MONEY AND MURDER

Simeon Lee had been brutally murdered. The old man was worth millions. Enough to make murder worth-while—for a lot of people.

HARRY, the good-for-nothing son who got plenty—and always needed more . . .

DAVID, who admitted he hated Simeon and who said he didn't care about the money . . .

PILAR, the mysterious beauty who was out for all she could get—and never bothered to hide it . . .

ALFRED, the devoted son who found that virtue didn't pay —but that maybe something else did . . .

HERE IS ONE OF THE MOST BAFFLING CRIMES POIROT'S BRILLIANT MIND EVER GRAPPLED WITH—A MURDER WITH TOO MANY SUSPECTS!

AGATHA CHRISTIE

A HOLIDAY FOR MURDER

ORIGINALLY PUBLISHED AS MURDER FOR CHRISTMAS

A NATIONAL GENERAL COMPANY

🙚

A HOLIDAY FOR MURDER
originally published under the title
MURDER FOR CHRISTMAS
*A Bantam Book / published by arrangement with
Dodd, Mead & Company, Inc.*

PRINTING HISTORY
Dodd, Mead edition published December 1938
Grosset & Dunlap edition published July 1940
2nd printing .... July 1941
Books, Inc. edition published December 1944
2nd printing ..... March 1945   3rd printing ... December 1945
4th printing .... May 1946
Bantam edition published June 1962

2nd printing .... July 1962	*9th printing .... July 1970*
3rd printing ... November 1962	*10th printing ..... March 1971*
4th printing .... January 1964	*11th printing .. September 1971*
5th printing .... June 1969	*12th printing ..... January 1972*
6th printing ... November 1969	*13th printing .... July 1972*
7th printing ... November 1969	*14th printing ... January 1973*
8th printing .... May 1970	*15th printing .... May 1973*

*Bantam Books are published by Bantam Books, Inc., a National
General company. Its trade-mark, consisting of the words "Bantam
Books" and the portrayal of a bantam, is registered in the United
States Patent Office and in other countries. Marca Registrada.
Bantam Books, Inc., 666 Fifth Avenue, New York, N.Y. 10019.*

PRINTED IN THE UNITED STATES OF AMERICA

My dear James,

You have always been one of the most faithful and kindly of my readers, and I was therefore seriously perturbed when I received from you a word of criticism.

You complained that my murders were getting too refined —anaemic, in fact! You yearned for a "good violent murder with lots of blood." A murder where there was no doubt about its being murder!

So this is your special story—written for you. I hope it may please.

Your affectionate sister-in-law,

Agatha

CONTENTS

Yet who would have thought the old man to have had so much blood in him?

MACBETH

I

STEPHEN PULLED up the collar of his coat as he walked briskly along the platform. Overhead a dim fog clouded the station. Large engines hissed superbly, throwing off clouds of steam into the cold raw air. Everything was dirty and smoke-grimed.

Stephen thought with revulsion:

"What a foul country—what a foul city!"

His first excited reaction to London—its shops, its restaurants, its well-dressed attractive women—had faded. He saw it now as a glittering rhinestone set in a dingy setting.

Supposing he were back in South Africa now. . . . He felt a quick pang of homesickness. Sunshine—blue skies—gardens of flowers—cool blue flowers—hedges of plumbago—blue convolvulus clinging to every little shanty.

And here—dirt, grime and endless incessant crowds—moving, hurrying, jostling. Busy ants running industriously about their ant hill.

For a moment he thought: "I wish I hadn't come. . . ."

Then he remembered his purpose and his lips set back in a grim line. No, by Hell, he'd go on with it! He'd planned this for years. He'd always meant to do—what he was going to do. Yes, he'd go on with it!

That momentary reluctance, that sudden questioning of himself: "Why? Is it worth it? Why dwell on the past? Why not wipe out the whole thing?"—all that was only weakness. He was not a boy to be turned this way and that by the whim of the moment. He was a man of forty, assured, purposeful. He would get on with it. He would do what he had come to England to do.

He got on the train and passed along the corridor, looking for a place. He had waved aside a porter and was carrying his own rawhide suitcase. He looked into carriage after carriage. The train was full. It was only three days before Christmas.

Stephen Farr looked distastefully at the crowded carriages. People! Incessant, innumerable people! And all so—so—what was the word—so *drab* looking! So alike, so horribly alike! Those that hadn't got faces like sheep had faces like rabbits, he thought. Some of them chattered and fussed. Some, heavy middle-aged men, grunted. More like pigs, those. Even the girls, slender egg-faced, scarlet-lipped, were of a depressing uniformity.

He thought with a sudden longing of open veldt, sun-baked and lonely. . . .

And then, suddenly, he caught his breath, looking into a carriage. This girl was different. Black hair, rich creamy pallor—eyes with the depth and darkness of night in them. The sad proud eyes of the South. . . . It was all wrong that this girl should be sitting in this train among these dull drab looking people—all wrong that she should be going into the dreary midlands of England. She should have been on a balcony, a rose between her lips, a piece of black lace draping her proud head, and there should have been dust and heat and the smell of blood—the smell of the bull-ring —in the air. . . . She should be somewhere splendid, not squeezed into the corner of a third class carriage.

He was an observant man. He did not fail to note the shabbiness of her little black coat and skirt, the cheap quality of her fabric gloves, the flimsy shoes and the defiant note of a flame-red handbag. Nevertheless splendour was the quality he associated with her. She *was* splendid, fine, exotic. . . .

What the Hell was she doing in this country of fogs and chills and hurrying industrious ants?

He thought: "I've got to know who she is and what she's doing here. . . . I've got to know. . . ."

II

Pilar sat squeezed up against the window and thought how very odd the English smelled. . . . It was what had struck her so far most forcibly about England—the difference of smell. There was no garlic and no dust and very little perfume. In this carriage now there was a smell of cold stuffiness—the sulphur smell of the trains—the smell of soap and another very unpleasant smell—it came, she thought, from the fur collar of the stout woman sitting beside her. Pilar sniffed delicately, imbibing the odour of moth balls reluctantly. It was a funny scent to choose to put on your-self, she thought.

2

A whistle blew, a stentorian voice cried out something and the train jerked slowly out of the station. They had started. She was on her way. . . .

Her heart beat a little faster. Would it be all right? Would she be able to accomplish what she had set out to do? Surely —surely—she had thought it all out so carefully. . . . She was prepared for every eventuality. Oh, yes, she would succeed— she must succeed. . . .

The curve of Pilar's red mouth curved upwards. It was suddenly cruel, that mouth. Cruel and greedy—like the mouth of a child or a kitten—a mouth that knew only its own desires and that was as yet unaware of pity.

She looked round her with the frank curiosity of a child. All these people—seven of them—how funny they were, the English! They all seemed so rich, so prosperous—their clothes—their boots— Oh! undoubtedly England was a very rich country as she had always heard. But they were not at all gay—no, decidedly not gay.

That was a handsome man standing in the corridor. . . . Pilar thought he was very handsome. She liked his deeply bronzed face and his high bridged nose and his square shoulders. More quickly than any English girl, Pilar had seen that the man admired her. She had not looked at him once directly, but she knew perfectly how often he had looked at her and exactly how he had looked.

She registered the facts without much interest or emotion. She came from a country where men looked at women as a matter of course and did not disguise the fact unduly. She wondered if he was an Englishman and decided that he was not.

"He is too alive, too real, to be English," Pilar decided. "And yet he is fair. He may be perhaps Americano." He was, she thought, rather like the actors she had seen in Wild West films.

An attendant pushed his way along the corridor.

"First lunch, please. First lunch. Take your seats for first lunch."

The other seven occupants of Pilar's carriage all held tickets for the first lunch. They rose in a body and the carriage was suddenly deserted and peaceful.

Pilar quickly pulled up the window which had been let down a couple of inches at the top by a militant looking grey-haired lady in the opposite corner. Then she sprawled comfortably back on her seat and peered out of the window at the northern suburbs of London. She did not turn her head at the sound of the door sliding back. It was the man from the corridor and Pilar knew, of course, that he had entered the carriage on purpose to talk to her.

She continued to look pensively out of the window.

Stephen Farr said:

"Would you like the window down at all?"

Pilar replied demurely:

"On the contrary. I have just shut it."

She spoke English perfectly, but with a slight accent.

During the pause that ensued Stephen thought:

"A delicious voice. It has the sun in it . . . it is warm like a summer night. . . ."

Pilar thought:

"I like his voice. It is big and strong. He is attractive—yes, he is attractive."

Stephen said:

"The train is very full."

"Oh, yes, indeed. The people go away from London, I suppose, because it is so black there."

Pilar had not been brought up to believe that it was a crime to talk to strange men in trains. She could take care of herself as well as any girl, but she had no rigid taboos.

If Stephen had been brought up in England he might have felt ill at ease at entering into conversation with a young girl. But Stephen was a friendly soul who found it perfectly natural to talk to anyone if he felt like it.

He smiled without any self-consciousness and said:

"London's rather a terrible place, isn't it?"

"Oh, yes. I do not like it at all."

"No more do I."

Pilar said:

"You are not English, no?"

"I'm British, but I come from South Africa."

"Oh, I see; that explains it."

"Have you just come from abroad?"

Pilar nodded.

"I come from Spain."

Stephen was interested.

"From Spain, do you? You're Spanish, then?"

"I am half Spanish. My mother was English. That is why I talk English so well."

"What about this war business?" asked Stephen.

"It is very terrible, yes—very sad. There has been damage done, quite a lot—yes."

"Which side are you on?"

Pilar's politics seemed to be rather vague. In the village where she came from, she explained, nobody had paid very much attention to the war. "It has not been near us, you understand. The Mayor, he is of course an officer of the Government, so he is for the Government, and the priest is for General Franco—but most of the people are so busy with the vines and the land, they have not time to go into these questions."

"So there wasn't any fighting round you?"

Pilar said that there had not been. "But then I drove in a car," she explained, "all across the country and there was much destruction. And I saw a bomb drop and it blew up a car—yes, and another destroyed a house. It was very exciting!"

Stephen Farr smiled a faintly twisted smile.

"So that's how it seemed to you?"

"It was a nuisance, too," explained Pilar. "Because I wanted to get on and the driver of my car, he was killed."

Stephen said, watching her:

"That didn't upset you?"

Pilar's great dark eyes opened very wide.

"Everyone must die! That is so, is it not? If it comes quickly from the sky—bouff—like that, it is as well as any other way One is alive for a time—yes, and then one is dead. That is what happens in this world."

Stephen Farr laughed.

"I don't think you are a pacifist."

"You do not think I am what?" Pilar seemed puzzled by a word which had not previously entered her vocabulary.

"Do you forgive your enemies, Señorita?"

Pilar shook her head.

"I have no enemies. But if I had——"

"Well?"

He was watching her, fascinated anew by the sweet cruel upward curving mouth.

Pilar said gravely:

"If I had an enemy—if anyone hated me and I hated them—then I would cut my enemy's throat like *this*. . . ."

She made a graphic gesture.

It was so swift and so crude that Stephen Farr was momentarily taken aback. He said:

"You're a bloodthirsty young woman!"

Pilar asked in a matter-of-fact tone:

"What would you do to your enemy?"

He started—stared at her, then laughed aloud.

"I wonder——" he said. "I wonder!"

Pilar said disapprovingly:

"But surely—you know."

He checked his laughter, drew in his breath and said in a low voice:

"Yes. I know. . . ."

Then, with a rapid change of manner, he asked:

"What made you come to England?"

Pilar replied with a certain demureness:

5

"I am going to stay with my relations—with my English relations."

"I see."

He leaned back in his seat, studying her—wondering what these English relations of whom she spoke were like—wondering what they would make of this Spanish stranger . . . trying to picture her in the midst of some sober British family at Christmas time.

Pilar asked:

"It is nice, South Africa, yes?"

He began to talk to her about South Africa. She listened with the pleased attention of a child hearing a story. He enjoyed her naïve but shrewd questions and amused himself by making a kind of exaggerated fairy story of it all.

The return of the proper occupants of the carriage put an end to this diversion. He rose, smiled into her eyes, and made his way out again into the corridor.

As he stood back for a minute in the doorway, to allow an elderly lady to come in, his eyes fell on the label of Pilar's obviously foreign straw case. He read the name with interest: *Miss Pilar Estravados*, then as his eye caught the address, it widened to incredulity and some other feeling. *Gorston Hall, Longdale, Addlesfield*.

He half turned, staring at the girl with a new expression —puzzled, resentful, suspicious. . . . He went out into the corridor and stood there smoking a cigarette and frowning to himself. . . .

III

In the big blue and gold drawing-room at Gorston Hall, Alfred Lee and Lydia, his wife, sat discussing their plans for Christmas. Alfred was a squarely built man of middle-age with a gentle face and mild brown eyes. His voice when he spoke was quiet and precise with a very clear enunciation. His head was sunk into his shoulders and he gave a curious impression of inertia. Lydia, his wife, was an energetic lean greyhound of a woman. She was amazingly thin, but all her movements had a swift startled grace about them.

There was no beauty in her careless haggard face, but it had distinction. Her voice was charming.

Alfred said:

"Father insists! There's nothing else for it."

Lydia controlled a sudden impatient movement. She said:

"Must you always give in to him?"

"He's a very old man, my dear—"

"Oh, I know—I know!"

"He expects to have his own way."

Lydia said drily:

"Naturally, since he has always had it! But sometime or other, Alfred, you will have to make a stand."

"What do you mean, Lydia?"

He stared at her, so palpably upset and startled, that for a moment she bit her lip and seemed doubtful whether to go on.

Alfred Lee repeated:

"What do you mean, Lydia?"

She shrugged her thin graceful shoulders.

She said, trying to choose her words cautiously:

"Your father is—inclined to be—tyrannical—"

"He's old."

"And will grow older. And consequently more tryannical. Where will it end? Already he dictates our lives to us completely. We can't make a plan of our own! If we do, it is always liable to be upset."

Alfred said:

"Father expects to come first. He is very good to us, remember."

"Oh! good to us!"

"*Very* good to us."

Alfred spoke with a trace of sternness.

Lydia said calmly:

"You mean financially?"

"Yes. His own wants are very simple. But he never grudges us money. You can spend what you like on dress and on this house and the bills are paid without a murmur. He gave us a new car only last week."

"As far as money goes, your father is very generous, I admit," said Lydia. "But in return he expects us to behave like slaves."

"Slaves?"

"That's the word I used. You *are* his slave, Alfred. If we have planned to go away and Father suddenly wishes us not to go, you cancel the arrangements and remain without a murmur! If the whim takes him to send us away, we go. . . . We have no lives of our own—no independence."

Her husband said distressfully:

"I wish you wouldn't talk like this, Lydia. It is very ungrateful. My father has done everything for us. . . ."

She bit off a retort that was on her lips. She shrugged those thin graceful shoulders once more.

Alfred said:

"You know, Lydia, the old man is very fond of you—"

His wife said clearly and distinctly:

"I am not at all fond of him."

"Lydia, it distresses me to hear you say things like that. It is so unkind——"

"Perhaps. But sometimes a compulsion comes over one to speak the truth."

"If Father guessed——"

"Your father knows perfectly well that I do not like him! It amuses him, I think."

"Really, Lydia, I am sure you are wrong there. He has often told me how charming your manner to him is."

"Naturally I've always been polite. I always shall be. I'm just letting you know what my real feelings are. I dislike your father, Alfred. I think he is a malicious and tyrannical old man. He bullies you and presumes on your affection for him. You ought to have stood up to him years ago."

Alfred said sharply:

"That will do, Lydia. Please don't say any more."

She sighed.

"I'm sorry. Perhaps I was wrong. . . . Let's talk of our Christmas arrangements. Do you think your brother David will really come?"

"Why not?"

She shook her head doubtfully.

"David is——queer. He's not been inside the house for years, remember. He was so devoted to your mother——he's got some feeling about this place."

"David always got on Father's nerves," said Alfred, "with his music and his dreamy ways. Father was, perhaps, a bit hard on him sometimes. But I think David and Hilda will come all right. Christmas time, you know."

"Peace and good will," said Lydia. Her delicate mouth curved ironically. "I wonder! George and Magdalene are coming. They said they would probably arrive to-morrow. I'm afraid Magdalene will be frightfully bored."

Alfred said with some slight annoyance:

"Why my brother George ever married a girl twenty years younger than himself I can't think! George was always a fool!"

"He's very successful in his career," said Lydia. "His constituents like him. I believe Magdalene works quite hard politically for him."

Alfred said slowly:

"I don't think I like her very much. She is very good-looking——but I sometimes think she is like one of those beautiful pears one gets——they have a rosy flush and a rather waxen appearance——" He shook his head.

"And they're bad inside?" said Lydia. "How funny you should say that, Alfred!"

"Why funny?"

She answered:

"Because—usually—you are such a gentle soul. You hardly ever say an unkind thing about anyone. I get annoyed with you sometimes because you're not sufficiently—oh, what shall I say?—sufficiently suspicious—not worldly enough!"

Her husband smiled.

"The world, I always think, is as you yourself make it."

Lydia said sharply:

"No! Evil is not only in one's mind. Evil exists! *You* seem to have no consciousness of the evil in the world. I have. I can feel it. I've always felt it—here in this house—" She bit her lip and turned away.

Alfred said: "Lydia—"

But she raised a quick admonitory hand, her eyes looking past him at something over his shoulder. Alfred turned.

A dark man with a smooth face was standing there deferentially.

Lydia said sharply:

"What is it, Horbury?"

Horbury's voice was low, a mere deferential murmur.

"It's Mr. Lee, madam. He asked me to tell you that there would be two more guests arriving for Christmas, and would you have rooms prepared for them."

Lydia said, "Two more guests?"

Horbury said smoothly: "Yes, madam, another gentleman and a young lady."

Alfred said wonderingly:

"A young lady?"

"That's what Mr. Lee said, sir."

Lydia said quickly:

"I will go up and see him—"

Horbury made one little step, it was a mere ghost of a movement but it stopped Lydia's rapid progress automatically.

"Excuse me, madam, but Mr. Lee is having his afternoon sleep. He asked specially that he should not be disturbed."

"I see," said Alfred. "Of course we won't distrub him."

"Thank you, sir."

Horbury withdrew.

Lydia said vehemently:

"How I dislike that man! He creeps about the house like a cat! One never hears him going or coming."

"I don't like him very much either. But he knows his job. It's not so easy to get a good male nurse attendant. And Father likes him; that's the main thing."

"Yes, that's the main thing, as you say. Alfred, what is this about a young lady? What young lady?"

Her husband shook his head.

"I can't imagine. I can't even think of anyone it might be likely to be."

They stared at each other. Then Lydia said, with a sudden twist of her expressive mouth:

"Do you know what I think, Alfred?"

"What?"

"I think your father has been bored lately. I think he is planning a little Christmas diversion for himself."

"By introducing two strangers into a family gathering?"

"Oh! I don't know what the details are—but I do fancy that your father is preparing to—amuse himself."

"I hope he *will* get some pleasure out of it," said Alfred gravely. "Poor old chap, tied by the leg, an invalid—after the adventurous life he has led."

Lydia said slowly:

"After the—adventurous life he has led."

The pause she made before the adjective gave it some special though obscure significance. Alfred seemed to feel it. He flushed and looked unhappy.

She cried out suddenly:

"How he ever had a son like you, I can't imagine! You two are poles apart. And he fascinates you—you simply worship him!"

Alfred said with a trace of vexation:

"Aren't you going a little far, Lydia? It's natural, I should say, for a son to love his father. It would be very unnatural not to do so."

Lydia said:

"In that case, most of the members of this family are—unnatural! Oh! don't let's argue! I apologize. I've hurt your feelings, I know. Believe me, Alfred, I really didn't mean to do that. I admire you enormously for your—your—*fidelity*. Loyalty is such a rare virtue in these days. Let us say, shall we, that I am jealous? Women are supposed to be jealous of their mothers-in-law—why not, then, of their fathers-in-law?"

He put a gentle arm round her.

"Your tongue runs away with you, Lydia. There's no reason for you to be jealous."

She gave him a quick remorseful kiss, a delicate caress on the tip of his ear.

"I know. All the same, Alfred, I don't believe I should have been in the least jealous of your mother. I wish I'd known her."

He sighed.

"She was a poor creature," he said.

His wife looked at him interestedly.

"So that's how she struck you . . . as a poor creature. . . . That's interesting."

He said dreamily:

"I remember her as nearly always ill. . . . Often in tears. . . ." He shook his head. "She had no spirit."

Still staring at him, she murmured very softly:

"How odd. . . ."

But as he turned a questioning glance on her, she shook her head quickly and changed the subject.

"Since we are not allowed to know who our mysterious guests are, I shall go out and finish my garden."

"It's very cold, my dear; a biting wind."

"I'll wrap up warmly."

She left the room. Alfred Lee, left alone, stood for some minutes motionless, frowning a little to himself, then he walked over to the big window at the end of the room. Outside was a terrace running the whole length of the house. Here, after a minute or two, he saw Lydia emerge, carrying a flat basket. She was wearing a big blanket coat. She set down the basket and began to work at a square stone sink slightly raised above ground level.

Her husband watched for some time. At last he went out of the room, fetched himself a coat and muffler and emerged onto the terrace by a side door. As he walked along he passed various other stone sinks arranged as miniature gardens, all the products of Lydia's agile fingers.

One represented a desert scene with smooth yellow sand, a little clump of green palm trees in coloured tin, and a procession of camels with one or two little Arab figures. Some primitive mud houses had been constructed of plasticine. There was an Italian garden with terraces and formal beds with flowers in coloured sealing-wax. There was an arctic one, too, with lumps of green glass for icebergs, and a little cluster of penguins. Next came a Japanese garden with a couple of beautiful little stunted trees, looking glass arranged for water, and bridges modeled out of plasticine.

He came at last to stand beside her where she was at work. She had laid down blue paper and covered it over with glass. Round this were lumps of rock piled up. At the moment she was pouring out coarse pebbles from a little bag and forming them into a beach. Between the rocks were some small cactuses.

Lydia was murmuring to herself:

"Yes, that's exactly right—exactly what I want. . . ."

Alfred said:

"What's this latest work of art?"

She started, for she had not heard him come up.

"This? Oh, it's the Dead Sea, Alfred. Do you like it?"

He said: "It's rather arid, isn't it? Oughtn't there to be more vegetation?"

She shook her head.

"It's my idea of the Dead Sea. It *is* dead, you see—"

"It's not so attractive as some of the others."

"It's not meant to be specially attractive."

Footsteps sounded on the terrace. An elderly butler, white-haired and slightly bowed, was coming towards them.

"Mrs. George Lee on the telephone, madam. She says will it be convenient if she and Mr. George arrive by the 5:20 to-morrow?"

"Yes, tell her that will be quite all right."

"Thank you, madam."

The butler hurried away. Lydia looked after him with a softened expression on her face.

"Dear old Tressilian. What a standby he is! I can't imagine what we should do without him."

Alfred agreed.

"He's one of the old school. He's been with us nearly forty years. He's devoted to us all."

Lydia nodded.

"Yes. He's like the faithful old retainers of fiction. I believe he'd lie himself blue in the face if it was necessary to protect one of the family!"

Alfred said:

"I believe he would. . . . Yes, I believe he would. . . ."

Lydia smoothed over the last bit of her shingle.

"There," she said. "That's ready."

"Ready?" Alfred looked puzzled.

She laughed.

"For Christmas, silly! For this sentimental family Christmas we're going to have."

IV

David was rereading the letter. Once he screwed it up into a ball and thrust it away from him. Then, reaching for it, he smoothed it out and read it again.

Quietly, without saying anything, his wife, Hilda, watched him. She noted the jerking muscle (or was it a nerve?) in his temple, the slight tremor of the long delicate hands, the nervous spasmodic movements of his whole body. When he pushed aside the lock of fair hair that always tended to stray down over his forehead and looked across at her with appealing blue eyes she was ready.

"Hilda, what shall we do about it?"

12

Hilda hesitated a minute before speaking. She had heard the appeal in his voice. She knew how dependent he was upon her—had always been ever since their marriage—knew that she could probably influence his decision finally and decisively. But for just that reason she was chary of pronouncing anything too final.

She said, and her voice had the calm soothing quality that can be heard in the voice of an experienced nannie in a nursery:

"It depends on how you feel about it, David."

A broad woman, Hilda, not beautiful, but with a certain magnetic quality. Something about her like a Dutch picture. Something warming and endearing in the sound of her voice. Something strong about her—the vital hidden strength that appeals to weakness. An overstout dumpy middle-aged woman—not clever—not brilliant—but with *something* about her that you couldn't pass over. Force! Hilda Lee had force!

David got up and began pacing up and down. His hair was practically untouched by grey. He was strangely boyish looking. His face had the mild quality of a Burne-Jones knight. It was, somehow, not very real. . . .

He said, and his voice was wistful:

"You know how I feel about it, Hilda. You must."

"I'm not sure."

"But I've told you—I've told you again and again! How I hate it all—the house and the country round and everything! It brings back nothing but misery. I hated every moment that I spent there! When I think of it—of all that *she* suffered—my mother. . . ."

His wife nodded sympathetically.

"She was so sweet, Hilda, and so patient. Lying there, often in pain, but bearing it—enduring everything. And when I think of my father"—his face darkened—"bringing all that misery into her life—humiliating her—boasting of his love affairs—constantly unfaithful to her and never troubling to conceal it."

Hilda Lee said:

"She should not have put up with it. She should have left him."

He said with a touch of reproof:

"She was too good to do that. She thought it was her duty to remain. Besides it was her home—where else should she go?"

"She could have made a life of her own."

David said fretfully:

"Not in those days! You don't understand. Women didn't behave like that. They put up with things. They endured patiently. She had us to consider. Even if she had divorced my father, what would have happened? He would probably have married again. There might have been a second family. *Our* interests might have gone to the wall. She had to think of all those considerations."

Hilda did not answer.

David went on:

"No, she did right. She was a saint! She endured to the end—uncomplainingly."

Hilda said: "Not quite uncomplainingly or you would not know so much, David!"

He said softly, his face lighting up:

"Yes—she told me things. . . . She knew how I loved her. When she died——"

He stopped. He ran his hands through his hair.

"Hilda, it was awful—horrible! The desolation! She was quite young still; she *needn't* have died. *He* killed her—my father! He was responsible for her dying. He broke her heart. I decided then that I'd not go on living under his roof. I broke away—got away from it all."

Hilda nodded.

"You were very wise," she said. "It was the right thing to do."

David said:

"Father wanted me to go into the works. That would have meant living at home. I couldn't have stood that. I can't think how Alfred stands it—how he has stood it all these years?"

"Did he never rebel against it?" asked Hilda with some interest. "I thought you told me something about his having given up some other career."

David nodded.

"Alfred was going into the Army. Father arranged it all. Alfred, the eldest, was to go into some cavalry regiment, Harry was to go into the works, so was I. George was to enter politics."

"And it didn't work out like that?"

David shook his head.

"Harry broke all that up! He was always frightfully wild. Got into debt—and all sorts of other troubles. Finally he went off one day with several hundred pounds that didn't belong to him leaving a note behind him saying an office stool didn't suit him and he was going to see the world."

"And you never heard any more of him?"

"Oh, yes, we did!" David laughed. "We heard quite often! He was always cabling for money from all over the world. He usually got it, too!"

"And Alfred?"

"Father made him chuck up the Army and come back and go into the works."

"Did he mind?"

"Very much to begin with. He hated it. But Father could always twist Alfred round his little finger. He's absolutely under Father's thumb still, I believe."

"And you—escaped!" said Hilda.

"Yes. I went to London and studied painting. Father told me plainly that if I went off on a fool's errand like that I'd get a small allowance from him during his lifetime and nothing when he died. I said I didn't care. He called me a young fool, and that was that! I've never seen him since."

Hilda said gently:

"And you haven't regretted it?"

"No, indeed. I realize I sha'n't ever get anywhere with my art. I shall never be a great artist—but we're happy enough in this cottage—we've got everything we want—all the essentials. And if I die, well, my life's insured for you."

He paused and then said:

"And now—*this!*"

He struck the letter with his open hand.

"I am sorry your father ever wrote that letter, if it upsets you so much," said Hilda.

David went on as though he had not heard her:

"Asking me to bring my wife for Christmas, expressing a hope that we may be all together for Christmas, a united family! What can it mean?"

Hilda said:

"Need it mean anything more than it says?"

He looked at her questioningly.

"I mean," she said, smiling, "that your father is growing old. He's beginning to feel sentimental about family ties. That does happen, you know."

"I suppose it does," said David slowly.

"He's an old man and he's lonely."

He gave her a quick look.

"You want me to go, don't you, Hilda?"

She said slowly:

"It seems a pity—not to answer an appeal. I'm old-fashioned, I daresay, but why not have peace and good will at Christmas time?"

"After all I've told you?"

"I know, dear, I know. But all that's in the *past*. It's all done and finished with."

"Not for me."

"No, *because you won't let it die.* You keep the past alive in your own mind."

"I can't forget."

"You *won't* forget—that's what you mean, David."

His mouth set in a firm line.

"We're like that, we Lees. We remember things for years—brood about them, keep memory green."

Hilda said with a touch of impatience:

"Is that anything to be proud of? I do not think so!"

He looked thoughtfully at her, a touch of reserve in his manner.

He said: "You don't attach much value to loyalty, then—loyalty to a memory?"

Hilda said:

"I believe the *present* matters—not the past! The past must go. If we seek to keep the past alive, we end, I think, by *distorting* it. We see it in exaggerated terms—a false perspective."

"I can remember every word and every incident of those days perfectly," said David passionately.

"Yes, but you *shouldn't*, my dear! It isn't natural to do so! You're applying the judgment of a boy to those days instead of looking back on them with the more temperate outlook of a man."

"What difference would that make?" demanded David.

Hilda hesitated. She was aware of unwisdom in going on, and yet there were things she badly wanted to say.

"I think," she said, "that you're seeing your father as a *Bogy!* You're exalting him into a kind of personification of Evil. Probably, if you were to see him now, you would realize that he was only a very ordinary man; a man, perhaps, whose passions ran away with him, a man whose life was far from blameless, but nevertheless merely a *man*—not a kind of inhuman Monster!"

"You don't understand! His treatment of my mother—"

Hilda said gravely:

"There is a certain kind of meekness—of submission—that brings out the worst in a man—whereas that same man, faced by spirit and determination, might be a different creature!"

"So you say it was her fault—"

Hilda interrupted him.

"No, of course I don't! I've no doubt your father treated your mother very badly indeed, but marriage is an extraordinary thing—and I doubt if any outsider—even a child of the marriage—has the right to judge. Besides, all this resentment on your part now cannot help your mother. It is all *gone*—it is behind you! What is left now is an old man, in feeble health, asking his son to come home for Christmas."

"And you want me to go?"

Hilda hesitated, then she suddenly made up her mind.

"Yes," she said, "I do. I want you to go and lay the Bogy once and for all."

V

George Lee, M.P. for Westeringham, was a somewhat corpulent gentleman of forty-one. His eyes were pale blue and slightly prominent with a suspicious expression, he had a heavy jowl, and a slow pedantic utterance.

He said now in a weighty manner:

"I have told you, Magdalene, that I think it my *duty* to go."

His wife shrugged her shoulders impatiently.

She was a slender creature, a platinum blonde with plucked eyebrows and a smooth egg-like face. It could, on occasions, look quite blank and devoid of any expression whatever. She was looking like that now.

"Darling," she said, "it will be perfectly grim, I am sure of it."

"Moreover," said George Lee, and his face lit up as an attractive idea occurred to him, "it will enable us to save considerably. Christmas is always an expensive time. We can put the servants on board wages."

"Oh, well!" said Magdalene. "After all, Christmas is pretty grim anywhere!"

"I suppose," said George, pursuing his own line of thought, "they will expect to have a Christmas dinner? A nice piece of beef, perhaps, instead of a turkey."

"Who? The servants? Oh, George, don't fuss so. You're always worrying about money."

"Somebody has to worry," said George.

"Yes, but it's absurd to pinch and scrape in all these little ways. Why don't you make your father give you some more money?"

"He already gives me a very handsome allowance."

"It's awful to be completely dependent on your father, as you are! He ought to settle some money on you outright."

"That's not his way of doing things."

Magdalene looked at him. Her hazel eyes were suddenly sharp and keen. The expressionless egg-like face showed sudden meaning.

"He's frightfully rich, isn't he, George? A kind of millionaire, isn't he?"

"A millionaire twice over, I believe."

Magdalene gave an envious sigh.

"How did he make it all? South Africa, wasn't it?"

"Yes, he made a big fortune there in his early days. Mainly diamonds."

"Thrilling!" said Magdalene.

"Then he came to England and started in business and his fortune has actually doubled or trebled itself, I believe."

"What will happen when he dies?" asked Magdalene.

"Father's never said much on the subject. Of course one can't exactly *ask*. I should imagine that the bulk of his money will go to Alfred and myself. Alfred, of course, will get the larger share."

"You've got other brothers, haven't you?"

"Yes, there's my brother David. I don't fancy *he* will get much. He went off to do art or some tomfoolery of that kind. I believe Father warned him that he would cut him out of his will and David said he didn't care."

"How silly," said Magdalene with scorn.

"There was my sister Jennifer, too. She went off with a foreigner—a Spanish artist—one of David's friends. But she died just over a year ago. She left a daughter, I believe. Father might leave a little money to her, but nothing much. And of course there's Harry—"

He stopped, slightly embarrassed.

"Harry?" said Magdalene, surprised. "Who is Harry?"

"Ah—er—my brother."

"I never knew you had another brother?"

"My dear, he wasn't a great—er—credit—to us. We don't mention him. His behaviour was disgraceful. We haven't heard anything of him for some years now. He's probably dead."

Magdalene laughed suddenly.

"What is it? What are you laughing at?"

Magdalene said:

"I was only thinking how funny it was that you—*you*, George, should have a disreputable brother! You're so very respectable."

"I should hope so," said George coldly.

Her eyes narrowed.

"Your father isn't—very respectable, George?"

"Really, Magdalene!"

"Sometimes the things he says make me feel quite uncomfortable."

George said: "Really, Magdalene, you surprise me. Does—er—does Lydia feel the same?"

"He doesn't say the same kind of things to Lydia," said Magdalene. She added angrily: "No, he never says them to *her*. I can't think why not."

George glanced at her quickly and then glanced away.

"Oh, well," he said vaguely. "One must make allowances. At Father's age—and with his health being so bad—"

He paused. His wife asked:

"Is he really—pretty ill?"

"Oh, I wouldn't say *that*. He's remarkably tough. All the same, since he wants to have his family round him at Christmas, I think we are quite right to go. It may be his last Christmas."

She said sharply:

"You *say* that, George, but really, I suppose, he may live for years?"

Slightly taken aback, her husband stammered:

"Yes—yes, of course he may."

Magdalene turned away.

"Oh, well," she said, "I suppose we're doing the right thing by going."

"I have no doubt about it."

"But I hate it! Alfred's so dull, and Lydia snubs me."

"Nonsense."

"She does. And I hate that beastly man-servant."

"Old Tressilian?"

"No, Horbury. Sneaking round like a cat and smirking."

"Really, Magdalene, I can't see that Horbury can affect you in any way!"

"He just gets on my nerves, that's all. But don't let's bother. We've got to go, I can see that. Won't do to offend the old man."

"No—no, that's just the point. About the servants' Christmas dinner—"

"Not now, George, some other time. I'll just ring up Lydia and tell her we'll come by the 5:20 to-morrow."

Magdalene left the room precipitately. After telephoning, she went up to her own room and sat down in front of the desk. She let down the flap and rummaged in its various pigeonholes. Cascades of bills came tumbling out. Magdalene sorted through them, trying to arrange them in some kind of order. Finally, with an impatient sigh, she bundled them up and thrust them back whence they had come. She passed a hand over her smooth platinum head.

"What on earth am I to do?" she murmured.

VI

On the first floor of Gorston Hall a long passage led to a big room overlooking the front drive. It was a room furnished in the more flamboyant of old-fashioned styles. It had heavy brocaded wallpaper, rich leather armchairs, large vases embossed with dragons, sculptures in bronze. . . . Everything in it was magnificent, costly and solid.

In a big grandfather armchair, the biggest and most imposing of all the chairs, sat the thin shriveled figure of an old man. His long claw-like hands rested on the arms of the chair. A gold-mounted stick was by his side. He wore an old shabby blue dressing-gown. On his feet were carpet slippers. His hair was white and the skin of his face was yellow.

A shabby insignificant figure, one might have thought. But the nose, aquiline and proud, and the eyes, dark and intensely alive, might cause an observer to alter his opinion. Here was fire and life and vigour. . . .

Old Simeon Lee cackled to himself, a sudden high cackle of amusement.

He said:

"You gave my message to Mrs. Alfred, hey?"

Horbury was standing beside his chair. He replied in his soft deferential voice:

"Yes, sir."

"Exactly in the words I told you? Exactly, mind?"

"Yes, sir. I didn't make a mistake, sir."

"No—you don't make mistakes. You'd better not make mistakes either—or you'll regret it! And what did she say, Horbury? What did Mr. Alfred say?"

Quietly, unemotionally, Horbury repeated what had passed. The old man cackled again and rubbed his hands together.

"Splendid . . . first rate . . . they'll have been thinking and wondering—all the afternoon! Splendid! I'll have 'em up now. Go and get them."

"Yes, sir."

Horbury walked noiselessly across the room and went out.

"And, Horbury—"

The old man looked round, then cursed to himself.

"Fellow moves like a cat. Never know where he is."

He sat quite still in his chair, his fingers caressing his chin till there was a tap on the door and Alfred and Lydia came in.

"Ah, there you are, there you are. Sit here, Lydia, my dear, by me. What a nice colour you've got."

"I've been out in the cold. It makes one's cheeks burn afterwards."

Alfred said:

"How are you, Father? Did you have a good rest this afternoon?"

"First rate—first rate. Dreamed about the old days! That was before I settled down and became a pillar of society."

He cackled with sudden laughter.

His daughter-in-law sat silently smiling with polite attention.

Alfred said:

"What's this, Father, about two extra being expected for Christmas?"

"Ah! that. Yes, I must tell you about that. It's going to be a grand Christmas for me this year—a grand Christmas. Let me see, George is coming and Magdalene—"

Lydia said:

"Yes, they are arriving to-morrow by the 5:20."

Old Simeon said:

"Poor stick, George! Nothing but a gasbag! Still, he *is* my son."

Alfred said:

"His constituents like him."

Simeon cackled again.

"They probably think he's honest. Honest! There never was a Lee who was honest yet."

"Oh, come now, Father."

"I except you, my boy. I except you."

"And David?" asked Lydia.

"David now. I'm curious to see the boy after all these years. He was a namby-pamby youngster. Wonder what his wife is like? At any rate *he* hasn't married a girl twenty years younger than himself, like that fool George!"

"Hilda wrote a very nice letter," said Lydia. "I've just had a wire from her confirming it and saying they are definitely arriving to-morrow."

Her father-in-law looked at her, a keen penetrating glance. He laughed.

"I never get any change out of Lydia," he said. "I'll say this for you, Lydia, you're a well-bred woman. Breeding tells. I know that well enough. A funny thing, though, heredity. There's only one of you that's taken after me—only one out of all the litter."

His eyes danced.

"Now guess who's coming for Christmas. I'll give you three guesses and I'll bet you a fiver you won't get the answer."

He looked from one face to the other. Alfred said, frowning:

"Horbury said you expected a young lady."

"That intrigued you—yes, I daresay it did. Pilar will be arriving any minute now. I gave orders for the car to go and meet her."

Alfred said sharply:

"*Pilar?*"

Simeon said:

"Pilar Estravados. Jennifer's girl. My granddaughter. I wonder what she'll be like?"

Alfred cried out:

"Good Heavens, Father, you never told me. . . ."

The old man was grinning.

"No, I thought I'd keep it a secret! Got Charlton to write out and fix things."

Alfred repeated, his tone hurt and reproachful:

"You never told me. . . ."

His father said, still grinning wickedly:

"It would have spoiled the surprise! Wonder what it will be like to have young blood under this roof again? I never saw Estravados. Wonder which the girl takes after—her mother or her father?"

"Do you really think it's wise, Father?" began Alfred. "Taking everything into consideration—"

The old man interrupted him.

"Safety—safety—you play for safety too much, Alfred! Always have! That hasn't been my way! Do what you want and be damned to it! That's what I say! The girl's my granddaughter—the only grandchild in the family! I don't care what her father was or what he did! She's my flesh and blood! And she's coming to live here in my house."

Lydia said sharply:

"She's coming to *live* here?"

He darted a quick look at her.

"Do you object?"

She shook her head. She said, smiling:

"I couldn't very well object to your asking someone to your own house, could I? No, I was wondering about—her."

"About her—what d'you mean?"

"Whether she would be happy here."

Old Simeon flung up his head.

"She's not got a penny in the world. She ought to be thankful!"

Lydia shrugged her shoulders.

Simeon turned to Alfred:

"You see? It's going to be a grand Christmas! All my children round me. *All* my children! There, Alfred, there's your clue. Now guess who the other visitor is."

Alfred stared at him.

"All my children! Guess, boy! *Harry,* of course! Your brother Harry!"

Alfred had gone very pale. He stammered:

"Harry—not Harry—"

"Harry himself!"

"But we thought he was dead!"

"Not he!"

22

"You—you are having him back here? After everything?"

"The prodigal son, eh? You're right! The fatted calf! We must kill the fatted calf, Alfred. We must give him a grand welcome."

Alfred said:

"He treated you—all of us—disgracefully. He—"

"No need to recite his crimes! It's a long list. But Christmas, you'll remember, is the season of forgiveness! We'll welcome the prodigal home."

Alfred rose. He murmured:

"This has been—rather a shock. I never dreamed that Harry would ever come inside these walls again."

Simeon leaned forward.

"You never liked Harry, did you?" he said softly.

"After the way he behaved to you—"

Simeon cackled. He said:

"Ah, but bygones must be bygones. That's the spirit for Christmas, isn't it, Lydia?"

Lydia, too, had gone pale. She said drily:

"I see that you have thought a good deal about Christmas this year."

"I want my family round me. Peace and good will. I'm an old man. Are you going, my dear?"

Alfred had hurried out. Lydia paused a moment before following him.

Simeon nodded his head after the retreating figure.

"It's upset him. He and Harry never got on. Harry used to jeer at Alfred. Called him old Slow and Sure."

Lydia's lips parted. She was about to speak, then as she saw the old man's eager expression, she checked herself. Her self-control, she saw, disappointed him. The perception of that fact enabled her to say:

"The hare and the tortoise? Ah, well, the tortoise wins the race."

"Not always," said Simeon. "Not always, my dear Lydia."

She said, still smiling:

"Excuse me, I must go after Alfred. Sudden excitements always upset him."

Simeon cackled.

"Yes, Alfred doesn't like changes. He always was a regular sobersides."

Lydia said:

"Alfred is very devoted to *you*."

"That seems odd to you, doesn't it?"

"Sometimes," said Lydia, "it does."

She left the room. Simeon looked after her.

He chuckled softly and rubbed his palms together.

"Lots of fun," he said. "Lots of fun still. I'm going to enjoy this Christmas."

With an effort he pulled himself upright and with the help of his stick shuffled slowly across the room.

He went to a big safe that stood at the corner of the room. He twirled the handle of the combination. The door came open and with shaking fingers he felt inside.

He lifted out a small chamois leather bag and opening it let a stream of uncut diamonds pass through his fingers.

"Well, my beauties, well. . . . Still the same—still my old friends. Those were good days—good days. . . . They sha'n't carve you and cut you about, my friends. *You* sha'n't hang round the necks of women or sit on their fingers or hang on their ears. You're *mine!* My old friends! We know a thing or two, you and I. I'm old, they say, and ill, but I'm not done for! Lots of life in the old dog yet. And there's still some fun to be got out of life. Still some fun—"

Part II ━━━━━━ DECEMBER 23RD

I

TRESSILIAN WENT to answer the doorbell. It had been an unusually aggressive peal and now, before he could make his slow way across the hall, it pealed out again.

Tressilian flushed. An ill-mannered, impatient way of ringing the bell at a gentleman's house! If it was a fresh lot of those carol singers he'd give them a piece of his mind.

Through the frosted glass of the upper half of the door he saw a silhouette—a big man in a slouch hat. He opened the door. As he had thought—a cheap flashy stranger—nasty pattern of suit he was wearing—loud! Some impudent begging fellow!

"Blessed if it isn't Tressilian," said the stranger. "How are you, Tressilian?"

Tressilian stared—took a deep breath—stared again. That bold arrogant jaw, the high bridged nose, the rollicking eye.

24

Yes, they had all been there years ago. More subdued then. . . .

He said with a gasp:

"Mr. Harry!"

Harry Lee laughed.

"Looks as though I'd given you quite a shock. Why? I'm expected, aren't I?"

"Yes, indeed, sir. Certainly, sir."

"Then why the surprise act?" Harry stepped back a foot or two and looked up at the house—a good solid mass of red brick, unimaginative but solid.

"Just the same ugly old mansion," he remarked. "Still standing, though, that's the main thing. How's my father, Tressilian?"

"He's somewhat of an invalid, sir. Keeps his room, and can't get about much. But he's wonderfully well, considering."

"The old sinner!"

Harry Lee came inside, let Tressilian remove his scarf and take the somewhat theatrical hat.

"How's my dear brother Alfred, Tressilian?"

"He's very well, sir."

Harry grinned.

"Looking forward to seeing me? Eh?"

"I expect so, sir."

"I don't! Quite the contrary. I bet it's given him a nasty jolt, my turning up! Alfred and I never did get on. Ever read your Bible, Tressilian?"

"Why, yes, sir, sometimes, sir."

"Remember the tale of the prodigal's return? The good brother didn't like it, remember, didn't like it at all! Good old stay-at-home Alfred doesn't like it either, I bet."

Tressilian remained silent looking down his nose. His stiffened back expressed protest. Harry clapped him on the shoulder.

"Lead on, old son," he said. "The fatted calf awaits me! Lead me right to it."

Tressilian murmured:

"If you will come this way into the drawing-room, sir. I am not quite sure where everyone is. . . . They were unable to send to meet you, sir, not knowing the time of your arrival."

Harry nodded. He followed Tressilian along the hall, turning his head to look about him as he went.

"All the old exhibits in their place, I see," he remarked. "I don't believe anything has changed since I went away twenty years ago."

25

He followed Tressilian into the drawing-room. The old man murmured:

"I will see if I can find Mr. or Mrs. Alfred," and hurried out.

Harry Lee had marched into the room and had then stopped, staring at the figure seated on one of the window sills. His eyes roamed incredulously over the black hair and the creamy exotic pallor.

"Good Lord!" he said. "Are you my father's seventh and most beautiful wife?"

Pilar slipped down and came towards him.

"I am Pilar Estravados," she announced. "And you must be my Uncle Harry, my mother's brother."

Harry said, staring:

"So that's who you are! Jenny's daughter."

Pilar said:

"Why did you ask me if I was your father's seventh wife? Has he really had six wives?"

Harry laughed.

"No, I believe he's only had one official one. Well—Pil—what's your name?"

"Pilar, yes."

"Well, Pilar, it really gives me quite a turn to see something like you blooming in this mausoleum."

"This—maus—please?"

"This museum of stuffed dummies! I always thought this house was lousy! Now I see it again I think it's lousier than ever!"

Pilar said in a shocked voice:

"Oh, no, it is very handsome here! The furniture is good and the carpets—thick carpets everywhere, and there are lots of ornaments. Everything is very good quality and very, very rich!"

"You're right there," said Harry, grinning. He looked at her with amusement. "You know I can't help getting a kick out of seeing you in the midst—"

He broke off as Lydia came rapidly into the room.

She came straight to him.

"How d'you do, Harry? I'm Lydia—Alfred's wife."

"How de do, Lydia?" He shook hands, examining her intelligent mobile face in a swift glance and approving mentally of the way she walked—very few women moved well.

Lydia in her turn took quick stock of him.

She thought:

"He looks a frightful tough—attractive, though. I wouldn't trust him an inch. . . ."

She said, smiling:

26

"How does it look after all these years? Quite different, or very much the same?"

"Pretty much the same." He looked round him. "This room's been done over."

"Oh! many times."

He said:

"I meant by you. You've made it—different."

"Yes, I expect so. . . ."

He grinned at her, a sudden impish grin that reminded her with a start of the old man upstairs.

"It's got more class about it now! I remember hearing that old Alfred had married a girl whose people came over with the Conqueror."

Lydia smiled.

She said:

"I believe they did. But they've rather run to seed since those days."

Harry said:

"How's old Alfred? Just the same blessed old stick-in-the-mud as ever?"

"I've no idea whether you will find him changed or not."

"How are the others? Scattered all over England?"

"No—they're all here for Christmas you know."

Harry's eyes opened.

"Regular Christmas family reunion? What's the matter with the old man? He used not to give a damn for sentiment. Don't remember his caring much for his family either. He must have changed!"

"Perhaps." Lydia's voice was dry.

Pilar was staring, her big eyes wide and interested.

Harry said:

"How's old George? Still the same skinflint? How he used to howl if he had to part with a halfpenny of his pocket money!"

Lydia said:

"George is in Parliament. He's member for Westeringham."

"What? Popeye in Parliament? Lord, that's good."

Harry threw back his head and laughed.

It was rich stentorian laughter—it sounded uncontrolled and brutal in the confined space of the room. Pilar drew in her breath with a gasp. Lydia flinched a little.

Then, at a movement behind him, Harry broke off his laugh and turned sharply. He had not heard anyone come in, but Alfred was standing there quietly. He was looking at Harry with an odd expression on his face.

Harry stood a minute, then a slow smile crept to his lips. He advanced a step.

"Why," he said, "it's Alfred!"

Alfred nodded.

"Hullo, Harry," he said.

They stood staring at each other. Lydia caught her breath. She thought:

"How absurd! Like two dogs—looking at each other. . . ."

Pilar's gaze widened even further. She thought to herself:

"How silly they look standing there . . . why do they not embrace? No, of course, the English do not do that. But they might *say* something. Why do they just *look?*"

Harry said at last:

"Well, well. Feels funny to be here again!"

"I expect so—yes. A good many years since you—got out."

Harry threw up his head. He drew his finger along the line of his jaw. It was a gesture that was habitual with him. It expressed belligerence.

"Yes," he said. "I'm glad to have come—" he paused to bring out the word with greater significance—"*home. . . .*"

II

"I've been, I suppose, a very wicked man," said Simeon Lee.

He was leaning back in his chair. His chin was raised and with one finger he was stroking his jaw reflectively. In front of him a big fire glowed and danced. Beside it sat Pilar, a little screen of papier-mâché held in her hand. With it she shielded her face from the blaze. Occasionally she fanned herself with it, using her wrist in a supple gesture. Simeon looked at her with satisfaction.

He went on talking, perhaps more to himself than to the girl, and yet stimulated by the fact of her presence.

"Yes," he said. "I've been a wicked man. What do you say to that, Pilar?"

Pilar shrugged her shoulders. She said:

"All men are wicked. The nuns say so. That is why one has to pray for them."

"Ah, but I've been more wicked than most." Simeon laughed. "I don't regret it, you know. No, I don't regret anything. I've enjoyed myself . . . every minute! They say you repent when you get old. That's bunkum. I don't repent. And as I tell you, I've done most things . . . all the good old sins! I've cheated and stolen and lied. . . . Lord, yes! And women! Always women! Someone told me the other day of an Arab chief who had a bodyguard of forty of his sons—all roughly the same age! Aha! Forty! I don't know about forty, but I bet I could produce a very fair bodyguard if I went about looking for the brats! Hey, Pilar, what do you think of that? Shocked?"

Pilar stared.

"No, why should I be shocked? Men always desire women. My father, too. That is why wives are so often unhappy and why they go to church and pray."

Old Simeon was frowning.

"I made Adelaide unhappy," he said. He spoke almost under his breath, to himself. "Lord, what a woman! Pink and white and pretty as they make 'em when I married her! And afterwards? Always wailing and weeping. It rouses the devil in a man when his wife is always crying. . . . She'd no guts, that's what was the matter with Adelaide. If she'd stood up to me! But she never did—not once. I believed when I married her that I was going to be able to settle down—raise a family, cut loose from the old life. . . ."

His voice died away. He stared—stared into the glowing heart of the fire.

"Raise a family. . . . God, what a family!" He gave a sudden shrill pipe of angry laughter. "Look at 'em—look at 'em! Not a child among them—to carry on! What's the matter with them? Haven't they got any of my blood in their veins? Not a son among 'em, legitimate or illegitimate. Alfred, for instance. Heavens above, how bored I get with Alfred! Looking at me with his dog's eyes. Ready to do anything I ask. Lord, what a fool! His wife, now—Lydia—I like Lydia. She's got spirit. She doesn't like me, though. No, she doesn't like me. But she has to put up with me for that nincompoop Alfred's sake." He looked over at the girl by the fire. "Pilar—remember—nothing is so boring as devotion."

She smiled at him. He went on, warmed by the presence of youth and strong femininity.

"George? What's George? A stick! A stuffed codfish! A pompous windbag with no brains and no guts—and mean about money as well! David? David always was a fool. A fool and a dreamer. His mother's boy. That was always David. Only sensible thing he ever did was to marry that solid comfortable-looking woman." He brought down his hand with a bang on the edge of his chair. "Harry's the best of 'em! Poor old Harry, the wrong 'un! But at any rate he's *alive!*"

Pilar agreed.

"Yes, he is nice. He laughs—laughs out loud—and throws his head back. Oh, yes, I like him very much."

The old man looked at her.

"You do, do you, Pilar? Harry always had a way with the girls. Takes after me there." He began to laugh, a slow wheezy chuckle. "I've had a good life—a very good life. Plenty of everything."

Pilar said:

"In Spain we have a proverb. It is like this: *Take what you like and pay for it, says God.*"

Simeon beat an appreciative hand on the arm of his chair.

"That's good. That's the stuff. Take what you like. . . . I've done that—all my life—taken what I wanted. . . ."

Pilar said, her voice high and clear, and suddenly arresting:

"And have you paid for it?"

Simeon stopped laughing to himself. He sat up and stared at her. He said: "What's that you say?"

"I said, have you paid for it, Grandfather?"

Simeon Lee said slowly:

"I—don't know. . . ."

Then, beating his fist on the arm of the chair, he cried out with sudden anger:

"What makes you say that, girl? What makes you say that?"

Pilar said: "I—wondered."

Her hand, holding the screen, was arrested. Her eyes were dark and mysterious. She sat, her head thrown back, conscious of herself, of her womanhood.

Simeon said: "You devil's brat. . . ."

She said softly:

"But you like me, Grandfather. You like me to sit here with you."

Simeon said:

"Yes, I like it. It's a long time since I've seen anything so young and beautiful . . . it does me good, warms my old bones. . . . And you're my own flesh and blood. . . . Good for Jennifer, she turned out to be the best of the bunch after all!"

Pilar sat there, smiling.

"Mind you, you don't fool me," said Simeon. "I know why you sit here so patiently and listen to me droning on. It's money—it's all money . . . or do you pretend you love your old grandfather?"

Pilar said:

"No, I do not love you. But I like you. I like you very much. You must believe that, for it is true. I think you have been wicked but I like that too. You are more real than the other people in this house. And you have interesting things to say. You have traveled and you have led a life of adventure. If I were a man I would be like that, too."

Simeon nodded.

"Yes, I believe you would. . . . We've gypsy blood in us, so it's always been said. It hasn't shown much in my children—except Harry—but I think it's come out in you. I can be patient, mind you, when it's necessary. I waited once fifteen years to get even with a man who'd done me an injury. That's another characteristic of the Lees. They don't forget! They'll avenge a wrong if they have to wait years to do it. A man swindled me. I waited fifteen years till I saw my chance—and then I struck. I ruined him. Cleaned him right out!"

He laughed softly.

Pilar said:

"That was in South Africa?"

"Yes. A grand country."

"You have been back there, yes?"

"I went back five years after I married. That was the last time."

"But before that? You were there for many years?"

"Yes."

"Tell me about it."

He began to talk. Pilar, shielding her face, listened.

His voice slowed, wearied. . . . He said:

"Wait, I'll show you something."

He pulled himself carefully to his feet. Then, with his stick, he limped slowly across the room. He opened the big safe. Turning, he beckoned her to him.

"There, look at these. Feel them—let them run through your fingers."

He looked into her wandering face and laughed.

"Do you know what they are? Diamonds, child, diamonds."

Pilar's eyes opened. She said as she bent over:

"But they are little pebbles, that is all."

Simeon laughed.

"They are uncut diamonds. That is how they are found —like this."

Pilar asked incredulously:

"And if they were cut they would be real diamonds?"

"Certainly."

"They would flash and sparkle?"

"Flash and sparkle."

Pilar said childishly:

"Oh-o-o, I cannot believe it!"

He was amused.

"It's quite true."

"They are valuable?"

"Fairly valuable. Difficult to say before they are cut—anyway this little lot is worth several thousands of pounds."

Pilar said, with a space between each two words:

"Several—thousands—of—pounds?"

"Say nine or ten thousand—they're biggish stones, you see."

Pilar asked, her eyes opening:

"But why do you not sell them then?"

"Because I like to have them here."

"But all that money?"

"I don't need the money."

"Oh—I see." Pilar looked impressed.

She said:

"But why do you not have them cut and made beautiful?"

"Because I prefer them like this." His face was set in a grim line. He turned away and began speaking to himself. "They take me back—the touch of them, the feel of them through my fingers. . . . It all comes back to me, the sunshine, and the smell of the veldt, the oxen—old Eb—all the boys—the evenings. . . ."

There was a soft tap on the door.

Simeon said:

"Put 'em back in the safe and bang it to."

Then he called: "Come in."

Horbury came in, soft and deferential.

He said:

"Tea is ready downstairs."

III

Hilda said:

"So there you are, David. I've been looking for you everywhere. Don't let's stay in this room, it's so frightfully cold."

David did not answer for a minute. He was standing looking at a chair, a low chair with faded satin upholstery.

He said abruptly:

"That's her chair . . . the chair she always sat in . . . just the same—it's just the same. Only faded, of course."

A little frown creased Hilda's broad forehead. She said:

"I see. Do let's come out of here, David, it's frightfully cold."

David took no notice. Looking round, he said:

"She sat in here mostly. I remember sitting on that stool there while she read to me. *Jack the Giant Killer*, that was it—*Jack the Giant Killer*. I must have been six years old then."

Hilda put a firm hand through his arm.

"Come back to the drawing-room, dear. There's no heating in this room."

He turned obediently, but she felt a little shiver go through him.

"Just the same," he murmured. "Just the same. As though time had stood still."

Hilda looked worried. She said in a cheerful, determined voice:

"I wonder where the others are? It must be nearly tea time."

David disengaged his arm and opened another door.

"There used to be a piano in here . . . oh, yes, here it is! I wonder if it's in tune?"

He sat down and opened the lid, running his hands lightly over the keys.

"Yes, it's evidently kept tuned."

He began to play.

His touch was good, the melody flowed out from under his fingers.

Hilda asked:

"What is that? I seem to know it and I can't quite remember."

He said:

"I haven't played it for years. *She* used to play it. One of Mendelssohn's *Songs Without Words*."

The sweet, over-sweet, melody filled the room. Hilda said: "Play some Mozart, do."

David shook his head. He began another Mendelssohn. Then, suddenly, he brought his hands down upon the keys in a harsh discord. He got up. He was trembling all over. Hilda went to him.

She said:

"David—David. . . ."

He said:

"It's nothing—it's nothing. . . ."

IV

The bell pealed aggressively. Tressilian rose from his seat in the pantry and went slowly out and along to the door.

The bell pealed again. Tressilian frowned. Through the frosted glass of the door he saw the silhouette of a man wearing a slouch hat.

Tressilian passed a hand over his forehead. Something worried him. It was as though everything was happening twice.

Surely this had happened before. Surely—

He drew back the latch and opened the door.

Then the spell broke. The man standing there said:

"Is this where Mr. Simeon Lee lives?"

"Yes. sir."

"I'd like to see him, please."

A faint echo of memory awoke in Tressilian. It was an intonation of voice that he remembered from the old days when Mr. Lee was first in England.

Tressilian shook his head dubiously.

"Mr. Lee is an invalid, sir. He doesn't see many people now. If you—"

The stranger interrupted.

He drew out an envelope and handed it to the butler.

"Please give this to Mr. Lee."

"Yes, sir."

V

Simeon Lee took the envelope. He drew out the single sheet of paper it held. He looked surprised. His eyebrows rose, but he smiled.

"By all that's wonderful!" he said.

Then to the butler:

"Show Mr. Farr up here, Tressilian."

"Yes, sir."

Simeon said:

"I was just thinking of old Ebenezer Farr. He was my partner out there in Kimberley. Now here's his son come along!"

Tressilian reappeared. He announced:

"Mr. Farr."

Stephen Farr came in with a trace of nervousness. He disguised it by putting on a little extra swagger. He said— and just for the moment his South African accent was more marked than usual—

"Mr. Lee?"

"I'm glad to see you. So you're Eb's boy."

Stephen Farr grinned rather sheepishly.

He said:

"My first visit to the old country. Father always told me to look you up if I did come."

"Quite right." The old man looked round. "This is my granddaughter, Pilar Estravados."

"How do you do?" said Pilar demurely.

Stephen Farr thought with a touch of admiration:

"Cool little devil. She was surprised to see me, but it only showed for a flash."

He said, rather heavily:

"I'm very pleased to make your acquaintance, Miss Estravados."

"Thank you," said Pilar.

Simeon Lee said:

"Sit down and tell me all about yourself. Are you in England for long?"

"Oh, I sha'n't hurry myself now I've really got here!"

Stephen laughed, throwing his head back.

Simeon Lee said:

"Quite right. You must stay here with us for a while."

"Oh, look here, sir. I can't butt in like that. It's only two days to Christmas."

"You must spend Christmas with us—unless you've got other plans?"

"Well, no, I haven't, but I don't like—"

Simeon said: "That's settled." He turned his head. "Pilar?"

"Yes, Grandfather."

"Go and tell Lydia we shall have another guest. Ask her to come up here."

Pilar left the room. Stephen's eyes followed her. Simeon noted the fact with amusement.

He said:

"You've come straight here from South Africa?"

"Pretty well."

They began to talk of that country.

Lydia entered a few minutes later.

Simeon said:

"This is Stephen Farr, son of my old friend and partner, Ebenezer Farr. He's going to be with us for Christmas if you can find room for him."

Lydia smiled.

"Of course." Her eyes took in the stranger's appearance. His bronzed face and blue eyes and the easy backward tilt of his head.

"My daughter-in-law," said Simeon.

Stephen said:

"I feel rather embarrassed—butting in on a family party like this."

"You're one of the family, my boy," said Simeon. "Think of yourself as that."

"You're too kind, sir."

Pilar reentered the room. She sat down quietly by the fire and picked up the hand screen. She used it as a fan, slowly tilting her wrist to and fro. Her eyes were demure and downcast.

35

Part III ——————DECEMBER 24TH

I

"DO YOU REALLY want me to stay on here, Father?" asked Harry. He tilted his head back. "I'm stirring up rather a hornet's nest you know."

"What do you mean?" asked Simeon sharply.

"Brother Alfred," said Harry. "Good brother Alfred! He, if I may say so, resents my presence here."

"The devil he does!" snapped Simeon. "I'm master in this house."

"All the same, sir, I expect you're pretty dependent on Alfred. I don't want to upset—"

"You'll do as I tell you," snapped his father.

Harry yawned.

"Don't know that I shall be able to stick a stay-at-home life. Pretty stifling to a fellow who's knocked about the world."

His father said:

"You'd better marry and settle down."

Harry said:

"Whom shall I marry? Pity one can't marry one's niece. Young Pilar is devilish attractive."

"You've noticed that?"

"Talking of settling down, fat George has done well for himself as far as looks go. Who was she?"

Simeon shrugged his shoulders.

"How should I know? George picked her up at a mannequin parade, I believe. She says her father was a retired naval officer."

Harry said:

"Probably a second mate of a coasting steamer. George will have a bit of trouble with her if he's not careful."

"George," said Simeon Lee, "is a fool."

Harry said:

"What did she marry him for? His money?"

Simeon shrugged his shoulders.

Harry said:

"Well, you think you can square Alfred all right?"

"We'll soon settle that," said Simeon grimly.

He touched a bell that stood on a table near him. Horbury appeared promptly. Simeon said:

"Ask Mr. Alfred to come here."

Horbury went out and Harry drawled:

"That fellow listens at doors!"

Simeon shrugged his shoulders.

"Probably."

Alfred hurried in. His face twitched when he saw his brother. Ignoring Harry, he said pointedly:

"You wanted me, Father?"

"Yes, sit down. I was just thinking we must reorganize things a bit now that we have two more people living in the house."

"Two?"

"Pilar will make her home here, naturally. And Harry is home for good."

Alfred said:

"Harry is coming to live here?"

"Why not, old boy?" said Harry.

Alfred turned sharply to him.

"I should think that you yourself would see that!"

"Well, sorry—but I don't."

"After everything that has happened? The disgraceful way you behaved. The scandal—"

Harry waved an easy hand.

"All that's in the past, old boy."

"You behaved abominably to Father after all he'd done for you."

"Look here, Alfred, it strikes me that's Father's business, not yours. If he's willing to forgive and forget—"

"I'm willing," said Simeon. "Harry's my son, after all, you know, Alfred."

"Yes, but—I resent it—for Father's sake."

Simeon said:

"Harry's coming here! I wish it. . . ." He laid a hand gently on the latter's shoulder. "I'm very fond of Harry."

Alfred got up and left the room. His face was white. Harry rose too and went after him laughing.

Simeon sat chuckling to himself. Then he started and looked round.

"Who the devil's that? Oh, it's you, Horbury. Don't creep about that way."

"I beg your pardon, sir."

"Never mind. Listen, I've got some orders for you. I want everybody to come up here after lunch—*everybody.*"

"Yes, sir."

"There's something else. When they come, you come with them. And when you get half-way along the passage *raise your voice,* so that I can hear. Any pretext will do. Understand?"

"Yes, sir."

Horbury went downstairs. He said to Tressilian:

"If you ask me, we *are* going to have a merry Christmas!"

Tressilian said sharply:

"What d'you mean?"

"You wait and see, Mr. Tressilian. It's Christmas Eve to-day and a nice Christmas spirit abroad, I don't think!"

II

They came into the room and paused at the doorway. Simeon was speaking into the telephone. He waved a hand to them.

"Sit down, all of you, I sha'n't be a minute."

He went on speaking into the telephone.

"Is that Charlton, Hodgkins & Brace? Is that you, Charlton? Simeon Lee speaking. Yes, isn't it? . . . Yes. . . . No, I wanted you to make a new will for me. . . . Yes, it's some time since I made the other. . . . Circumstances have altered. . . . Oh, no, no hurry. Don't want you to spoil your Christmas. Say Boxing Day or the day after. Come along and I'll tell you what I want done. No, that's quite all right. I sha'n't be dying just yet."

He replaced the receiver, then looked round at the eight members of his family. He cackled and said:

"You're all looking very glum. What is the matter?"

Alfred said:

"You sent for us. . . ."

Simeon said quickly:

"Oh, sorry—nothing portentous about it. Did you think it was a family council? No, I'm just rather tired to-day, that's all. None of you need come up after dinner. I shall go to bed. I want to be fresh for Christmas Day."

He grinned at them. George said portentously:

"Of course. . . . Of course. . . ."

Simeon said:

"Grand old institution, Christmas! Promotes solidarity of family feeling. What do *you* think, Magdalene, my dear?"

Magdalene Lee jumped. Her rather silly little mouth flew open and then shut itself. She said:

"Oh— Oh, *yes!*"

Simon said:

"Let me see, you lived with a retired naval officer"—he paused—"your *father*—don't suppose you made much of Christmas; it needs a big family for that!"

"Well—well—yes, perhaps it does."

Simeon's eyes slid past her.

"Don't want to talk of anything unpleasant at this time of year, but you know, George, I'm afraid I'll have to cut down your allowance a bit. My establishment here is going to cost me a bit more to run in future."

George got very red.

"But look here, Father, you can't do that!"

Simeon said softly:

"Oh, I can't?"

"My expenses are very heavy already. Very heavy. As it is, I don't know how I make both ends meet. It needs the most rigorous economy."

"Let your wife do a bit more of it," said Simeon. "Women are good at that sort of thing. They often think of economies where a man would never have dreamed of them. And a clever woman can make her own clothes. My wife, I remember, was clever with her needle. About all she *was* clever with—a good woman but deadly dull—"

David sprang up. His father said:

"Sit down, boy, you'll knock something over—"

David said:

"My mother—"

Simeon said:

"Your mother had the brains of a louse! And it seems to me she's transmitted those brains to her children." He raised himself up suddenly. A red spot appeared in each cheek. His voice came high and shrill. "You're not worth a penny piece, any of you! I'm sick of you all! You're not *men!* You're weaklings—a set of namby-pamby weaklings— Pilar's worth any two of you put together! I'll swear to Heaven I've got a better son somewhere in the world than any of you even if you are born the right side of the blanket!"

"Here, Father, hold hard," cried Harry.

He had jumped up and stood there, a frown on his usually good-humoured face.

Simeon snapped:

"The same goes for *you!* What have *you* ever done? Whined to me for money from all over the world! I tell you I'm sick of the sight of you all! Get out!"

He leaned back in his chair, panting a little.

Slowly, one by one his family went out. George was red and indignant, Magdalene looked frightened. David was pale and quivering. Harry blustered out of the room. Alfred went like a man in a dream. Lydia followed him with her head held high. Only Hilda paused in the doorway and came slowly back.

She stood over him and he started when he opened his eyes and found her standing there. There was something menacing in the solid way she stood there quite immovably.

He said irritably:

"What is it?"

Hilda said:

"When your letter came I believed what you said—that you wanted your family round you for Christmas. I persuaded David to come."

Simeon said:

"Well, what of it?"

Hilda said slowly:

"You *did* want your family round you—but not for the purpose you said! You wanted them there, didn't you, in order to set them all by the ears? God help you, it's your idea of *fun!*"

Simeon chuckled.

He said:

"I always had rather a specialized sense of humour. I don't expect anyone else to appreciate the joke. *I'm* enjoying it!"

She said nothing. A vague feeling of apprehension came over Simeon Lee. He said sharply:

"What are you thinking about?"

Hilda Lee said slowly:

"I'm afraid. . . ."

Simeon said:

"You're afraid—of me?"

Hilda said:

"Not *of* you. I'm afraid—*for* you!"

Like a judge who has delivered sentence, she turned away. She marched, slowly and heavily, out of the room. . . .

Simeon sat staring at the door.

Then he got to his feet and made his way over to the safe.

He murmured:

"Let's have a look at my beauties. . . ."

III

The doorbell rang about a quarter to eight.

Tressilian went to answer it. He returned to his pantry to find Horbury there, picking up the coffee cups off the tray and looking at the mark on them.

"Who was it?" said Horbury.

"Superintendent of Police—Mr. Sugden—mind what you're doing!"

Horbury had dropped one of the cups with a crash.

"Look at that now," lamented Tressilian. "Eleven years I've had the washing up of those and never one broken and now you come along touching things you've no business to touch and look what happens!"

"I'm sorry, Mr. Tressilian. I am indeed," the other apologized. His face was covered with perspiration. "I don't know how it happened. Did you say a Superintendent of Police had called?"

"Yes, Mr. Sugden."

The valet passed a tongue over pale lips.

"What—what did he want?"

"Collecting for the Police Orphanage."

"Oh!" The valet straightened his shoulders. In a more natural voice he said:

"Did he get anything?"

"I took up the book to old Mr. Lee, and he told me to fetch the Superintendent up and to put the sherry on the table."

"Nothing but begging this time of year," said Horbury. "The old devil's generous, I will say that for him, in spite of his other failings."

Tressilian said with dignity:

"Mr. Lee has always been an open-handed gentleman."

Horbury nodded.

"It's the best thing about him! Well, I'll be off now."

"Going to the pictures?"

"I expect so. Ta ta, Mr. Tressilian."

He went through the door that led to the servants' hall.

Tressilian looked up at the clock hanging on the wall.

He went into the dining-room and laid the rolls in the napkins.

Then, after assuring himself that everything was as it should be, he sounded the gong in the hall.

As the last note died away the Superintendent came down the stairs. Superintendent Sugden was a large, handsome man. He wore a tightly buttoned blue suit and moved with a sense of his own importance!

He said affably:

"I rather think we shall have a frost to-night. Good thing; the weather's been very unseasonable lately."

Tressilian said, shaking his head:

"The damp affects my rheumatism."

The Superintendent said that rheumatism was a painful complaint and Tressilian let him out by the front door.

The old butler refastened the door and came back slowly into the hall. He passed his hand over his eyes and sighed. Then he stretched his back as he saw Lydia pass into the drawing-room. George Lee was just coming down the stairs. Tressilian hovered ready. When the last guest, Magdalene, had entered the drawing-room, he made his own appearance, murmuring:

"Dinner is served."

In his way Tressilian was a connoisseur of ladies' dress. He always noted and criticized the gowns of the ladies as he circled round the table, decanter in hand.

Mrs. Alfred, he noted, had got on her new flowered black and white taffeta. A bold design, very striking, but she could carry it off, though many ladies couldn't. The dress Mrs. George had on was a pretty model, he was pretty sure of that. Must have cost a pretty penny! He wondered how Mr. George would like paying for it! Mr. George didn't like spending money—he never had. Mrs. David now, a nice lady, but didn't have any idea of how to dress. For her figure, plain black velvet would have been the best. Figured velvet, and crimson at that, was a bad choice. Miss Peela, now, it didn't matter what she wore; with her figure and her hair she looked well in anything. A flimsy cheap little white gown it was, though. Still, Mr. Lee would soon see to that! Taken to her wonderful, he had. Always was the same way when a gentleman was elderly. A young face could do anything with him!

"Hock or claret?" murmured Tressilian in a deferential whisper in Mrs. George's ear. Out of the tail of his eye he noted that Walter, the footman, was handing the vegetables before the gravy again—after all he had been told!

Tressilian went round with the soufflé. It struck him, now that his interest in the ladies' toilets and his misgivings over Walter's deficiencies were a thing of the past, that everyone was very silent to-night. At least, not exactly silent—Mr. Harry was talking enough for twenty—no, not Mr. Harry, the South African gentleman. And the others were talking too, but only, as it were, in spasms. There was something a little—queer about them.

Mr. Alfred, for instance, he looked downright ill. As though he had had a shock or something. Quite dazed he

42

looked and just turning over the food on his plate without eating it. The mistress she was worried about him. Tressilian could see that. Kept looking down the table towards him—not noticeably, of course—just quietly. Mr. George was very red in the face—gobbling his food, he was, without tasting it. He'd get a stroke one day if he wasn't careful. Mrs. George wasn't eating. Slimming, as likely as not. Miss Peela seemed to be enjoying her food all right and talking and laughing up at the South African gentleman. Properly taken with her, he was. Didn't seem to be anything on *their* minds!

Mr. David? Tressilian felt worried about Mr. David. Just like his mother, he was, to look at. And remarkably young looking still. But nervous—there, he'd knocked over his glass.

Tressilian whisked it away, mopped up the stream deftly. It was all over. Mr. David hardly seemed to notice what he had done. Just sat staring in front of him with a white face.

Thinking of white faces, funny the way Horbury had looked in the pantry just now when he'd heard a police officer had come to the house . . . almost as though—

Tressilian's mind stopped with a jerk. Walter had dropped a pear off the dish he was handing. Footmen were no good nowadays! They might be stable boys the way they went on!

He went round with the port. Mr. Harry seemed a bit distrait to-night. Kept looking at Mr. Alfred. Never had been any love lost between those two, not even as boys. Mr. Harry, of course, had always been his father's favourite and that had rankled with Mr. Alfred. Mr. Lee had never cared for Mr. Alfred much. A pity, when Mr. Alfred always seemed so devoted to his father.

There, Mrs. Alfred was getting up now. She swept round the table. Very nice that design on the taffeta, that cape suited her. A very graceful lady.

He went out to the pantry, closing the dining-room door on the gentlemen with their port.

He took the coffee tray into the drawing-room. The four ladies were sitting there rather uncomfortably, he thought. They were not talking. He handed round the coffee in silence.

He went out again. As he went into his pantry he heard the dining-room door open. David Lee came out and went along the hall to the drawing-room.

Tressilian went back into his pantry. He read the riot act to Walter. Walter was nearly, if not quite, impertinent!

Tressilian, alone in his pantry, sat down rather wearily.

He had a feeling of depression. Christmas Eve, and all this strain and tension . . . he didn't like it!

With an effort he roused himself. He went to the drawing-room and collected the coffee cups. The room was empty except for Lydia who was standing half concealed by the window curtain at the far end of the room. She was standing there looking out into the night.

From the next room the piano sounded.

Mr. David playing. But why, Tressilian asked himself, did Mr. David play the *Dead March?* For that's what it was. Oh, indeed, things were very wrong.

He went slowly along the hall and back into his pantry.

It was then he first heard the noise from overhead . . . a crashing of china, the overthrowing of furniture—a series of cracks and bumps.

"Good gracious!" thought Tressilian. "Whatever is the master doing? What's happening up there?"

And then, clear and high, came a scream—a horrible high wailing scream that died away in a choke or gurgle.

Tressilian stood there a moment paralyzed, then he ran out into the hall and up the broad staircase. Others were with him. That scream had been heard all over the house.

They raced up the stairs and round the bend, past a recess with statues gleaming white and eerie, and along the straight passage to Simeon Lee's door. Mr. Farr was there already and Mrs. David. She was leaning back against the wall and he was twisting at the door handle.

"The door's locked," he was saying. "The door's locked!"

Harry Lee pushed past and wrested it from him. He, too, turned and twisted at the handle.

"Father!" he shouted. "Father, let us in."

He held up his hand and in the silence they all listened. There was no answer. No sound from inside the room.

The front doorbell rang but no one paid any attention to it. Stephen Farr said:

"We've got to break the door down. It's the only way."

Harry said:

"That's going to be a tough job. These doors are good solid stuff. Come on, Alfred."

They heaved and strained. Finally they went and got an oak bench and used it as a battering ram. The door gave at last. Its hinges splintered and the door sank shuddering from its frame.

For a minute they stood there huddled together looking in. What they saw was a sight that no one of them ever forgot. . . .

There had clearly been a terrific struggle. Heavy furniture was overturned. China vases lay splintered on the floor. In the middle of the hearthrug in front of the blazing fire, lay Simeon Lee in a great pool of blood . . . blood was splashed all round. The place was like a shambles.

44

There was a long shuddering sigh and then two voices spoke in turn. Strangely enough the words they uttered were both quotations.

David Lee said:

"The mills of God grind slowly. . . ."

Lydia's voice came like a fluttering whisper:

"Who would have thought the old man to have had so much blood in him?"

IV

Superintendent Sugden had rung the bell three times. Finally, in desperation he pounded on the knocker.

A scared Walter at length opened the door.

"Oh—er," he said. A look of relief came over his face. "I was just ringing up the police."

"What for?" said Superintendent Sugden sharply. "What's going on here?"

Walter whispered:

"It's old Mr. Lee. *He's been done in. . . ."*

The Superintendent pushed past him and ran up the stairs. He came into the room without anyone being aware of his entrance. As he entered he saw Pilar bend forward and pick up something from the floor. He saw David Lee standing with his hands over his eyes.

He saw the others huddled into a little group. Alfred Lee alone had stepped near his father's body. He stood now quite close, looking down. His face was blank.

George Lee was saying importantly:

"Nothing must be touched—remember that—*nothing*—till the police arrive. That is *most* important."

"Excuse me," said Sugden.

He pushed his way forward, gently thrusting the ladies aside.

Alfred Lee recognized him.

"Ah," he said. "It's you, Superintendent Sugden. You've got here very quickly."

"Yes, Mr. Lee." Superintendent Sugden did not waste time on explanations. "What's all this?"

"My father," said Alfred Lee, "has been killed—*murdered. . . ."*

His voice broke.

Magdalene began suddenly to sob hysterically.

Superintendent Sugden held up a large official hand.

He said authoritatively:

"Will everybody kindly leave the room except Mr. Lee and —er—Mr. George Lee. . . ."

They moved slowly towards the door, reluctantly, like sheep. Superintendent Sugden intercepted Pilar suddenly.

"Excuse me, miss," he said pleasantly. "Nothing must be touched or disturbed."

She stared at him. Stephen Farr said impatiently:

"Of course not. She understands that."

Superintendent Sugden said, still in the same pleasant manner:

"You picked up something from the floor just now?"

Pilar's eyes opened. She stared and said incredulously: *"I did?"*

Superintendent Sugden was still pleasant. His voice was just a little firmer.

He said:

"Yes, I saw you. . . ."

"Oh!"

"So please give it to me. It's in your hand now."

Slowly Pilar unclosed her hand. There lay in it a wisp of rubber and a small object made of wood. Superintendent Sugden took them, enclosed them in an envelope and put them away in his breast pocket.

He said:

"Thank you."

He turned away. Just for a minute Stephen Farr's eyes showed a startled respect. It was as though he had underestimated the large handsome superintendent.

They went slowly out of the room. Behind them they heard the Superintendent's voice saying officially:

"And now, if you please—"

V

"Nothing like a wood fire," said Colonel Johnson as he threw on an additional log and then drew his chair nearer to the blaze. "Help yourself," he added, hospitably calling attention to the tantalus and syphon that stood near his guest's elbow.

The guest raised a polite hand in negation. Cautiously, he edged his own chair nearer to the blazing logs, though he was of the opinion that the opportunity for roasting the soles of one's feet (like some medieval torture) did not offset the cold draught that swirled round the back of the shoulders.

Colonel Johnson, Chief Constable of Middleshire, might be of the opinion that nothing could beat a wood fire, but Hercule Poirot was of the opinion that central heating could and did every time!

"Amazing business, that Cartwright case," remarked the host reminiscently. "Amazing man! Enormous charm of manner. Why, when he came here with you, he had us all eating out of his hand."

He shook his head.

"We'll never have anything like that case!" he said. "Nicotine poisoning is rare, fortunately."

"There was a time when you would have considered all poisoning un-English," suggested Hercule Poirot. "A device of foreigners! Unsportsmanlike!"

"I hardly think we could say that," said the Chief Constable. "Plenty of poisoning by arsenic—probably a good deal more than has ever been suspected."

"Possibly, yes."

"Always an awkward business, a poisoning case," said Johnson. "Conflicting testimony of the experts—then doctors are usually so extremely cautious in what they say. Always a difficult case to take to a jury. No, if one *must* have murder (which Heaven forbid) give me a straightforward case. Something where there's no ambiguity about the cause of death."

Poirot nodded.

"The bullet wound, the cut throat, the crushed-in skull? It is there your preference lies?"

"Oh, don't call it a preference, my dear fellow. Don't harbour the idea that I *like* murder cases! Hope I never have another. Anyway, we ought to be safe enough during your visit."

Poirot began modestly:

"My reputation—"

But Johnson had gone on.

"Christmas time," he said. "Peace, good will—and all that kind of thing. Good will all round."

Hercule Poirot leaned back in his chair. He joined his fingertips. He studied his host thoughtfully.

He murmured:

"It is, then, your opinion, that Christmas time is an unlikely season for crime?"

"That's what I said."

"Why?"

"Why?" Johnson was thrown slightly out of his stride. "Well, as I've just said—season of good cheer and all that!"

Hercule Poirot murmured:

"The British, they are so sentimental!"

Johnson said stoutly:

"What if we are? What if we do like the old ways, the old traditional festivities? What's the harm?"

"There is no harm. It is all most charming! But let us

for a moment examine *facts*. You have said that Christmas is a season of good cheer. That means, does it not, a lot of eating and drinking? It means, in fact, the *over*eating! And with the overeating there comes the indigestion! And with the indigestion there comes the irritability!"

"Crimes," said Colonel Johnson, "are not committed from irritability."

"I am not so sure! Take another point. There is, at Christmas, a spirit of good will. It is, as you say, 'the thing to do.' Old quarrels are patched up, those who have disagreed, consent to agree once more, even if it is only temporarily."

Johnson nodded.

"Bury the hatchet, that's right."

Poirot pursued his theme.

"And families now, families who have been separated throughout the year assemble once more together. Now under these conditions, my friend, you must admit that there will occur a great amount of *strain*. People who do not *feel* amiable are putting great pressure on themselves to *appear* amiable! There is at Christmas time a great deal of *hypocrisy*, honourable hypocrisy, hypocrisy undertaken *pour le bon motif, c'est entendu,* but nevertheless hypocrisy!"

"Well, I shouldn't put it quite like that myself," said Colonel Johnson doubtfully.

Poirot beamed upon him.

"No, no. It is *I* who am putting it like that, not *you!* I am pointing out to you that under these conditions— mental strain, physical *malaise*—it is highly probable that dislikes that were before merely mild, and disagreements that were trivial, might suddenly assume a more serious character. The result of pretending to be a more amiable, a more forgiving, a more high-minded person than one really is, has sooner or later the effect of causing one to behave as a more disagreeable, a more ruthless and an altogether more unpleasant person than is actually the case! If you dam the stream of natural behaviour, *mon ami,* sooner or later the dam bursts and a cataclysm occurs!"

Colonel Johnson looked at him doubtfully.

"Never know when you're serious and when you're pulling my leg," he grumbled.

Poirot smiled at him.

"I am not serious! Not in the least am I serious! But all the same, it is true what I say—artificial conditions bring about their natural reaction.

Colonel Johnson's man-servant entered the room.

"Superintendent Sugden on the phone, sir."

"Right. I'll come."

With a word of apology the Chief Constable left the room.

He returned some three minutes later. His face was grave and perturbed.

"Damn it all!" he said. "Case of murder! On Christmas Eve, too!"

Poirot's eyebrows rose.

"It is that definitely—murder, I mean?"

"Eh? Oh, no other solution possible! Perfectly clear case. Murder—and a brutal murder at that!"

"Who is the victim?"

"Old Simeon Lee. One of the richest men we've got! Made his money in South Africa originally. Gold—no, diamonds, I believe. He sunk an immense fortune in manufacturing some particular gadget of mining machinery. His own invention, I believe. Anyway, it's paid him hand over fist! They say he's a millionaire twice over."

Poirot said:

"He was well liked, yes?"

Johnson said slowly:

"Don't think anyone liked him. Queer sort of chap. He's been an invalid for some years now. I don't know very much about him myself. But of course he is one of the big figures of the county."

"So this case, it will make a big stir?"

"Yes. I must get over to Longdale as fast as I can."

He hesitated, looking at his guest. Poirot answered the unspoken question.

"You would like that I should accompany you?"

Johnson said awkwardly:

"Seems a shame to ask you. But, well, you know how it is! Superintendent Sugden is a good man, none better; painstaking, careful, thoroughly sound—but—well, he's not an *imaginative* chap in any way. Should like very much, as you are here, benefit of your advice."

He halted a little over the end part of his speech, making it somewhat telegraphic in style. Poirot responded quickly.

"I shall be delighted. You can count on me to assist you in any way I can. We must not hurt the feelings of the good Superintendent. It will be his case—not mine. I am only the unofficial consultant."

Colonel Johnson said warmly:

"You're a good fellow, Poirot."

With those words of commendation, the two men started out.

It was a constable who opened the front door to them and saluted. Behind him, Superintendent Sugden advanced down the hall and said:

"Glad you've got here, sir. Shall we come into this room here on the left—Mr. Lee's study? I'd like to run over the main outlines. The whole thing's a rum business."

He ushered them into a small room on the left of the hall. There was a telephone there and a big desk covered with papers. The walls were lined with bookcases.

The Chief Constable said:

"Sugden, this is M. Hercule Poirot. You may have heard of him. Just happened to be staying with me. Superintendent Sugden."

Poirot made a little bow and looked the other man over. He saw a tall man with square shoulders and a military bearing who had an aquiline nose, a pugnacious jaw and a large flourishing chestnut coloured moustache. Sugden stared hard at Hercule Poirot after acknowledging the introduction. Hercule Poirot stared hard at Superintendent Sugden's moustache. Its luxuriance seemed to fascinate him.

The Superintendent said:

"Of course I have heard of you, Mr. Poirot. You were in this part of the world some years ago if I remember rightly. Death of Sir Bartholomew Strange. Poisoning case. Nicotine. Not my district but of course I heard all about it."

Colonel Johnson said impatiently:

"Now, then, Sugden, let's have the facts. A clear case, you said."

"Yes, sir, it's murder right enough—not a doubt of that. Mr. Lee's throat was cut—jugular vein severed I understand from the doctor. But there's something very odd about the whole matter."

"You mean—"

"I'd like you to hear my story first, sir. These are the circumstances: This afternoon, after five o'clock, I was rung up by Mr. Lee at Addlesfield police station. He sounded a bit odd over the phone—asked me to come and see him at eight o'clock this evening—made a special point of the time. Moreover, he instructed me to say to the butler that I was collecting subscriptions for some Police charity."

The Chief Constable looked up sharply.

"Wanted some plausible pretext to get you into the house?"

"That's right, sir. Well, naturally, Mr. Lee is an important person, and I acceded to his request. I got here a little before eight o'clock, and represented myself as seeking sub-scriptions for the Police Orphanage. The butler went away and returned to tell me that Mr. Lee would see me. Thereupon he showed me up to Mr. Lee's room which is situated on the next floor, immediately over the dining-room."

Superintendent Sugden paused, drew a breath and then proceeded in a somewhat official manner with his report.

"Mr. Lee was seated in a chair by the fireplace. He was wearing a dressing-gown. When the butler had left the room and closed the door, Mr. Lee asked me to sit down near him. He then said rather hesitatingly that he wanted to give me particulars of a robbery. I asked him what had been taken. He replied that he had reason to believe that diamonds (uncut diamonds, I think he said) to the value of several thousand pounds had been stolen from his safe."

"Diamonds, eh?" said the Chief Constable.

"Yes, sir. I asked him various routine questions but his manner was very uncertain and his replies were somewhat vague in character. At last he said: 'You must understand, Superintendent, that I may be mistaken in this matter.' I said: 'I do not quite understand, sir. Either the diamonds are missing, or they are not missing—one or the other.' He replied: 'The diamonds are certainly missing, but it is just possible, Superintendent, that their disappearance may be simply a rather foolish kind of practical joke.' Well, that seemed odd to me, but I said nothing. He went on: 'It is difficult for me to explain in detail, but what it amounts to is this: So far as I can see only two persons can possibly have the stones. One of those persons might have done it as a joke. If the other person took them, then they have definitely been stolen.' I said: 'What exactly do you want me to do, sir?' He said quickly: 'I want you, Superintendent, to return here in about an hour—no, make it a little more than that—say, nine-fifteen. At that time I shall be able to tell you definitely whether I have been robbed or not.' I was a little mystified, but I agreed and went away."

Colonel Johnson commented:

"Curious—very curious. What do you say, Poirot?"

Hercule Poirot said:

"May I ask, Superintendent, what conclusions you yourself drew?"

The Superintendent stroked his jaw as he replied carefully:

"Well, various ideas occurred to me, but on the whole, I figured it out this way. There was no question of any practical joke. The diamonds had been stolen all right. But the old gentleman wasn't sure who'd done it. It's my opinion that he was speaking the truth when he said that it might have been one of two people—and of those two people one was a servant and the other was a *member of the family*."

Poirot nodded appreciatively.

"*Très bien.* Yes, that explains his attitude very well."

"Hence his desire that I should return later. In the interval he meant to have an interview with the person in question. He would tell them that he had already spoken of the matter to the police but that if restitution were promptly made he could hush the matter up."

Colonel Johnson said:

"And if the suspect didn't respond?"

"In that case, he meant to place the investigation in our hands."

Colonel Johnson frowned and twisted his moustache. He demurred.

"Why not take that course *before* calling you in?"

"No, no, sir." The Superintendent shook his head. "Don't you see, if he had done that, it might have been bluff. It wouldn't have been half so convincing. The person might say to himself: 'The old man won't call the police in, no matter what he suspects!' But if the old gentleman says to him, 'I've *already spoken to the Police*, the Superintendent has only just left.' Then the thief asks the butler, say, and the butler confirms that. He says, 'Yes, the Superintendent was here just before dinner.' Then the thief is convinced the old gentleman means business and it's up to him to cough up the stones."

"H'm, yes, I see that," said Colonel Johnson. "Any idea, Sugden, who this 'member of the family' might be?"

"No, sir."

"No indication whatsoever?"

"None."

Johnson shook his head. Then he said:

"Well, let's get on with it."

Superintendent Sugden resumed his official manner.

"I returned to the house, sir, at nine-fifteen precisely. Just as I was about to ring the front doorbell, I heard a scream from inside the house and then a confused sound of shouts and a general commotion. I rang several times and also used the knocker. It was three or four minutes before the door was answered. When the footman at last opened it I could see that something momentous had occurred. He was shaking all over and looked as though he was about to faint. He gasped out that Mr. Lee had been murdered. I ran hastily upstairs. I found Mr. Lee's room in a state of wild confusion. There had evidently been a severe struggle. Mr. Lee himself was lying in a pool of blood in front of the fireplace with his throat cut."

The Chief Constable said sharply:

"He couldn't have done it himself?"

Sugden shook his head.

"Impossible, sir. For one thing there were the chairs and tables overturned and the broken crockery and ornaments and then there was no sign of the razor or knife with which the crime had been committed."

The Chief Constable said thoughtfully:

"Yes, that seems conclusive. Anyone in the room?"

"Most of the family were there, sir. Just standing round."

Colonel Johnson said sharply:

"Any ideas, Sugden?"

The Superintendent said slowly:

"It's a bad business, sir. It looks to me as though one of them must have done it. I don't see how anyone from outside could have done it and got away in that time."

"What about the window? Closed or open?"

"There are two windows in the room, sir. One was closed and locked. The other was open a few inches at the bottom —but it was fixed in that position by a burglar screw and moreover, I've tried it and it's stuck fast—hasn't been opened for years, I should say. Also the wall outside is quite smooth and unbroken—no ivy or creepers. I don't see how anyone could have left that way."

"How many doors in the room?"

"Just one. The room is at the end of a passage. That door was locked on the inside. When they heard the noise of the struggle and the old man's dying scream and rushed upstairs they had to break down the door to get in."

Johnson said sharply:

"And who was in the room?"

Superintendent Sugden replied gravely:

"Nobody was in the room, sir, except the old man who had been killed not more than a few minutes previously."

VII

Colonel Johnson stared at Sugden for some minutes before he spluttered:

"Do you mean to tell me, Superintendent, that this is one of those damned cases you get in detective stories where a man is killed in a locked room by some apparently supernatural agency?"

A very faint smile agitated the Superintendent's moustache as he replied gravely:

"I do not think it's quite as bad as that, sir."

Colonel Johnson said:

53

"Suicide. It must be suicide!"

"Where's the weapon, if so? No, sir, suicide won't do."

"Then how did the murderer escape? By the window?"

Sugden shook his head.

"I'll take my oath he didn't do that."

"But the door was locked, you say, on the inside."

The Superintendent nodded. He drew a key from his pocket and laid it on the table.

"No fingerprints," he announced. "But just look at that key, sir. Take a look at it with that magnifying glass there."

Poirot bent forward. He and Johnson examined the key together. The Chief Constable uttered an exclamation.

"By Jove, I get you. Those faint scratches on the end of the barrel. You see 'em, Poirot?"

"But, yes, I see. That means, does it not, that the key was turned from outside the door—turned by means of a special implement that went through the keyhole and gripped the barrel—possibly an ordinary pair of pliers would do it."

The Superintendent nodded.

"It can be done all right."

Poirot said:

"The idea being, then, that the death would be thought to be suicide, since the door was locked and no one was in the room?"

"That was the idea, Mr. Poirot, not a doubt of it, I should say."

Poirot shook his head doubtfully.

"But the disorder in the room! As you say, that by itself wiped out the idea of suicide. Surely the murderer would first of all have set the room to rights."

Superintendent Sugden said:

"But he hadn't *time*, Mr. Poirot. That's the whole point. He hadn't time. Let's say he counted on catching the old gentleman unawares. Well, that didn't come off. There was a struggle—a struggle heard plainly in the room underneath and what's more the old gentleman called out for help. Everyone came rushing up. The murderer only had time to nip out of the room and turn the key from the outside."

"That is true," Poirot admitted. "Your murderer, he may have made the bungle. But why, oh, why, did he not at least leave the weapon? For naturally, if there is no weapon, it cannot be suicide! That was an error most grave."

Superintendent Sugden said stolidly:

"Criminals usually make mistakes. That's our experience."

Poirot gave a slight sigh. He murmured:

"But all the same, in spite of his mistakes, he has escaped, this criminal."

54

"I don't think he has exactly *escaped*."

"You mean he is in the house still?"

"I don't see where else he can be. It was an inside job."

"But, *tout de même*," Poirot pointed out gently, "he has escaped to this extent. *You do not know who he is.*"

Superintendent Sugden said gently but firmly:

"I rather fancy that we soon shall. We haven't done any questioning of the household yet."

Colonel Johnson cut in:

"Look here, Sugden, one thing strikes me. Whoever turned that key from the outside must have had some knowledge of the job. That's to say he probably had had criminal experience. Those sort of tools aren't easy to manage."

"You mean it was a professional job, sir?"

"That's what I mean."

"It does look like it," the other admitted. "Following up that, it looks as though there were a professional thief among the servants. That would explain the diamonds being taken and the murder would follow on logically from that."

"Well, anything wrong with that theory?"

"It's what I thought myself to begin with. But it's difficult. There are eight servants in the house, six of them are women and of those six, five have been here for four years and more. Then there's the butler and the footman. The butler has been here for close on forty years—bit of a record that, I should say. The footman's local, son of the gardener and brought up here. Don't see very well how he can be a professional. The only other person is Mr. Lee's valet attendant. He's comparatively new but he was out of the house—still is—went out just before eight o'clock."

Colonel Johnson said:

"Have you got a list of just who exactly was in the house?"

"Yes, sir. I got it from the butler." He took out his notebook. "Shall I read it to you?"

"Please, Sugden."

"Mr. and Mrs. Alfred Lee. Mr. George Lee, M.P., and his wife. Mr. Henry Lee. Mr. and Mrs. David Lee. Miss" (the Superintendent paused a little, taking the words carefully) "Pillar" (he pronounced it like a piece of architecture) "Estravados. Mr. Stephen Farr. Then for the servants: Edward Tressilian, butler. Walter Champion, footman. Emily Reeves, cook. Queenie Jones, kitchenmaid. Gladys Spent, head housemaid. Grace Best, second housemaid. Beatrice Moscombe, third housemaid. Joan Kench, betweenmaid. Sydney Horbury, valet attendant."

"That's the lot, eh?"

"That's the lot, sir."

"Any idea where everybody was at the time of the murder?"

"Only roughly. As I told you, I haven't questioned anybody yet. According to Tressilian, the gentlemen were in the dining-room still. The ladies had gone to the drawing-room. Tressilian had served coffee. According to his statement he had just got back to his pantry when he heard a noise upstairs. It was followed by a scream. He ran out into the hall and upstairs in the wake of the others."

Colonel Johnson said:

"How many of the family live in the house and who are just staying here?"

"Mr. and Mrs. Alfred Lee live here. The others are just visiting."

Johnson nodded.

"Where are they all?"

"I asked them to stay in the drawing-room until I was ready to take their statements."

"I see. Well, we'd better go upstairs and take a look at the doings."

The Superintendent led the way up the broad stairs and along the passage.

As he entered the room where the crime had taken place Johnson drew a deep breath.

"Pretty horrible," he commented.

He stood for a minute studying the overturned chairs, the smashed china and the blood-bespattered débris.

A thin elderly man stood up from where he had been kneeling by the body and gave a nod.

"Evening, Johnson," he said. "Bit of a shambles, eh?"

"I should say it was. Got anything for us, doctor?"

The doctor shrugged his shoulders. He grinned.

"I'll let you have the scientific language at the inquest! Nothing complicated about it. Throat cut like a pig. He bled to death in less than a minute. No sign of the weapon."

Poirot went across the room to the windows. As the Superintendent had said, one was shut and bolted. The other was open about four inches at the bottom. A thick patent screw of the kind known many years ago as an anti-burglar screw secured it in that position.

Sugden said:

"According to the butler that window was never shut, wet or fine. There's a linoleum mat underneath it in case rain beat in, but it didn't much, as the overhanging roof protects it."

Poirot nodded.

He came back to the body and stared down at the old man.

The lips were drawn back from the bloodless gums in something that looked like a snarl. The fingers were curved like claws.

Poirot said:

"He does not seem a strong man, no."

The doctor said:

"He was pretty tough, I believe. He'd survived several pretty bad illnesses that would have killed most men."

Poirot said:

"I do not mean that. I mean, he was not big, not strong physically."

"No, he's frail enough."

Poirot turned from the dead man. He bent to examine an overturned chair, a big chair of mahogany. Beside it was a round mahogany table and the fragments of a big china lamp. Two other smaller chairs lay near by, also the smashed fragments of a decanter and two glasses, a heavy glass paperweight was unbroken, some miscellaneous books, a big Japanese vase smashed in pieces, and a bronze statuette of a naked girl completed the débris.

Poirot bent over all these exhibits, studying them gravely but without touching them. He frowned to himself as though perplexed.

The Chief Constable said:

"Anything strike you, Poirot?"

Hercule Poirot sighed. He murmured:

"Such a frail shrunken old man—and yet—all this."

Johnson looked puzzled. He turned away and said to the sergeant who was busy at his work:

"What about prints?"

"Plenty of them, sir, all over the room."

"What about the safe?"

"No good. Only prints on that are those of the old gentleman himself."

Johnson turned to the doctor.

"What about bloodstains?" he asked. "Surely whoever killed him must have got blood on him."

The doctor said doubtfully:

"Not necessarily. Bleeding was almost entirely from the jugular vein. That wouldn't spout like an artery."

"No, no. Still, there seems a lot of blood about."

Poirot said:

"Yes, there is a lot of blood—it strikes one, that. A lot of blood."

Superintendent Sugden said respectfully:

"Do you—er—does that suggest anything to you, Mr. Poirot?"

Poirot looked about him. He shook his head perplexedly. He said:

"There is something here—some violence. . . ." He stopped a minute, then went on. "Yes, that is it—*violence*. . . . And blood—an insistence on *blood*. . . . There is—how shall I put it?—there is *too much blood*. Blood on the chairs, on the tables, on the carpet. . . . The blood ritual? Sacrificial blood? Is that it? Perhaps. Such a frail old man, so thin, so shriveled, so dried up—and yet—in his death—*so much blood*. . . ."

His voice died away. Superintendent Sugden, staring at him with round startled eyes, said in an awed voice:

"Funny—that's what she said—the lady. . . ."

Poirot said sharply:

"What lady? What was it she said?"

Sugden answered:

"Mrs. Lee—Mrs. Alfred. Stood over there by the door and half whispered it. It didn't make sense to me."

"What did she say?"

"Something about who would have thought the old gentleman had so much blood in him. . . ."

Poirot said softly:

"*Yet who would have thought the old man to have had so much blood in him?* The words of Lady Macbeth. She said that. . . . Ah, that is interesting. . . ."

VIII

Alfred Lee and his wife came into the small study where Poirot, Sugden and the Chief Constable were standing waiting. Colonel Johnson came forward.

"How do you do, Mr. Lee? We've never actually met, but as you probably know, I'm Chief Constable of the County. Johnson's my name. I can't tell you how distressed I am by this."

Alfred, his brown eyes like those of a suffering dog, said hoarsely:

"Thank you. It's terrible—quite terrible. I—this is my wife."

Lydia said in her quiet voice:

"It has been a frightful shock to my husband—to all of us—but particularly to him."

Her hand was on her husband's shoulder.

Colonel Johnson said:

"Won't you sit down, Mrs. Lee? Let me introduce M. Hercule Poirot."

Hercule Poirot bowed. His eyes went interestedly from husband to wife.

Lydia's hand pressed gently on Alfred's shoulder.

"Sit down, Alfred."

Alfred sat. He murmured:

"Hercule Poirot. Now who—who—"

He passed his hand in a dazed fashion over his forehead.

Lydia Lee said:

"Colonel Johnson will want to ask you a lot of questions, Alfred."

The Chief Constable looked at her with approval. He was thankful that Mrs. Alfred Lee was turning out to be such a sensible and competent woman.

Alfred said:

"Of course. Of course. . . ."

Johnson said to himself:

"Shock seems to have knocked him out completely. Hope he can pull himself together a bit."

Aloud he said:

"I've got a list here of everybody who was in the house to-night. Perhaps you'll tell me, Mr. Lee, if it is correct?"

He made a slight gesture to Sugden and the latter pulled out his notebook and once more recited the list of names.

The businesslike procedure seemed to restore Alfred Lee to something more like his usual self. He had regained command of himself, his eyes no longer looked dazed and staring. When Sugden finished, he nodded in agreement.

"That's quite right," he said.

"Do you mind telling me a little more about your guests? Mr. and Mrs. George Lee and Mr. and Mrs. David Lee are, I gather, relatives."

"They are my two younger brothers and their wives."

"They are staying here only?"

"Yes, they came to us for Christmas."

"Mr. Henry Lee is also a brother?"

"Yes."

"And your two other guests? Miss Estravados and Mr. Farr?"

"Miss Estravados is my niece. Mr. Farr is the son of my father's one-time partner in South Africa."

"Ah, an old friend."

Lydia intervened.

"No, actually we had never seen him before until yesterday."

"I see. But you invited him to stay with you for Christmas?"

Alfred hesitated, then looked towards his wife. She said clearly:

"Mr. Farr turned up quite unexpectedly yesterday. He happened to be in the neighbourhood and came to call upon my father-in-law. When my father-in-law found he was the son of his old friend and partner he insisted on his remaining with us for Christmas."

Colonel Johnson said:

"I see. That explains the household. As regards the servants, Mrs. Lee, do you consider them all trustworthy?"

Lydia considered for a moment before replying. Then she said:

"Yes, I am quite sure they are all thoroughly reliable. They have mostly been with us for many years. Tressilian, the butler, has been here since my husband was a young child. The only newcomers are the betweenmaid, Joan, and the nurse-valet who attended on my father-in-law."

"What about them?"

"Joan is rather a silly little thing. That is the worst that can be said of her. I know very little about Horbury. He has been here just over a year. He was quite competent at his job and my father-in-law seemed satisfied with him."

Poirot said acutely:

"But you, madam, were not so satisfied?"

Lydia shrugged her shoulders slightly.

"It was nothing to do with me."

"But you are the mistress of the house, madam. The servants are your concern?"

"Oh, yes, of course. But Horbury was my father-in-law's personal attendant. He did not come under my jurisdiction."

"I see."

Colonel Johnson said:

"We come now to the events of to-night. I'm afraid this will be painful for you, Mr. Lee, but I would like your account of what happened."

Alfred said in a low voice:

"Of course."

Colonel Johnson said, prompting him:

"When, for instance, did you last see your father?"

A slight spasm of pain crossed Alfred's face as he replied in a low voice:

"It was after tea. I was with him for a short time. Finally I said good-night to him and left him at—let me see—about a quarter to six."

Poirot observed:

"You said good-night to him? You did not then expect to see him again that evening?"

60

"No. My father's supper, a light meal, was always brought to him at seven. After that he sometimes went to bed early or sometimes sat up in his chair, but he did not expect to see any members of the family again unless he specially sent for them."

"Did he often send for them?"

"Sometimes. If he felt like it."

"But it was not the ordinary procedure?"

"No."

"Go on, please, Mr. Lee."

Alfred continued:

"We had our dinner at eight o'clock. Dinner was over and my wife and the other ladies had gone into the drawing-room." His voice faltered. His eyes began to stare again. "We were sitting there—at the table . . . suddenly there was the most astounding noise overhead. Chairs overturning, furniture crashing, breaking glass and china and then— Oh, God" (he shuddered), "I can hear it still—my father screamed—a horrible long-drawn scream—the scream of a man in mortal agony. . . ."

He raised shaking hands to cover his face. Lydia stretched out her hand and touched his sleeve. Colonel Johnson said gently:

"And then?"

Alfred said in a broken voice:

"I think—just for a minute we were *stunned*. Then we sprang up and went out of the door and up the stairs to my father's room. The door was locked. We couldn't get in. It had to be broken open. Then, when we did get in, we saw—"

His voice died away.

Johnson said quickly:

"There's no need to go into that part of it, Mr. Lee. To go back a little, to the time you were in the dining-room. Who was there with you when you heard the cry?"

"Who was there? Why, we were all—No, let me see. My brother was there—my brother Harry."

"Nobody else?"

"No one else."

"Where were the other gentlemen?"

Alfred sighed and frowned in an effort of remembrance.

"Let me see—it seems so long ago—yes, like years— what did happen? Oh, of course, George had gone to telephone. Then we began to talk of family matters and Stephen Farr said something about seeing we wanted to discuss things and he took himself off. He did it very nicely and tactfully."

"And your brother David?"

Alfred frowned.

"David? Wasn't he there? No, of course he wasn't. I don't quite know when he slipped away."

Poirot said gently:

"So you had the family matters to discuss?"

"Er—yes."

"That is to say, you had matters to discuss with *one* member of your family?"

Lydia said:

"What do you mean, M. Poirot?"

He turned quickly to her.

"Madam, your husband says that Mr. Farr left them because he saw they had affairs of the family to discuss. But it was not a *conseil de famille*, since M. David was not there and M. George was not there. It was, then, a discussion between two members of the family only."

Lydia said:

"My brother-in-law, Harry, had been abroad for a great number of years. It was natural that he and my husband should have things to talk over."

"Ah! I see. It was like that."

She shot him a quick glance, then turned her eyes away. Johnson said:

"Well, that seems clear enough. Did you notice anyone else as you ran upstairs to your father's room?"

"I—really I don't know. I think so. We all came from different directions. But I'm afraid I didn't notice—I was so alarmed. That terrible cry. . . ."

Colonel Johnson passed quickly to another subject.

"Thank you, Mr. Lee. Now there is another point. I understand that your father had some valuable diamonds in his possession."

Alfred looked rather surprised.

"Yes," he said. "That is so."

"Where did he keep them?"

"In the safe in his room."

"Can you describe them at all?"

"They were rough diamonds—that is, uncut stones."

"Why did your father have them there?"

"It was a whim of his. They were stones he had brought with him from South Africa. He never had them cut. He just liked keeping them in his possession. As I say, it was a whim of his."

"I see," said the Chief Constable.

From his tone it was plain that he did not see. He went on:

"Were they of much value?"

"My father estimated their value at about ten thousand pounds."

62

"In fact they were very valuable stones?"

"Yes."

"It seems a curious idea to keep such stones in a bed-room safe."

Lydia interposed:

"My father-in-law, Colonel Johnson, was a somewhat curious man. His ideas were not the conventional ones. It definitely gave him pleasure to handle those stones."

"They recalled, perhaps, the past to him," said Poirot.

She gave him a quick appreciative look.

"Yes," she said. "I think they did."

"Were they insured?" asked the Chief Constable.

"I think not."

Johnson leaned forward. He asked quietly:

"Did you know, Mr. Lee, that those stones had been stolen?"

"What?" Alfred Lee stared at him.

"Your father said nothing to you of their disappearance?"

"Not a word."

"You did not know that he had sent for Superintendent Sugden here and had reported the loss to him?"

"I hadn't the faintest idea of such a thing!"

The Chief Constable transferred his gaze.

"What about you, Mrs. Lee?"

Lydia shook her head.

"I heard nothing about it."

"As far as you knew the stones were still in the safe?"

"Yes."

She hesitated and then asked:

"Is that why he was killed? For the sake of those stones?"

Colonel Johnson said:

"That is what we are going to find out!"

He went on:

"Have you any idea, Mrs. Lee, who could have engineered such a theft?"

She shook her head.

"No, indeed. I am sure the servants are all honest. In any case it would be very difficult for them to get at the safe. My father-in-law was always in his room. He never came downstairs."

"Who attended to the room?"

"Horbury. He made the bed and dusted. The second house-maid went in to do the grate and lay the fire every morning, otherwise Horbury did everything."

Poirot said:

"So Horbury would be the person with the best opportunity?"

"Yes."

"Do you think that it was he who stole the diamonds, then?"

"It is possible, I suppose . . . he had the best opportunity. Oh! I don't know what to think."

Colonel Johnson said:

"Your husband has given us his account of the evening. Will you do the same, Mrs. Lee? When did you last see your father-in-law?"

"We were all up in his room this afternoon—before tea. That was the last time I saw him."

"You did not see him later to bid him good-night?"

"No."

Poirot said:

"Do you usually go and say good-night to him?"

Lydia said sharply:

"No."

The Chief Constable went on:

"Where were you when the crime took place?"

"In the drawing-room."

"You heard the noise of the struggle?"

"I think I heard something heavy fall. Of course the room is over the dining-room, not the drawing-room, so I wouldn't have heard so much."

"But you heard the cry?"

Lydia shuddered.

"Yes, I heard that . . . it was horrible . . . like—like a soul in Hell. I knew at once something dreadful had happened. I hurried out and followed my husband and Harry up the stairs."

"Who else was in the drawing-room at the time?"

Lydia frowned.

"Really—I can't remember. David was next door in the music room, playing Mendelssohn. I think Hilda had gone to join him."

"And the other two ladies?"

Lydia said slowly:

"Magdalene went to telephone. I can't remember whether she had come back or not. I don't know where Pilar was."

Poirot said gently:

"In fact you may have been quite alone in the drawing-room?"

"Yes—yes—as a matter of fact I believe I was."

Colonel Johnson said:

"About these diamonds. We ought, I think, to make quite sure about them. Do you know the combination of your father's safe, Mr. Lee? I see it is of a somewhat old-fashioned pattern."

"You will find it written down in a small notebook he

carried in the pocket of his dressing-gown."

"Good. We will go and look presently. It will be better, perhaps, if we interview the other members of the house party first. The ladies may want to get to bed."

Lydia stood up.

"Come, Alfred." She turned to them. "Shall I sent them in to you?"

"One by one, if you wouldn't mind, Mrs. Lee."

"Certainly."

She moved towards the door. Alfred followed her.

Suddenly, at the last moment, he swung round.

"Of course," he said. He came quickly back to Poirot. "You are Hercule Poirot! I don't know where my wits have been. I should have realized at once. . . ."

He spoke quickly, in a low excited voice.

"It's an absolute godsend, your being here! You must find out the truth, M. Poirot. Spare no expense! I will be responsible for any expense. *But find out.* . . . My poor father —killed by someone—killed with the utmost brutality! You *must* find out, M. Poirot. My father has got to be avenged."

Poirot answered quietly:

"I can assure you, M. Lee, that I am prepared to do my utmost to assist Colonel Johnson and Superintendent Sugden."

Alfred Lee said:

"I want you to work for *me*. My father has got to be avenged."

He began to tremble violently. Lydia had come back. She went up to him and drew his arm through hers.

"Come, Alfred," she said. "We must get the others."

Her eyes met Poirot's. They were eyes that kept their own secrets. They did not waver.

Poirot said softly:

"Who would have thought the old man—"

She interrupted him:

"Stop! Don't say that!"

Poirot murmured:

"You said it, madam."

She breathed softly:

"I know . . . I remember . . . it was—so horrible."

Then she went abruptly out of the room, her husband beside her.

IX

George Lee was solemn and correct.

"A terrible business," he said, shaking his head. "A terrible, terrible business. I can only believe that it must—er—have been the work of a *lunatic!"*

Colonel Johnson said politely:

"That is your theory?"

"Yes. Yes, indeed. A homicidal maniac. Escaped, perhaps, from some mental Home in the vicinity."

Superintendent Sugden put in:

"And how do you suggest this—er—lunatic gained admittance to the house, Mr. Lee? And how did he leave it?"

George shook his head.

"That," he said firmly, "is for the police to discover."

Sugden said:

"We made the round of the house at once. All windows were closed and barred. The side door was locked, so was the front door. Nobody could have left by the kitchen premises without being seen by the kitchen staff."

George Lee cried:

"But that's absurd! You'll be saying next that my father was never murdered at all!"

"He was murdered all right," said Superintendent Sugden. "There's no doubt about that."

The Chief Constable cleared his throat and took up the questioning.

"Just where were you, Mr. Lee, at the time of the crime?"

"I was in the dining-room. It was just after dinner. No, I was, I think, in this room. I had just finished telephoning."

"You had been telephoning?"

"Yes. I had put a call through to the Conservative agent in Westeringham—my constituency. Some urgent matters."

"And it was after that that you heard the scream?"

George Lee gave a slight shiver.

"Yes, very unpleasant. It—er—froze my marrow. It died away in a kind of choke or gurgle."

He took out a handkerchief and wiped his forehead where the perspiration had broken out.

"Terrible business," he muttered.

"And then you hurried upstairs?"

"Yes."

"Did you see your brothers, Mr. Alfred and Mr. Harry Lee?"

"No, they must have gone up just ahead of me, I think."

"When did you last see your father, Mr. Lee?"

"This afternoon. We were all up there."

"You did not see him after that?"

"No."

The Chief Constable paused, then he said:

"Were you aware that your father kept a quantity of valuable uncut diamonds in the safe in his bedroom?"

George Lee nodded.

"A most unwise procedure," he said pompously. "I often told him so. He might have been murdered for them—I mean—that is to say—"

Colonel Johnson cut in:

"Are you aware that these stones have disappeared?"

George's jaw dropped. His protuberant eyes stared.

"Then he *was* murdered for them?"

The Chief Constable said slowly:

"He was aware of their loss and reported it to the police some hours before his death."

George said:

"But then—I don't understand—I—"

Hercule Poirot said gently:

"We, too, do not understand. . . ."

X

Harry Lee came into the room with a swagger. For a moment Poirot stared at him, frowning. He had a feeling that somewhere he had seen this man before. He noted the features, the high bridged nose, the arrogant poise of the head, the line of the jaw and he realized that though Harry Lee was a big man and his father had been a man of merely middle height yet there had been a good deal of resemblance between them.

He noted something else, too. For all his swagger, Harry Lee was nervous. He was carrying it off with a swing, but the anxiety underneath was real enough.

"Well, gentlemen," he said, "what can I tell you?"

Colonel Johnson said:

"We shall be glad of any light you can throw on the events of this evening."

Harry Lee shook his head.

"I don't know anything at all. It's all pretty horrible and utterly unexpected."

Poirot said:

"You have recently returned from abroad, I think, Mr. Lee?"

Harry turned to him quickly.

"Yes. Landed in England a week ago."

Poirot said:

"You had been away a long time?"

Harry Lee lifted up his chin and laughed.

"You might as well hear straight away—someone will soon tell you! I'm the prodigal son, gentlemen! It's nearly twenty years since I last set foot in this house."

"But you returned—now. Will you tell us why?" asked Poirot.

With the same appearance of frankness Harry answered readily enough.

"It's the good old parable still. I got tired of the husks that the swine do eat—or don't eat, I forget which. I thought to myself that the fatted calf would be a welcome exchange. I had had a letter from my father suggesting that I come home. I obeyed the summons and came. That's all."

Poirot said:

"You came for a short visit—or a long one?"

Harry said:

"I came home—for good!"

"Your father was willing?"

"The old man was delighted." He laughed again. The corners of his eyes crinkled engagingly. "Pretty boring for the old man living here with Alfred! Alfred's a dull stick—very worthy and all that, but poor company. My father had been a bit of a rip in his time. He was looking forward to my company."

"And your brother and his wife, were they pleased that you were to live here?"

Poirot asked the question with a slight lifting of his eyebrows.

"Alfred? Alfred was livid with rage. Don't know about Lydia. She was probably annoyed on Alfred's behalf. But I've no doubt she'd be quite pleased in the end. I like Lydia. She's a delightful woman. I should have got on with Lydia. But Alfred was quite another pair of shoes." He laughed again. "Alfred's always been as jealous as Hell of me. He's always been the good dutiful stay-at-home stick-in-the-mud son. And what was he going to get for it in the end? What the good boy of the family always gets. A kick in the pants. Take it from me, gentlemen, virtue doesn't pay."

He looked from one face to another.

"Hope you're not shocked by my frankness. But after all, it's the truth you're after. You'll drag out all the family dirty linen into the light of day in the end. I might as well display mine straight away. I'm not particularly broken-hearted by my father's death—after all, I hadn't seen the old devil since I was a boy—but nevertheless he was my father and he was murdered. I'm all out for revenge on the murderer." He stroked his jawbone, watching them. "We're rather hot on revenge in our family. None of the Lees forget easily. I mean to make sure that my father's murderer is caught and hanged."

"I think you can trust us to do our best in that line, Mr. Lee," said Sugden.

"If you don't I shall take the law into my own hands," said Harry Lee.

The Chief Constable said sharply:

"Have you any ideas on the subject of the murderer's identity, then, Mr. Lee?"

Harry shook his head.

"No," he said slowly. "No—I haven't. You know—it's rather a jolt. Because I've been thinking about it—and I don't see that it can have been an outside job. . . ."

"Ah," said Sugden, nodding his head.

"And if so," said Harry Lee. "Then someone here in the house killed him. . . . But who the devil could have done it? Can't suspect the servants. Tressilian has been here since the year one. The half-witted footman? Not on your life. Horbury, now, he's a cool customer, but Tressilian tells me he was out at the pictures. So what do you come to? Passing over Stephen Farr (and why the devil should Stephen Farr come all the way from South Africa and murder a total stranger?) there's only the family. And for the life of me I can't see one of us doing it. Alfred? He adored Father. George? He hasn't got the guts. David? David's always been a moon dreamer. He'd faint if he saw his own finger bleed. The wives? Women don't go and slit a man's throat in cold blood. So who did? Blessed if I know. But it's damned disturbing."

Colonel Johnson cleared his throat—an official habit of his—and said:

"When did you last see your father this evening?"

"After tea. He'd just had a row with Alfred. About your humble servant. The old man was no end bucked with himself. He always liked stirring up trouble. In my opinion that's why he kept my arrival dark from the others. Wanted to see the fur fly when I blew in unexpectedly! That's why he talked about altering his will, too."

Poirot stirred softly. He murmured:

"So your father mentioned his will?"

"Yes. In front of the whole lot of us. Watching us like a cat to see how we reacted. Just told the lawyer chap to come over and see him about it after Christmas."

Poirot asked:

"What changes did he contemplate making?"

Harry Lee grinned.

"He didn't tell us that! Trust the old fox! I imagine—or shall we say I hoped—that the change was to the advantage of your humble servant! I should imagine I'd been cut out of any former wills. Now, I rather fancy, I was to go back. Nasty blow for the others. Pilar, too—he'd taken a fancy to her. She was in for something good, I should imagine. You haven't seen her yet? My Spanish niece. She's a beautiful creature, Pilar—with the lovely warmth of the South—and its cruelty. Wish I wasn't a mere uncle!"

"You say your father took to her?"

Harry nodded.

"She knew how to get round the old man. Sat up there with him a good deal. I bet she knew just what she was after! Well, he's dead now. No wills can be altered in Pilar's favour—nor mine either, worse luck!"

He frowned, paused a minute, and then went on with a change of tone.

"But I'm wandering from the point. You wanted to know what was the last time I saw my father? As I've told you it was after tea—might have been a little past six. The old man was in good spirits then—a bit tired perhaps. I went away and left him with Horbury. I never saw him again."

"Where were you at the time of his death?"

"In the dining-room with brother Alfred. Not a very harmonious after dinner session. We were in the middle of a pretty sharp argument when we heard the noise overhead. Sounded as though ten men were wrestling up there. And then poor old Father screamed. It was like killing a pig. The sound of it paralyzed Alfred. He just sat there with his jaw dropping. I fairly shook him back to life and we started off upstairs. The door was locked. Had to break it open. Took some doing, too. How the devil that door came to be locked I can't imagine! There was no one in the room but Father, and I'm damned if anyone could have got away through the windows."

Superintendent Sugden said:

"The door was locked from the outside."

"What?" Harry stared. "But I'll swear the key was on the *inside*."

Poirot murmured:

"So you noticed that?"

Harry Lee said sharply:

"I do notice things. It's a habit of mine."

He looked sharply from one face to the other.

"Is there anything more you want to know, gentlemen?"

Johnson shook his head.

"Thank you, Mr. Lee, not for the moment. Perhaps you will ask the next member of the family to come along?"

"Certainly I will."

He walked to the door and went out without looking back.

The three men looked at each other.

Colonel Johnson said:

"What about it, Sugden?"

The Superintendent shook his head doubtfully. He said:

"He's afraid of something. I wonder why. . . ."

XI

Magdalene Lee paused effectively in the doorway. One long slender hand touched the burnished platinum sheen of her hair. The leaf-green velvet frock she wore clung to the delicate lines of her figure. She looked very young and a little frightened.

The three men were arrested for a moment looking at her. Johnson's eyes showed a sudden surprised admiration. Superintendent Sugden's showed no animation, merely the impatience of a man anxious to get on with his job. Hercule Poirot's eyes were deeply appreciative (as she saw) but the appreciation was not for her beauty but for the effective use she made of it. She did not know that he was thinking to himself

"Jolie mannequin, la petite. Elle se pose tout naturellement. Elle a les yeux dures."

Colonel Johnson was thinking:

"Damned good-looking girl. George Lee will have trouble with her if he doesn't look out. Got an eye for a man all right."

Superintendent Sugden was thinking:

"Empty headed, vain piece of goods. Hope we get through with her quickly."

Colonel Johnson rose.

"Will you sit down, Mrs. Lee? Let me see, you are—?"

"Mrs. George Lee."

She accepted the chair with a warm smile of thanks. "After all," the glance seemed to say, "although you *are* a man and a policeman, you are not so dreadful after all."

The tail end of the smile included Poirot. Foreigners were so susceptible where women were concerned. About Superintendent Sugden she did not bother.

She murmured, twisting her hands together in a pretty distress:

"It's all so terrible. I feel so frightened."

"Come, come, Mrs. Lee," said Colonel Johnson kindly but briskly. "It's been a shock, I know, but it's all over now. We just want an account from you of what happened this evening."

She cried out:

"But I don't know anything about it—I don't indeed."

For a minute the Chief Constable's eyes narrowed. He said gently:

"No, of course not."

"We only arrived here yesterday. George *would* make me come here for Christmas! I wish we hadn't. I'm sure I shall never feel the same again!"

"Very upsetting—yes."

"I hardly know George's family, you see. I'd only seen Mr. Lee once or twice—at our wedding and once since. Of course I've seen Alfred and Lydia more often, but they're really all quite strangers to me."

Again the wide-eyed frightened child look. Again Hercule Poirot's eyes were appreciative—and again he thought to himself:

"*Elle joue très bien la comédie, cette petite. . . .*"

"Yes, yes," said Colonel Johnson. "Now just tell me about the last time you saw your father-in-law—Mr. Lee—alive."

"Oh! *that!* That was this afternoon. It was dreadful!"

Johnson said quickly:

"Dreadful? Why?"

"They were so angry!"

"Who was angry?"

"Oh! all of them. . . . I don't mean George. His father didn't say anything to him. But all the others."

"What happened exactly?"

"Well, when we got there—he asked for all of us—he was speaking into the telephone—to his lawyers about his will. And then he told Alfred he was looking very glum. I think that was because of Harry coming home to live. Alfred was very upset about that, I believe. You see years ago Harry did something quite dreadful. And then he said something about his wife (she's dead long ago); she had had the brains of a louse, he said, and David sprang up and looked as though he'd like to murder him— Oh!" She stopped suddenly, her eyes alarmed. "I didn't *mean* that— I didn't mean it at all!"

Colonel Johnson said soothingly:

"Quite—quite; figure of speech, that was all."

"Hilda, that's David's wife, quieted him down and—well, I think that's all. Mr. Lee said he didn't want to see anyone again that evening. So we all went away."

"And that was the last time you saw him?"

"Yes. Until—until—"

She shivered.

Colonel Johnson said:

"Yes, quite so. Now where were you at the time of the crime?"

"Oh—let me see. I think I was in the drawing-room."

"Aren't you sure?"

Magdalene's eyes flickered a little, the lids drooped over them.

She said:

"Of course! How stupid of me. . . . I'd gone to telephone. One gets so mixed up."

"You were telephoning, you say? In this room?"

"Yes; that's the only telephone except the one upstairs in my father-in-law's room."

Superintendent Sugden said:

"Was anybody else in the room with you?"

Her eyes widened.

"Oh, no, I was quite alone."

"Had you been here long?"

"Well—a little time. It takes some time to put a call through in the evening."

"It was a trunk call, then?"

"Yes. To Westeringham."

"I see."

"And then?"

"And then there was that awful scream—and everybody running—and the door being locked and having to break it down. Oh! it was like a *nightmare!* I shall always always remember it!"

"No, no." Colonel Johnson's tone was mechanically kind. He went on:

"Did you know that your father-in-law kept a quantity of valuable diamonds in his safe?"

"No, did he?" Her tone was quite frankly thrilled. "Real diamonds?"

Hercule Poirot said:

"Diamonds worth about ten thousand pounds."

"Oh!" It was a soft gasping sound—holding in it the essence of feminine cupidity.

"Well," said Colonel Johnson, "I think that's all for the present. We needn't bother you any further, Mrs. Lee."

"Oh, thank you."

She stood up—smiled from Johnson to Poirot—the smile of a grateful little girl, then she went out walking with her head held high and her palms a little turned outwards.

Colonel Johnson called:

"Will you ask your brother-in-law, Mr. David Lee, to come here?"

Closing the door after her, he came back to the table.

"Well," he said, "what do you think? We're getting at some of it now! You notice one thing. George Lee was telephoning when he heard the scream! His wife was telephoning when she heard it! That doesn't fit—it doesn't fit at all."

He added:

"What do you think, Sugden?"

The Superintendent said slowly:

"I don't want to speak offensively of the lady, but I should say that though she's the kind who would be first class at getting money out of a gentleman, I don't think she's the kind who'd cut a gentleman's throat. That wouldn't be her line at all."

"Ah, but one never knows, *mon vieux*," murmured Poirot.

The Chief Constable turned round to him.

"And you, Poirot, what do you think?"

Hercule Poirot leaned forward. He straightened the blotter in front of him, and flicked a minute speck of dust from a candlestick. He answered:

"I would say that the character of the late Mr. Simeon Lee begins to emerge for us. It is there, I think, that the whole importance of this case lies . . . in the character of the dead man."

Superintendent Sugden turned a puzzled face to him.

"I don't quite get you, Mr. Poirot," he said. "What exactly has the character of the deceased got to do with his murder?"

Poirot said dreamily:

"The character of the victim has always something to do with his or her murder. The frank and unsuspicious mind of Desdemona was the direct cause of her death. A more suspicious woman would have seen Iago's machinations and circumvented them much earlier. The uncleanness of Marat directly invited his end in a bath. From the temper of Mercutio's mind came his death at the sword's point."

Colonel Johnson pulled his moustache.

"What exactly are you getting at, Poirot?"

"I am telling you that because Simeon Lee was a certain kind of man, he set in motion certain forces, which forces in the end brought about his death."

"You don't think the diamonds had anything to do with it then?"

Poirot smiled at the honest perplexity in Johnson's face.

"*Mon cher*," he said. "It was because of Simeon Lee's peculiar character that he kept ten thousand pounds' worth of uncut diamonds in his safe! You have not there the action of every man."

"That's very true, Mr. Poirot," said Superintendent Sugden, nodding his head with the air of a man who at last sees what a fellow conversationalist is driving at. "He was a queer one, Mr. Lee was. He kept those stones there so he could take them out and handle them and get the feeling of the past back. Depend upon it, that's why he never had them cut."

Poirot nodded energetically.

"Precisely—precisely. I see you have great acumen, Superintendent."

The Superintendent looked a little doubtful at the compliment, but Colonel Johnson cut in.

"There's something else, Poirot. I don't know whether it has struck you—"

"*Mais oui,*" said Poirot. "I know what you mean. Mrs. George Lee, she let the cat out of the bag more than she knew! She gave us a pretty impression of that last family meeting. She indicates, oh! so naïvely, that Alfred was angry with his father—and that David looked as 'though he could murder him.' Both those statements, I think, were true. But from them we can draw our own reconstruction. What did Simeon Lee assemble his family for—why should they have arrived in time to hear him telephoning to his lawyer? *Parbleu,* it was no error, that. He *wanted* them to hear it! The poor old one, he sits in his chair and he has lost the diversions of his younger days. So he invents a new diversion for himself. He amuses himself by playing upon the cupidity and the greed of human nature—yes, and on its emotions and its passions, too! But from that arises one further deduction. In his game of rousing the greed and emotion of his children, he would not omit anyone. He must, logically and necessarily, have had his dig at Mr. George Lee as well as at the others! His wife is carefully silent about that. At her, too, he may have shot a poisoned arrow or so. We shall find out, I think, from others what Simeon Lee had to say to George Lee and George Lee's wife—"

He broke off. The door opened and David Lee came in.

XII

David Lee had himself well in hand. His demeanour was calm—almost unnaturally so. He came up to them, drew a chair forward and sat down, looking with grave interrogation at Colonel Johnson.

The electric light touched the fair peak of hair that grew on his forehead and showed up the sensitive modeling of the cheek bones. He looked absurdly young to be the son of that shriveled old man who lay dead upstairs.

"Yes, gentlemen," he said, "what can I tell you?"

Colonel Johnson said:

"I understand, Mr. Lee, that there was a kind of family meeting held in your father's room this afternoon?"

"There was. But it was quite informal. I mean, it was not a family council or anything of that kind."

"What took place there?"

David Lee answered calmly:

"My father was in a difficult mood. He was an old man and an invalid; of course, one had to make allowances for him. He seemed to have assembled us there in order to—well —vent his spite upon us."

"Can you remember what he said?"

David said quietly:

"It was really all rather foolish. He said we were no use— any of us—that there wasn't a single man in the family! He said Pilar (that is my Spanish niece) was worth two of any of us. He said—" David stopped.

Poirot said:

"Please, Mr. Lee, the exact words, if you can."

David said reluctantly:

"He spoke rather coarsely—said he hoped that somewhere in the world he had better sons—even if they were born the wrong side of the blanket. . . ."

His sensitive face showed distaste for the words he was repeating. Superintendent Sugden looked up suddenly alert. Leaning forward, he said:

"Did your father say anything in particular to your brother, Mr. George Lee?"

"To George? I don't remember. Oh, yes, I believe he told him he would have to cut down expenses in future, he'd have to reduce his allowance. George was very upset, got as red as a turkey cock. He spluttered and said he couldn't possibly manage with less. My father said quite coolly that he'd have to. He said he'd better get his wife to help him economize— rather a nasty dig that—George has always been the economical one—saves and stints on every penny. Magdalene, I fancy, is a bit of a spender—she has extravagant tastes."

Poirot said:

"So that she, too, was annoyed?"

"Yes. Besides, my father worded something else rather crudely, mentioned her as having lived with a naval officer— of course he really meant her father, but it sounded rather dubious. Magdalene went scarlet. I don't blame her."

Poirot said:

"Did your father mention his late wife, your mother?"

The red blood ran in waves up David's temples. His hands clenched themselves on the table in front of him, trembling slightly.

He said in a low choked voice:

"Yes, he did. He insulted her."

Colonel Johnson said:

"What did he say?"

David said abruptly:

"I don't remember. Just some slighting reference."

Poirot said softly:

"Your mother has been dead some years?"

David said shortly:

"She died when I was a boy."

"She was not—perhaps—very happy in her life here?"

David gave a scornful laugh.

"Who could be happy with a man like my father? My mother was a saint. She died a broken-hearted woman."

Poirot went on:

"Your father was, perhaps, distressed by her death?"

David said abruptly:

"I don't know. I left home."

He paused and then said:

"Perhaps you may not be aware of the fact that when I came on this visit I had not seen my father for nearly twenty years. So you see I can't tell you very much about his habits or his enemies or what went on here."

Colonel Johnson asked:

"Did you know that your father kept a lot of valuable diamonds in the safe in his bedroom?"

David said indifferently:

"Did he? Seems a foolish sort of thing to do."

Johnson said:

"Will you describe briefly your own movements?"

"Mine? Oh, I went away from the dinner table fairly quickly. It bores me, this sitting round over port. Besides I could see that Alfred and Harry were working up for a quarrel. I hate rows. I slipped away and went to the music room and played the piano."

Poirot asked:

"The music room, it is next to the drawing-room, is it not?"

"Yes. I played there for some time—till—till the thing happened."

"What did you hear exactly?"

"Oh! a far-off noise of furniture being overturned somewhere upstairs. And then a pretty ghastly cry." He clenched his hands again. "Like a soul in Hell. God, it was awful!"

Johnson said:

"Were you alone in the music room?"

"Eh? No, my wife, Hilda, was there. She'd come in from the drawing-room. We—we went up with the others."

He added quickly and nervously:

"You don't want me, do you, to describe what—what I saw there?"

Colonel Johnson said:

"No, quite unnecessary. Thank you, Mr. Lee, there's nothing more. You can't imagine, I suppose, who would be likely to want to murder your father?"

David Lee said recklessly:

"I should think—quite a lot of people! I don't know of anyone definite."

He went out rapidly, shutting the door loudly behind him.

XIII

Colonel Johnson had had no time to do more than clear his throat when the door opened again and Hilda Lee came in.

Hercule Poirot looked at her with interest. He had to admit to himself that the wives these Lees had married were an interesting study. The swift intelligence and greyhound grace of Lydia, the meretricious airs and graces of Magdalene, and now the solid comfortable strength of Hilda. She was, he saw, younger than her rather dowdy style of hairdressing and unfashionable clothes made her appear. Her mouse brown hair was unflecked with grey and her steady hazel eyes set in the rather podgy face shone out like beacons of kindliness. She was, he thought, a nice woman.

Colonel Johnson was talking in his kindliest tone.

"—a great strain on all of you," he was saying. "I gather from your husband, Mrs. Lee, that this is the first time you have been to Gorston Hall?"

She bowed her head.

"Were you previously acquainted with your father-in-law, Mr. Lee?"

Hilda replied in her pleasant voice:

"No. We were married soon after David left home. He always wanted to have nothing to do with his family. Until now we have not seen any of them."

"How then, did this visit come about?"

"My father-in-law wrote to David. He stressed his age and his desire that all his children should be with him this Christmas."

"And your husband responded to this appeal?"

Hilda said:

"His acceptance was, I am afraid, all my doing. I—misunderstood the situation."

Poirot interposed. He said:

"Will you be so kind as to explain yourself a little more clearly, madam? I think what you can tell us may be of value."

She turned to him immediately.

She said:

"At that time I had never seen my father-in-law. I had no idea what his real motive was. I assumed that he was old and lonely and that he really wanted to be reconciled to all his children."

"And what was his real motive, in your opinion, madam?"

Hilda hesitated a moment. Then she said slowly:

"I have no doubt—no doubt at all—that what my father-in-law really wanted was not to promote peace but to stir up strife."

"In what way?"

Hilda said in a low voice:

"It amused him to—to appeal to the worst instincts in human nature. There was—how can I put it—a kind of diabolical impishness about him. He wished to set every member of the family at loggerheads with each other."

Johnson said sharply:

"And did he succeed?"

"Oh, yes," said Hilda Lee. "He succeeded."

Poirot said:

"We have been told, madam, of a scene that took place this afternoon. It was, I think, rather a violent scene."

She bowed her head.

"Will you describe it to us—as truthfully as possible if you please."

She reflected a minute.

"When we went in my father-in-law was telephoning."

"To his lawyer, I understand?"

"Yes, he was suggesting that Mr.—was it Charlton?—I don't quite remember the name—should come over as he, my father-in-law, wanted to make a new will. His old one, he said, was quite out of date."

Poirot said:

"Think carefully, madam, in your opinion, did your father-in-law deliberately ensure that you should all overhear this conversation, or was it just by *chance* that you overheard it?"

Hilda Lee said:

"I am almost sure that he meant us to overhear."

"With the object of fomenting doubt and suspicion among you?"

"Yes."

"So that, really, he may not have meant to alter his will at all?"

She demurred.

"No, I think that part of it was quite genuine. He probably did wish to make a new will—but he enjoyed underlining the fact."

"Madam," said Poirot. "I have no official standing and my questions, you understand, are not perhaps those that an

English officer of the law would ask. But I have a great desire to know what form you think that new will would have taken. I am asking, you perceive, not for your knowledge, but simply for your opinion. *Les femmes,* they are never slow to form opinions, *Dieu merci.*"

Hilda Lee smiled a little.

"I don't mind saying what I think. My husband's sister Jennifer married a Spaniard, Juan Estravados. Her daughter, Pilar, has just arrived here. She is a very lovely girl—and she is, of course, the only grandchild in the family. Old Mr. Lee was delighted with her. He took a tremendous fancy to her. In my opinion he wished to leave her a considerable sum in his new will. Probably he had only left her a small portion or even nothing at all in an old one."

"Did you know your sister-in-law at all?"

"No, I never met her. Her Spanish husband died in tragic circumstances, I believe, soon after the marriage. Jennifer herself died a year ago. Pilar was left an orphan. This is why Mr. Lee sent for her to come and live with him in England."

"And the other members of the family, did they welcome her coming?"

Hilda said quietly:

"I think they all liked her. It was very pleasant to have someone young and alive in the house."

"And she, did she seem to like being here?"

Hilda said slowly:

"I don't know. It must seem cold and strange to a girl brought up in the South—in Spain."

Johnson said:

"Can't be very pleasant being in Spain just at present. Now, Mrs. Lee, we'd like to hear your account of the conversation this afternoon."

Poirot murmured:

"I apologize. I have made the digressions."

Hilda Lee said:

"After my father-in-law finished telephoning, he looked round at us and laughed and said we all looked very glum. Then he said that he was tired and should go to bed early. Nobody was to come up and see him this evening. He said he wanted to be in good form for Christmas Day. Something like that.

"Then—" Her brows knit in an effort of remembrance. "I think he said something about its being necessary to be one of a large family to appreciate Christmas, and then he went on to speak of money. He said it would cost him more to run this house in future. He told George and Magdalene they would have to economize. Told her she ought to make her own clothes. Rather an old-fashioned idea, I'm afraid. I don't wonder it annoyed her. He said his own wife had been clever with her needle."

Poirot said gently:

"Is that all that he said about her?"

Hilda flushed.

"He made a slighting reference to her brains. My husband was very devoted to his mother, and that upset him very much. And then, suddenly, Mr. Lee began shouting at us all. He worked himself up about it. I can understand, of course, how he felt—"

Poirot said gently, interrupting her:

"How did he feel?"

She turned her tranquil eyes upon him.

"He was disappointed, of course," she said. "Because there are no grandchildren—no boys, I mean—no Lees to carry on. I can see that that must have festered for a long time. And suddenly he couldn't keep it in any longer and vented his rage against his sons—saying they were a lot of namby-pamby old women—something like that. I felt sorry for him, then, because I realized how his pride was hurt by it."

"And then?"

"And then," said Hilda slowly, "we all went away."

"That was the last you saw of him?"

She bowed her head.

"Where were you at the time the crime occurred?"

"I was with my husband in the music room. He was playing to me."

"And then?"

"We heard tables and chairs overturned upstairs and china being broken—some terrible struggle. And then that awful scream as his throat was cut. . . ."

Poirot said:

"Was it such an awful scream? Was it"—he paused— "*like a soul in Hell?*"

Hilda Lee said:

"It was worse than that!"

"What do you mean, madam?"

"It was like someone *who had no soul* . . . it was in-human like a beast. . . ."

Poirot said gravely:

"So—you have judged him, madam?"

She raised a hand in sudden distress. Her eyes fell and she stared down at the floor.

XIV

Pilar came into the room with the wariness of an animal who suspects a trap. Her eyes went quickly from side to side. She looked not so much afraid as deeply suspicious.

Colonel Johnson rose and put a chair for her. Then he said:

"You understand English, I suppose, Miss Estravados?" Pilar's eyes opened wide. She said:

"Of course. My mother was English. I am really very English indeed."

A faint smile came to Colonel Johnson's lips, as his eyes took in the black gloss of her hair, the proud dark eyes and the curling red lips. Very English! An incongruous term to apply to Pilar Estravados.

He said:

"Mr. Lee was your grandfather. He sent for you to come from Spain. And you arrived a few days ago. Is that right?"

Pilar nodded.

"That is right. I had—oh! a lot of adventures getting out of Spain—there was a bomb from the air and the chauffeur he was killed—where his head had been there was all blood. And I could not drive a car, so for a long way I had to walk—and I do not like walking. I never walk. My feet were sore—but sore—"

Colonel Johnson smiled.

He said:

"At any rate you arrived here. Had your mother spoken to you of your grandfather much?"

Pilar nodded cheerfully.

"Oh, yes, she said he was an old devil."

Hercule Poirot smiled.

He said:

"And what did you think of him when you arrived, mademoiselle?"

Pilar said:

"Of course he was very, very old. He had to sit in a chair—and his face was all dried up. But I liked him all the same. I think that when he was a young man, he must have been handsome—very handsome, like you," said Pilar to Superintendent Sugden. Her eyes dwelt with naïve pleasure on his handsome face which had turned brick red at the compliment.

Colonel Johnson stifled a chuckle. It was one of the few occasions when he had seen the stolid Superintendent taken aback.

"But, of course," Pilar continued regretfully, "he could ever have been as big as you."

Hercule Poirot sighed.

"You like, then, big men, señorita?" he inquired.

Pilar agreed enthusiastically.

"Oh, yes, I like a man to be very big, tall, and the shoulers broad and very, very strong."

Colonel Johnson said sharply:

"Did you see much of your grandfather when you arived here?"

Pilar said:

"Oh, yes. I went to sit with him. He told me things—hat he had been a very wicked man, and all the things he lid in South Africa."

"Did he ever tell you that he had diamonds in the safe n his room?"

"Yes, he showed them to me. But they were not like liamonds—they were just like pebbles—very ugly—very ugly ndeed."

Superintendent Sugden said shortly:

"So he showed them to you, did he?"

"Yes."

"He didn't give you any of them?"

Pilar shook her head.

"No, he did not. I thought that perhaps one day he would—f I were very nice to him and came often to sit with him. Because old gentlemen they like very much young girls."

Colonel Johnson said:

"Do you know that those diamonds have been stolen?"

Pilar opened her eyes very wide.

"Stolen?"

"Yes, have you any idea who might have taken them?"

Pilar nodded her head.

"Oh, yes," she said. "It would be Horbury."

"Horbury? You mean the valet?"

"Yes."

"Why do you think that?"

"Because he has the face of a thief. His eyes go so, from side to side, he walks softly and listens at doors. He is like a cat. And all cats are thieves."

"H'm," said Colonel Johnson. "We'll leave it at that. Now I understand that all the family were up in your grandfather's room this afternoon, and that some—er—angry words passed."

Pilar nodded and smiled.

"Yes," she said. "It was great fun. Grandfather made them, oh! so angry!"

"Oh, you enjoyed it, did you?"

"Yes. I like to see people get angry. I like it very much. But here in England they do not get angry like they do in Spain. In Spain they take out their knives and they curse and shout. In England they do nothing, just get very red in the face and shut up their mouths tight."

"Do you remember what was said?"

Pilar seemed rather doubtful.

"I am not sure. Grandfather said they were no good— that they had not got any children. He said I was better than any of them. He liked me, very much."

"Did he say anything about money or a will?"

"A will—no, I don't think so. I don't remember."

"What happened?"

"They all went away—except Hilda—the fat one, David's wife, she stayed behind."

"Oh, she did, did she?"

"Yes. David looked very funny. He was all shaking and, oh! so white. He looked as though he might be sick."

"And what then?"

"Then I went and found Stephen. We danced to the gramophone."

"Stephen Farr?"

"Yes. He is from South Africa—he is the son of Grandfather's partner. He is very handsome, too. Very brown and big and he has nice eyes."

Johnson asked:

"Where were you when the crime occurred?"

"You ask where I was?"

"Yes."

"I had gone into the drawing-room with Lydia. And then I went up to my room and did my face. I was going to dance again with Stephen. And then, far away, I heard a scream and everyone was running, so I went too. And they were trying to break down Grandfather's door. Harry did it with Stephen, they are both big, strong men."

"Yes?"

"And then—crash—down it went—and we all looked in. Oh, such a sight—everything smashed and knocked over and Grandfather lying in a lot of blood, and his throat was cut like *this*"—she made a vivid, dramatic gesture at her own neck—"right up under his ear."

She paused, having obviously enjoyed her narrative.

Johnson said:

"The blood didn't make you feel ill?"

She stared.

"No, why should it? There is usually blood when people are killed. There was, oh! so much blood everywhere!"

Poirot said:

"Did anyone say anything?"

Pilar said:

"David said such a funny thing—what was it? Oh, yes. The mills of God—that is what he said"—she repeated it with emphasis on each word—"*the—mills—of—God*— What does that mean? Mills are what make flour, are they not?"

Colonel Johnson said:

"Well, I don't think there is anything more just now, Miss Estravados."

Pilar got up obediently. She flashed a quick, charming smile at each man in turn.

"I will go now then."

She went out.

Colonel Johnson said:

"*The mills of God grind slowly, yet they grind exceeding small.* And David Lee said that!"

XV

As the door opened once more, Colonel Johnson looked up. For a moment he took the entering figure to be that of Harry Lee, but as Stephen Farr advanced into the room he saw his error.

"Sit down, Mr. Farr," he said.

Stephen sat. His eyes, cool, intelligent eyes, went from one to the other of the three men. He said:

"I'm afraid I sha'n't be of much use to you. But please ask me anything that you think may help. Perhaps I'd better explain to start with exactly who I am. My father, Ebenezer Farr, was Simeon Lee's partner in South Africa in the old days. I'm talking of over forty years ago."

He paused.

"My dad talked to me a lot about Simeon Lee—what a personality he was. He and Dad cleaned up a good bit together. Simeon Lee went home with a fortune and my father didn't do badly either. My father always told me that when I came to this country I was to look up Mr. Lee. I said once that it was a long time ago and that he'd probably not know who I was, but Dad scoffed at the idea. He said, 'When two men have been through what Simeon and I went through, they don't forget.' Well, my father died a couple of years ago. This year I came over to England for the first time, and I thought I'd act on Dad's advice and look up Mr. Lee."

With a slight smile he went on:

"I was just a little nervous when I came along here, but I needn't have been. Mr. Lee gave me a warm welcome and absolutely insisted that I should stay with the family over

85

Christmas. I was afraid I was butting in, but he wouldn't hear of a refusal."

He added rather shyly:

"They were all very nice to me—Mr. and Mrs. Alfred Lee couldn't have been nicer. I'm terribly sorry for them that all this should come upon them."

"How long have you been here, Mr. Farr?"

"Since yesterday."

"Did you see Mr. Lee to-day at all?"

"Yes, I had a chat with him this morning. He was in good spirits then and anxious to hear about a lot of people and places."

"That was the last time you saw him?"

"Yes."

"Did he mention to you that he kept a quantity of uncut diamonds in his safe?"

"No."

He added before the other could speak:

"Do you mean that this business was murder and robbery?"

"We're not sure yet," said Johnson. "Now to come to the events of this evening, will you tell me in your own words what you were doing?"

"Certainly. After the ladies left the dining-room I stayed and had a glass of port. Then I realized that the Lees had family business they wanted to discuss and that my being there was hampering them, so I excused myself and left them."

"And what did you do then?"

Stephen Farr leaned back in his chair. His forefinger caressed his jaw. He said rather woodenly:

"I—er—went along to a big room with a parquet floor—kind of ballroom, I fancy. There's a gramophone there and dance records. I put some records on."

Poirot said:

"It was possible, perhaps, that someone might join you there?"

A very faint smile curved Stephen Farr's lips. He answered:

"It was possible, yes. One always hopes."

And he grinned outright.

Poirot said:

"Señorita Estravados is very beautiful."

Stephen answered:

"She's easily the best thing to look at that I've seen since I came to England."

"Did Miss Estravados join you?" asked Colonel Johnson.

Stephen shook his head.

"I was still there when I heard the rumpus. I came out into the hall and ran hell for leather to see what was the matter. I helped Harry Lee to break the door down."

"And that's all you have to tell us?"

"Absolutely all, I'm afraid."

Hercule Poirot leaned forward. He said softly:

"But I think, Monsieur Farr, that you could tell us a good deal if you liked."

Farr said sharply:

"What d'you mean?"

"You can tell us of something that is very important in this case—the character of Mr. Lee. You say that your father talked much of him to you. What manner of a man was it that he described to you?"

Stephen Farr said slowly:

"I think I see what you're driving at. What was Simeon Lee like in his young days? Well—you want me to be frank, I suppose?"

"If you please."

"Well, to begin with, I don't think that Simeon Lee was a highly moral member of society. I don't mean that he was exactly a crook, but he sailed pretty near the wind. His morals were nothing to boast about anyway. He had charm, though, a good deal of it. And he was fantastically generous. No one with a hard luck story ever appealed to him in vain. He drank a bit, but not overmuch; was attractive to women and had a sense of humour. All the same, he had a queer revengeful streak in him. Talk of the elephant never forgets and you talk of Simeon Lee. My father told me of several cases where Lee waited years to get even with someone who'd done him a nasty turn."

Superintendent Sugden said:

"Two might play at that game. You've no knowledge, I suppose, Mr. Farr, of anyone Simeon Lee had done a bad turn to out there? Nothing out of the past that could explain the crime committed here this evening?"

Stephen Farr shook his head.

"He had enemies, of course, must have had, being the man he was. But I know of no specific case. Besides," his eyes narrowed, "I understand (as a matter of fact I've been questioning Tressilian) there have been no strangers in or near the house this evening."

Hercule Poirot said:

"With the exception of yourself, M. Farr."

Stephen Farr swung round upon him.

"Oh, so that's it? Suspicious stranger within the gates! Well, you won't find anything of that kind. No back history of Simeon Lee doing Ebenezer Farr down, and Eb's son coming over to revenge his dad! No," he shook his head, "Simeon and Ebenezer had nothing against each other. I came here, as I've told you, out of sheer curiosity. And moreover, I should imagine a gramophone is as good an alibi as anything else. I never stopped putting on records— somebody must have heard them. One record wouldn't give me time to race away upstairs—these passages are a mile long, anyway—slit an old man's throat, wash off the blood and get back again before the others came rushing up. The idea's farcical!"

Colonel Johnson said:

"We're not making any insinuations against you, Mr. Farr."

Stephen Farr said:

"I didn't care much for the tone of Mr. Hercule Poirot's voice."

"That," said Hercule Poirot, "is unfortunate!"

He smiled benignly at the other.

Stephen Farr looked angrily at him.

Colonel Johnson interposed quickly:

"Thank you, Mr. Farr. That will be all for the present. You will, of course, not leave this house."

Stephen Farr nodded. He got up and left the room, walking with a freely swinging stride.

As the door closed behind him, Johnson said:

"There goes X, the unknown quantity. His story seems straightforward enough. All the same, he's the dark horse. He *might* have pinched those diamonds—might have come here with a bogus story just to gain admittance. You'd better get his fingerprints, Sugden, and see if he's known."

"I've already got them," said the Superintendent with a dry smile.

"Good man. You don't overlook much. I suppose you're on to all the obvious lines?"

Superintendent Sugden checked off on his fingers:

"Check up on those telephone calls—times, etc. Check up on Horbury. What time he left, who saw him go. Check up all entrances and exits. Check up on staff generally. Check up financial position of members of family. Get on to the lawyers and check up on will. Search house for the weapon and for bloodstains on clothing—also, possibly diamonds hidden somewhere."

"That covers everything, I think," said Colonel Johnson approvingly. "Can you suggest anything, M. Poirot?"

Poirot shook his head. He said:

"I find the Superintendent admirably thorough."

Sugden said gloomily:

"It won't be any joke looking through this house for the

missing diamonds. Never saw so many ornaments and knick-knacks in my life."

"The hiding places are certainly abundant," Poirot agreed.

"And there's really nothing you would suggest, Poirot?"

The Chief Constable looked a little disappointed—rather like a man whose dog has refused to do its trick.

Poirot said:

"You will permit that I take a line of my own?"

"Certainly—certainly," said Johnson at the same moment as Superintendent Sugden said rather suspiciously:

"What line?"

"I would like," said Hercule Poirot, "to converse—very often—very frequently—with members of the family."

"You mean you'd like to have another shot at questioning them?" asked the Colonel, a little puzzled.

"No, no, not to question—to converse!"

"Why?" asked Sugden.

Hercule Poirot waved an emphatic hand.

"In conversation, points arise! If a human being converses much, it is impossible for him to avoid the truth!"

Sugden said:

"Then you think someone is lying?"

Poirot sighed.

"*Mon cher,* everyone lies—in parts like the egg of the English curate. It is profitable to separate the harmless lies from the vital ones."

Colonel Johnson said sharply:

"All the same, it's incredible, you know. Here's a particularly crude and brutal murder—and whom have we as suspects? Alfred Lee and his wife—both charming, well-bred, quiet people. George Lee, who's a member of parliament and the essence of respectability. His wife? She's just an ordinary modern lovely. David Lee seems a gentle creature and we've got his brother Harry's word for it that he can't stand the sight of blood. His wife seems a nice, sensible woman—quite commonplace. Remains the Spanish niece and the man from South Africa. Spanish beauties have hot tempers, but I don't see that attractive creature slitting the old man's neck in cold blood, especially as from what has come out she had every reason to keep him alive—at any rate until he had signed a new will. Stephen Farr's a possibility—that is to say, he may be a professional crook and have come here after the diamonds. The old man discovered the loss and Farr slit his throat to keep him quiet. That could have been so—that gramophone alibi isn't too good."

Poirot shook his head.

"My dear friend," he said. "Compare the physique of M. Stephen Farr and old Simeon Lee. If Farr decided to kill the old man he could have done it in a minute—Simeon Lee couldn't possibly have put up that fight against him. Can one believe that that frail old man and that magnificent specimen of humanity struggled for some minutes overturning chairs and breaking china? To imagine such a thing is fantastic!"

Colonel Johnson's eyes narrowed.

"You mean," he said, "that it was a *weak* man who killed Simeon Lee?"

"Or a woman!" said the Superintendent.

XVI

Colonel Johnson looked at his watch.

"Nothing much more that I can do here. You've got things well in hand, Sugden. Oh, just one thing. We ought to see the butler fellow. I know you've questioned him, but we know a bit more about things now. It's important to get confirmation of just where everybody says he was at the time of the murder."

Tressilian came in slowly. The Chief Constable told him to sit down.

"Thank you, sir. I will, if you don't mind. I've been feeling very queer—very queer indeed. My legs, sir, and my head."

Poirot said gently:

"You have had the shock, yes."

The butler shuddered.

"Such—such a violent thing to happen. In this house! Where everything has always gone on so quietly."

Poirot said:

"It was a well-ordered house, yes? But not a happy one?"

"I wouldn't like to say that, sir."

"In the old days when all the family was at home, was it happy then?"

Tressilian said slowly:

"It wasn't, perhaps, what one would call very harmonious, sir."

"The late Mrs. Lee was somewhat of an invalid, was she not?"

"Yes, sir, very poorly she was."

"Were her children fond of her?"

"Mr. David, he was devoted to her. More like a daughter than a son. And after she died, he broke away, couldn't face living here any longer."

Poirot said:

"And Mr. Harry? What was he like?"

"Always rather a wild young gentleman, sir, but good-hearted. Oh, dear, gave me quite a turn it did, when the bell rang—and then again, so impatient like, and I opened the door and there was a strange man and then Mr. Harry's voice said: 'Hullo, Tressilian. Still here, eh? Just the same as ever.' "

Poirot said sympathetically:

"It must have been the strange feeling, yes, indeed."

Tressilian said, a little pink flush showing in his cheek:

"It seems sometimes, sir, as though the past isn't the past! I believe there's been a play on in London about something like that. There's something in it, sir—there really is. There's a feeling comes over you—as though you'd done everything before. It just seems to me as though the bell rings and I go to answer it and there's Mr. Harry—even if it should be Mr. Farr or some other person—I'm just saying to myself —*but I've done this before. . . .*"

Poirot said:

"That is very interesting—very interesting."

Tressilian looked at him gratefully.

Johnson, somewhat impatient, cleared his throat and took charge of the conversation.

"Just want to get various times checked correctly," he said. "Now when the noise upstairs started I understand that only Mr. Alfred Lee and Mr. Harry Lee were in the dining-room. Is that so?"

"I really couldn't tell you, sir. All the gentlemen were there when I served coffee to them—but that would be about a quarter of an hour earlier."

"Mr. George Lee was telephoning. Can you confirm that?"

"I think somebody did telephone, sir. The bell rings in my pantry, and when anybody takes off the receiver to call a number, there's just a faint noise on the bell. I do remember hearing that, but I didn't pay any attention to it."

"You don't know exactly when it was?"

"I couldn't say, sir. It was after I had taken coffee to the gentlemen, that is all I can say."

"Do you know where any of the ladies were at the time I mentioned?"

"Mrs. Alfred was in the drawing-room, sir, when I went for the coffee tray. That was just a minute or two before I heard the cry upstairs."

Poirot asked:

"What was she doing?"

"She was standing by the far window, sir. She was holding the curtain a little back and looking out."

"And none of the other ladies was in the room?"

"No, sir."

"Do you know where they were?"

"I couldn't say at all, sir."

"You don't know where anyone else was?"

"Mr. David, I think, was playing in the music room next to the drawing-room."

"You heard him playing?"

"Yes, sir." Again the old man shivered. "It was like a sign, sir, so I felt afterwards. It was the *Dead March* he was playing. Even at the time, I remember, it gave me the creeps."

"It is curious, yes," said Poirot.

"Now about this fellow, Horbury, the valet," said the Chief Constable. "Are you definitely prepared to swear that he was out of the house by eight o'clock?"

"Oh, yes, sir. It was just after Mr. Sugden arrived. I remember particular because he broke a coffee cup."

Poirot said:

"Horbury broke a coffee cup?"

"Yes, sir—one of the old Worcester ones. Eleven years I've washed them up and never one broken till this evening."

Poirot said:

"What was Horbury doing with the coffee cups?"

"Well, of course, sir, he'd no business to have been handling them at all. He was just holding one up, admiring it like, and I happened to mention that Mr. Sugden had called and he dropped it."

Poirot said:

"Did you say 'Mr. Sugden' or did you mention the word police?"

Tressilian looked a little startled.

"Now I come to think of it, sir, I mentioned that the Police Superintendent had called."

"And Horbury dropped the coffee cup?" said Poirot.

"Seems suggestive, that," said the Chief Constable. "Did Horbury ask any questions about the Superintendent's visit?"

"Yes, sir, asked what he wanted here. I said he'd come collecting for the Police Orphanage and had gone up to Mr. Lee."

"Did Horbury seem relieved when you said that?"

"Do you know, sir, now you mention it, he certainly did. His manner changed at once. Said Mr. Lee was a good old chap and free with his money—rather disrespectfully he spoke—and then he went off."

"Which way?"

"Out through the door to the servants' hall."

Sugden interposed:

"All that's O.K., sir. He passed through the kitchen where

the cook and the kitchenmaid saw him, and out through the back door."

"Now listen, Tressilian, and think carefully. Is there any means by which Horbury could return to the house without anyone seeing him?"

The old man shook his head.

"I don't see how he could have done so, sir. All the doors are locked on the inside."

"Supposing he had had a key?"

"The doors are bolted as well."

"How does he get in when he comes?"

"He has a key to the back door, sir. All the servants come in that way."

"He *could* have returned that way, then?"

"Not without passing through the kitchen, sir. And the kitchen would be occupied till well after half-past nine or a quarter to ten."

Colonel Johnson said:

"That seems conclusive. Thank you, Tressilian."

The old man got up and with a bow left the room. He returned, however, a minute or two later.

"Horbury has just returned, sir. Would you like to see him now?"

"Yes, please, send him in at once."

XVII

Sydney Horbury did not present a very prepossessing appearance. He came into the room and stood rubbing his hands together, and darting quick looks from one person to another. His manner was unctuous.

Johnson said:

"You're Sydney Horbury?"

"Yes, sir."

"Valet attendant to the late Mr. Lee?"

"Yes, sir. It's terrible, sir, isn't it? You could have knocked me down with a feather when I heard from Gladys. Poor old gentleman——"

Johnson cut him short.

"Just answer my questions, please."

"Yes, sir, certainly, sir."

"What time did you go out to-night, and where have you been?"

"I left the house just before eight, sir. I went to the 'Superb,' sir, just five minutes' walk away. *Love in Old Seville* was the picture, sir."

"Anyone who saw you there?"

"The young lady in the box office, sir, she knows me. And the Commissionaire at the door. He knows me, too. And—er—as a matter of fact I was with a young lady, sir. I met her there by appointment."

"Oh, you did, did you? What's her name?"

"Doris Buckle, sir. She works in the Combined Dairies, sir, 23 Markham Road."

"Good, we'll look into that. Did you come straight home?"

"I saw my young lady home first, sir. Then I came straight back. You'll find it's quite all right, sir. I didn't have anything to do with this. I was—"

Colonel Johnson said curtly:

"Nobody's accusing you of having anything to do with it."

"No, sir, of course not, sir. But it's not very pleasant when a murder happens in a house."

"Nobody said it was. Now then, how long had you been in Mr. Lee's service?"

"Just over a year, sir."

"Did you like your place here?"

"Yes, sir. I was quite satisfied. The pay was good. Mr. Lee was rather difficult sometimes, but of course I'm used to attending on invalids."

"You've had previous experience?"

"Oh, yes, sir. I was with Major West and with the Honourable Jasper Finch—"

"You can give all these particulars to Sugden later. What I want to know is this—at what time did you last see Mr. Lee this evening?"

"It was about half-past seven, sir. Mr. Lee had a light supper brought to him every evening at seven o'clock. I then prepared him for bed. After that he would sit in front of the fire in his dressing-gown till he felt like going to bed."

"What time was that, usually?"

"It varied, sir. Sometimes he would go to bed as early as eight o'clock—that is, if he felt tired. Sometimes he would sit up till eleven or after."

"What did he do when he did want to go to bed?"

"Usually he rang for me, sir."

"And you assisted him to bed?"

"Yes, sir."

"But this was your evening out—did you always have Friday?"

"Yes, sir, Friday was my regular day."

"What happened then when Mr. Lee wanted to go to bed?"

"He would ring his bell and either Tressilian or Walter would see to him."

"He was not helpless? He could move about?"

"Yes, sir, but not very easily. Rheumatoid arthritis was

94

what he suffered from, sir. He was worse some days than others."

"Did he never go into another room in the daytime?"

"No, sir. He preferred to be in just the one room. Mr. Lee wasn't luxurious in his tastes. It was a big room with plenty of air and light in it."

"Mr. Lee had his supper at seven, you say?"

"Yes, sir. I took the tray away and put out the sherry and two glasses on the bureau."

"Why did you do that?"

"Mr. Lee's orders."

"Was that usual?"

"Sometimes. It was the rule that none of the family came to see Mr. Lee in the evening unless he invited them. Some evenings he liked to be alone. Other evenings he'd send down and ask Mr. Alfred, or Mrs. Alfred, or both of them to come up after dinner."

"But as far as you know he had not done so on this occasion? That is, he had not sent a message to any member of the family requesting their presence?"

"He hadn't sent any message by *me*, sir."

"So that he wasn't expecting any of the family?"

"He might have asked one of them personally, sir."

"Of course."

Horbury continued:

"I saw that everything was in order, wished Mr. Lee goodnight and left the room."

Poirot asked:

"Did you make up the fire before you left the room?"

The valet hesitated.

"It wasn't necessary, sir. It was well built up."

"Could Mr. Lee have done that himself?"

"Oh, no, sir. I expect Mr. Harry Lee had done it."

"Mr. Harry Lee was with him when you came in before supper?"

"Yes, sir. He went away when I came."

"What was the relationship between the two as far as you could judge?"

"Mr. Harry Lee seemed in very good spirits, sir. Throwing back his head and laughing a good deal."

"And Mr. Lee?"

"He was quiet, and rather thoughtful."

"I see. Now there's something more I want to know, Horbury. What can you tell us about the diamonds Mr. Lee kept in his safe?"

"Diamonds, sir? I never saw any diamonds."

"Mr. Lee kept a quantity of uncut stones there. You must have seen him handling them."

"Those funny little pebbles, sir? Yes, I did see him with them once or twice. But I didn't know they were diamonds. He was showing them to the foreign young lady only yesterday—or was it the day before?"

Colonel Johnson said abruptly:

"Those stones have been stolen."

Horbury cried out:

"I hope you don't think, sir, that *I* had anything to do with it!"

"I'm not making any accusations," said Johnson. "Now then, is there anything you can tell us that has any bearing on this matter?"

"The diamonds, sir? Or the murder?"

"Both."

Horbury considered. He passed his tongue over his pale lips. At last he looked up with eyes that were a shade furtive.

"I don't think there's anything, sir."

Poirot said softly:

"Nothing you've overheard, say, in the course of your duties, which might be helpful."

The valet's eyelids flickered a little.

"No, sir, I don't think so, sir. There was a little awkwardness between Mr. Lee—and some members of his family."

"Which members?"

"I gathered there was a little trouble over Mr. Harry Lee's return. Mr. Alfred Lee resented it. I understand he and his father had a few words about it—but that was all there was to it. Mr. Lee didn't accuse him for a minute of having taken any diamonds. And I'm sure Mr. Alfred wouldn't do such a thing."

Poirot said quickly:

"His interview with Mr. Alfred was *after* he had discovered the loss of the diamonds, was it not, though?"

"Yes, sir."

Poirot leaned forward.

"I thought, Horbury," he said softly, *"that you did not know of the theft of the diamonds until we informed you of it just now? How then, do you know that Mr. Lee had discovered his loss before he had this conversation with his son?"*

Horbury turned brick red.

"No use lying. Out with it," said Sugden. "When did you know?"

Horbury said sullenly:

"I heard him telephoning to someone about it."

"You weren't in the room?"

"No, outside the door. Couldn't hear much—only a word or two."

"What did you hear exactly?" asked Poirot sweetly.

"I heard the words robbery and diamonds and I heard him say, 'I don't know who to suspect'—and I heard him say something about this evening at eight o'clock."

Superintendent Sugden nodded.

"That was to me he was speaking, my lad. About ten after five, was it?"

"That's right, sir."

"And when you went into his room afterwards, did he look upset?"

"Just a bit, sir. Seemed absent-minded and worried."

"So much so that you got the wind up—eh?"

"Look here, Mr. Sugden, I won't have you saying things like that. Never touched any diamonds, I didn't, and you can't prove I did. I'm not a thief."

Superintendent Sugden, unimpressed, said:

"That remains to be seen." He glanced questioningly at the Chief Constable, received a nod and went on: "That'll do for you, my lad. Sha'n't want you again tonight."

Horbury went out gratefully in haste.

Sugden said appreciatively:

"Pretty bit of work, M. Poirot. You trapped him as neatly as I've ever seen it done. He may be a thief or he may not, but he's certainly a first class liar!"

"An unprepossessing person," said Poirot.

"Nasty bit of goods," agreed Johnson. "Question is, what do we think of his evidence?"

Sugden summarized the position neatly.

"Seems to me there are three possibilities: No. 1: Horbury's a thief *and* a murderer. No. 2: Horbury's a thief but *not* a murderer. No. 3: Horbury's an innocent man. Certain amount of evidence for No. 1. He overheard telephone call and knew the theft had been discovered. Gathered from old man's manner that he was suspected. Made his plans accordingly. Went out ostentatiously at eight o'clock and cooked up an alibi. Easy enough to slip out of a theater and return there unnoticed. He'd have to be pretty sure of the girl, though, that she wouldn't give him away. I'll see what I can get out of her to-morrow."

"How, then, did he manage to reenter the house?" asked Poirot.

"That's more difficult," Sugden admitted. "But there might be ways. Say one of the women servants unlocked a side door for him."

Poirot raised his eyebrows quizzically.

"He places then his life at the mercy of two women? With *one* woman it would be taking a big risk—with *two, eh bien* —I find the risk fantastic!"

Sugden said:

"Some criminals think they can get away with anything!"

He went on:

"Let's take No. 2: Horbury pinched those diamonds. He took 'em out of the house to-night and has possibly passed them on to some accomplice. That's quite easy going and highly probable. Now we've got to admit that somebody else chose this night to murder Mr. Lee. That somebody being quite unaware of the diamond complication. It's possible, of course, but it's a bit of a coincidence.

"Possibility No. 3: Horbury's innocent. Somebody else both took the diamonds and murdered the old gentleman. There it is; it's up to us to get at the truth."

Colonel Johnson yawned. He looked again at his watch and got up.

"Well," he said, "I think we'll call it a night, eh? Better just have a look in the safe before we go. Odd thing if those wretched diamonds were there all the time."

But the diamonds were not in the safe. They found the combination where Alfred Lee had told them, in the small notebook taken from the dressing-gown pocket of the dead man. In the safe they found an empty chamois leather bag. Among the papers the safe contained, only one was of interest.

It was a will dated some fifteen years previously. After various legacies and bequests, the provisions were simple enough. Half Simeon Lee's fortune went to Alfred Lee. The other half was to be divided in equal shares among his remaining children—Harry, George, David and Jennifer.

Part IV ------ DECEMBER 25TH

I

IN THE BRIGHT sun of Christmas noon, Poirot walked in the gardens of Gorston Hall. The Hall itself was a large solidly built house with no special architectural pretensions.

Here on the south side was a broad terrace flanked with a hedge of clipped yew. Little plants grew in the interstices of the stone flags and at intervals along the terrace there were stone sinks arranged as miniature gardens.

Poirot surveyed them with benign approval. He murmured to himself:

"C'est bien imaginé, ça!"

In the distance he caught sight of two figures going towards an ornamental sheet of water some three hundred yards away. Pilar was easily recognizable as one of the figures and he thought at first the other was Stephen Farr, then he saw that the man with Pilar was Harry Lee. Harry seemed very attentive to his attractive niece. At intervals he flung his head back and laughed, then bent once more attentively towards her.

"Assuredly, there is one who does not mourn," Poirot murmured to himself.

A soft sound behind him made him turn. Magdalene Lee was standing there. She too, was looking at the retreating figures of the man and girl. She turned her head and smiled enchantingly at Poirot.

She said:

"It's such a glorious sunny day! One can hardly believe in all the horrors of last night, can one, M. Poirot?"

"It is difficult, truly, madam."

Magdalene sighed.

"I've never been mixed up in tragedy before. I've—I've really only just grown up. I stayed a child too long, I think. . . . That's not a good thing to do."

Again she sighed. She said:

"Pilar, now, seems so extraordinarily self-possessed. . . . I suppose it's the Spanish blood? It's all very odd, isn't it?"

"What is odd, madam?"

"The way she turned up here, out of the blue!"

Poirot said:

"I have learned that Mr. Lee had been searching for her for some time. He had been in correspondence with the Consulate in Madrid and with the Vice-Consul at Aliquara where her mother died."

"He was very secretive about it all," said Magdalene. "Alfred knew nothing about it. No more did Lydia."

"Ah!" said Poirot.

Magdalene came a little nearer to him. He could smell the delicate perfume she used.

"You know, M. Poirot, there's some story connected with Jennifer's husband, Estravados. He died quite soon after the marriage and there's some mystery about it. Alfred and Lydia know. I believe it was something—rather disgraceful. . . ."

"That," said Poirot, "is sad indeed."

Magdalene said:

"My husband feels—and I agree with him—that the family ought to have been told more about the girl's antecedents. After all, if her father was a *criminal*—"

She paused, but Hercule Poirot said nothing. He seemed to be admiring such beauties of nature as could be seen in the winter season in the grounds of Gorston Hall.

Magdalene said:

"I can't help feeling that the manner of my father-in-law's death was somehow *significant*. It—it was so very *un-English*."

Hercule Poirot turned slowly. His grave eyes met hers in innocent inquiry.

"Ah," he said. "The Spanish touch, you think?"

"Well, they *are* cruel, aren't they?" Magdalene spoke with an effect of childish appeal. "All those bull fights and things!"

Hercule Poirot said pleasantly:

"You are saying that in your opinion Señorita Estravados cut her grandfather's throat?"

"Oh! no, M. Poirot!" Magdalene was vehement. She was shocked. "I never said anything of the kind! Indeed I didn't!"

"Well," said Poirot. "Perhaps you did not."

"But I *do* think that she is—well, a suspicious person. The furtive way she picked up something from the floor of that room last night, for instance."

A different note crept into Hercule Poirot's voice. He said sharply:

"She picked up something from the floor last night?"

Magdalene nodded. Her childish mouth curved spitefully.

"Yes, as soon as we got into the room. She gave a quick glance round to see if anyone was looking and then pounced on it. But the Superintendent man saw her, I'm glad to say, and made her give it up."

"What was it that she picked up? Do you know, madam?"

"No. I wasn't near enough to see." Magdalene's voice held regret. "It was something quite small."

Poirot frowned to himself.

"It is interesting, that," he murmured to himself.

Magdalene said quickly:

"Yes, I thought you ought to know about it. After all, we don't know *anything* about Pilar's upbringing and what her life has been like. Alfred is always so unsuspicious and dear Lydia is so casual." Then she murmured: "Perhaps I'd better go and see if I can help Lydia in any way. There may be letters to write."

She left him with a smile of satisfied malice on her lips.

Poirot remained on the terrace, lost in thought.

To him there came Superintendent Sugden. The Police Superintendent looked gloomy. He said:

"Good-morning, Mr. Poirot. Doesn't seem quite the right thing to say Merry Christmas, does it?"

"*Mon cher collègue*, I certainly do not observe any traces of merriment on your countenance. If you had said, 'Merry Christmas,' I should not have replied, 'Many of them!'"

"I don't want another one like this one and that's a fact," said Sugden.

"You have made the progress, yes?"

"I've checked up on a good many points. Horbury's alibi is holding water all right. The Commissionaire at the movie theater saw him go in with the girl, and saw him come out with her at the end of the performance, and seems pretty positive he didn't leave and couldn't have left and returned during the performance. The girl swears quite definitely he was with her in the theater all the time."

Poirot's eyebrows rose.

"I hardly see, then, what more there is to say?"

The cynical Sugden said:

"Well, one never knows with girls! Lie themselves black in the face for the sake of a man."

"That does credit to their hearts," said Hercule Poirot.

Sugden growled:

"That's a foreign way of looking at it. It's defeating the ends of justice."

Hercule Poirot said:

"Justice is a very strange thing. Have you ever reflected on it?"

Sugden stared at him. He said:

"You're a queer one, Mr. Poirot."

"Not at all. I follow a logical train of thought. But we will not enter into a dispute on the question. It is your belief, then, that this demoiselle from the milk shop is not speaking the truth?"

Sugden shook his head.

"No," he said. "It's not like that at all. As a matter of fact I think she *is* telling the truth. She's a simple kind of girl and I think if she was telling me a pack of lies, I'd spot it."

Poirot said:

"You have the experience, yes."

"That's just it, Mr. Poirot. One does know, more or less, after a lifetime of taking down statements when a person's lying and when they're not. No, I think the girl's evidence is genuine, and if so Horbury *couldn't* have murdered old Mr. Lee, and that brings us right back to the people in the house."

He drew a deep breath.

"One of 'em did it, Mr. Poirot. One of 'em did it. But *which?*"

"You have no new data?"

"Yes, I've had a certain amount of luck over the telephone calls. Mr. George Lee put through a call to Westeringham at two minutes to nine. That call lasted under six minutes."

"Aha!"

"As you say! Moreover *no other call* was put through—to Westeringham or anywhere else."

"Very interesting," said Poirot, with approval. "M. George Lee says he has just finished telephoning when he hears the noise overhead—but actually he had finished telephoning nearly *ten minutes before that*. Where was he in those ten minutes? Mrs. George Lee says that *she* was telephoning—but actually she never put through a call at all. Where was *she?*"

Sugden said:

"I saw you talking to her, Mr. Poirot?"

His voice held a question, but Poirot replied:

"You are in error!"

"Eh?"

"*I* was not talking to *her*—she was talking to *me!*"

"Oh—" Sugden seemed to be about to brush the distinction aside impatiently; then, as its significance sank in, he said:

"*She* was talking to *you*, you say?"

"Most definitely. She came out here for that purpose."

"What did she have to say?"

"She wished to stress certain points—the un-English character of the crime—the possibly undesirable antecedents of Miss Estravados on the paternal side—the fact that Miss Estravados had furtively picked up something from the floor last night."

"She told you that, did she?" said Sugden with interest.

"Yes. What was it that the señorita picked up?"

Sugden sighed.

"I could give you three hundred guesses! I'll show it to you. It's the sort of thing that solves the whole mystery in detective stories! If you can make anything out of it, I'll retire from the police force!"

"Show it to me."

Sugden took an envelope from his pocket and tilted its contents onto the palm of his hand. A faint grin showed on his face.

"There you are. What do you make of it?"

On the Superintendent's broad palm lay a little triangular piece of pink rubber and a small wooden peg.

His grin broadened, as Poirot picked up the articles and frowned over them.

"Make anything of them, Mr. Poirot?"

"This little piece of stuff might have been cut from a sponge bag?"

"It was. It comes from a sponge bag in Mr. Lee's room. Somebody with sharp scissors just cut a small triangular piece out of it. Mr. Lee may have done it himself for all I know. But it beats me *why* he should do it. Horbury can't throw any light on the matter. As for the peg, it's about the size of a cribbage peg, but they're usually made of ivory. This is just rough wood—whittled out of a bit of deal, I should say."

"Most remarkable," murmured Poirot.

"Keep 'em if you like," said Sugden kindly. "*I* don't want them."

"*Mon ami*, I would not deprive you of them!"

"They don't mean anything at all to you?"

"I must confess—nothing whatever!"

"Splendid!" said Sugden with heavy sarcasm, returning them to his pocket. "We *are* getting on!"

Poirot said:

"Mrs. George Lee, she recounts that the young lady stooped and picked these bagatelles up in a furtive manner. Should you say that that was true?"

Sugden considered the point.

"N-o," he said hesitatingly. "I shouldn't quite go as far as that. She didn't look guilty—nothing of that kind—but she did set about it rather—well—quickly and quietly—if you know what I mean. *And she didn't know I'd seen her do it!* That I'm sure of—she jumped when I rounded on her."

Poirot said thoughtfully:

"Then there *was* a reason—but what conceivable reason could there have been? That little piece of rubber is quite fresh—it has not been used for anything—it can have no meaning whatsoever and yet—"

Sugden said impatiently:

"Well, you can worry about it if you like, Mr. Poirot. I've got other things to think about."

Poirot asked:

"The case stands—where, in your opinion?"

Sugden took out his notebook.

"Let's get down to *facts*. To begin with there are the people who *couldn't* have done it. Let's get them out of the way first—"

"They are?"

"Alfred and Harry Lee. They've got a definite alibi. Also Mrs. Alfred Lee, since Tressilian saw her in the drawing-room only about a minute before the row started upstairs. Those three are clear. Now for the others. Here's a list. I've put it this way for clearness."

He handed the book to Poirot.

At the time of the crime

George Lee	was	?
Mrs. George Lee	was	?
David Lee	was	playing piano in music room (confirmed by his wife)
Mrs. David Lee	was	in music room (confirmed by husband)
Miss Estravados	was	in her bedroom (no confirmation)
Stephen Farr	was	in ballroom playing gramophone (confirmed by three of staff who could hear the music in servants' hall)

Poirot said, handing back the list:
"And therefore?"

"And therefore," said Sugden, "George Lee could have killed the old man. Mrs. George Lee could have killed him, Pilar Estravados could have killed him and *either Mr. or Mrs. David Lee could have killed him,* but not *both.*"

"You do not, then, accept that alibi?"

Superintendent Sugden shook his head emphatically.

"Not on your life! Hus and and wife—devoted to each other! They may be in it together, or if one of them did it, the other is ready to swear to an alibi. I look at it this way. *Someone* was in the music room, playing the piano. It *may* have been David Lee. It probably *was,* since he was an acknowledged musician, but there's nothing to say his wife was there too *except her word and his.* In the same way, it *may* have been Hilda Lee who was playing that piano while David Lee crept upstairs and killed his father! No, it's an absolutely different case from the two brothers in the dining-room. Alfred Lee and Harry Lee don't love each other. Neither of them would perjure himself for the other's sake."

"What about Stephen Farr?"

"He's a possible suspect because that gramophone alibi is a bit thin. On the other hand it's the sort of alibi that's really sounder than a good cast-iron dyed-in-the-wool alibi which ten to one has been faked up beforehand!"

Poirot bowed his head thoughtfully.

"I know what you mean. It is the alibi of a man *who did not know that he would be called upon to provide such a thing.*"

"Exactly! And anyway, somehow, I don't believe a stranger was mixed up in this thing."

Poirot said quickly:

"I agree with you. It is here a *family* affair. It is a poison that works in the blood—it is intimate—it is deep-seated. There is here, I think, *hate* and *knowledge.* . . ."

He waved his hands.

"I do not know—it is difficult!"

Superintendent Sugden had waited respectfully, but without being much impressed. He said:

"Quite so, Mr. Poirot. But we'll get at it, never fear, with elimination and logic. We've got the *possibilities* now—the people with *opportunity.* George Lee, Magdalene Lee, David Lee, Hilda Lee, Pilar Estravados and I'll add Stephen Farr. Now we come to *motive.* Who had a *motive* for putting old Mr. Lee out of the way? There again we can wash out certain people. Miss Estravados, for one. I gather that as the will stands now, she doesn't get anything at all. If Simeon Lee had died before her mother, her mother's share would have come down to her (unless her mother willed it otherwise) but as Jennifer Estravados predeceased Simeon Lee, that particular legacy reverts to the other members of the family. So it was definitely to Miss Estravados' interests to keep the old man alive. He'd taken a fancy to her, it's pretty certain he'd have left her a good slice of money when he made a new will. She had everything to lose and nothing to gain by his murder. You agree to that?"

"Perfectly."

"There remains, of course, the possibility that she cut his throat in the heat of a quarrel but that seems extremely unlikely to me. To begin with, they were on the best of terms, and she hadn't been here long enough to bear him a grudge about anything. It therefore seems highly unlikely that Miss Estravados has anything to do with the crime—except that you might argue that to cut a man's throat is an un-English sort of thing to do, as your friend Mrs. George put it."

"Do not call her *my* friend," said Poirot hastily. "Or I shall speak of *your* friend, Miss Estravados, who finds you such a handsome man!"

He had the pleasure of seeing the Superintendent's official poise upset again. The police officer turned crimson. Poirot looked at him with malicious amusement.

He said, and there was a wistful note in his voice:

"It is true that your moustache is superb. . . . Tell me, do you use for it a special pomade?"

"Pomade? Good Lord, no!"

"What do you use?"

"Use? Nothing at all. It—it just *grows*."

Poirot sighed.

"You are favoured by nature." He caressed his own well-groomed black moustache, then sighed. "However expensive the preparation," he murmured, "to restore the natural colour does somewhat impoverish the quality of the hair."

Superintendent Sugden, uninterested in hairdressing problems, was continuing in a stolid manner:

"Considering the *motive* for the crime, I should say that we can probably wash out Mr. Stephen Farr. It's just *possible* that there was some hanky-panky between his father and Mr. Lee and the former suffered, but I doubt it. Farr's manner was too easy and assured when he mentioned that subject. He was quite confident—and I don't think he was acting. No, I don't think we'll find anything there."

"I do not think you will," said Poirot.

"And there's one other person with a motive for keeping old Mr. Lee alive. His son Harry. It's true that he benefits under the will, but I don't believe *he was aware of the fact.* Certainly couldn't have been *sure* of it! The general impression seemed to be that Harry had been definitely cut out of his share of the inheritance at the time he cut loose. But now he was on the point of coming back into favour! It was all to his advantage that his father should make a new will. He wouldn't be such a fool as to kill him now. Actually, as we know, he *couldn't* have done it. You see, we're getting on, we're clearing quite a lot of people out of the way."

"How true. Very soon there will be nobody left!"

Sugden grinned.

"We're not going as far as that! We've got George Lee and his wife, and David Lee and Mrs. David. They all benefit by the death, and George Lee, from all I can make out, is grasping about money. Moreover, his father was threatening to cut down supplies. So we've George Lee with motive *and* opportunity!"

"Continue," said Poirot.

"And we've got Mrs. George! As fond of money as a cat is fond of cream, and I'd be prepared to bet she's heavily in debt at the minute! She was jealous of the Spanish girl. She was quick to spot that the other was gaining an ascendency over the old man. She'd heard him say that he was sending for the lawyer. So she struck quickly. You could make out a case."

"Possibly."

106

"Then there's David Lee and his wife. They inherit under the present will, but I don't believe, somehow, that the money motive would be particularly strong in their case."

"No?"

"No. David Lee seems to be a bit of a dreamer—not a mercenary type. But he's—well, he's *odd*. As I see it, there are three possible motives for this murder. There's the diamond complication, there's the will, and there's—well—just plain *hate*."

"Ah, you see that, do you?"

Sugden said:

"Naturally. It's been present in my mind all along. *If* David Lee killed his father, I don't think it was for money. And if he was the criminal it might explain the—well, the blood letting!"

Poirot looked at him appreciatively.

"Yes, I wondered when you would take that into consideration. *So much blood*—that is what Mrs. Alfred said. It takes one back to ancient rituals—to blood sacrifice, to the anointing with the blood of the sacrifice. . . ."

Sugden said, frowning:

"You mean whoever did it was mad?"

"*Mon cher*—there are all sorts of deep instincts in man of which he himself is unaware. The craving for blood—the demand for sacrifice!"

Sugden said doubtfully:

"David Lee looks a quiet harmless fellow."

Poirot said:

"You do not understand the psychology. David Lee is a man who lives in the past—a man in whom the memory of his mother is still very much alive. He kept away from his father for many years because he could not forgive his father's treatment of his mother. He came here, let us suppose, to forgive. *But he may not have been able to forgive*. . . . We do know one thing—that when David Lee stood by his father's dead body, some part of him was appeased and satisfied. *The mills of God grind slowly, yet they grind exceeding small*. Retribution! Payment! The wrong wiped out by expiation!"

Sugden gave a sudden shudder. He said:

"Don't talk like that, Mr. Poirot. You give me quite a turn. It may be that it's as you say. If so, Mrs. David knows—and means to shield him all she knows how. I can imagine her doing that. On the other hand I can't imagine her being a murderess. She's such a comfortable commonplace sort of woman."

Poirot looked at him curiously.

"So she strikes you like that?" he murmured.

"Well, yes—a homely body, if you know what I mean!"

"Oh! I know what you mean perfectly!"

Sugden looked at him.

"Come now, Mr. Poirot; you've got ideas about this case, let's have them."

Poirot said slowly:

"I have ideas, yes, but they are rather nebulous. Let me first hear your summing up of the case."

"Well, it's as I said—three possible motives. Hate, gain—and this diamond complication. Take the facts chronologically:

"3:30. Family gathering. Telephone conversation to lawyer overheard by all the family. Then the old man lets loose on his family, tells them where they all get off. They slink out like a lot of scared rabbits."

"Hilda Lee remained behind," said Poirot.

"So she did. But not for long. Then about six Alfred has an interview with his father—unpleasant interview. Harry is to be reinstated. Alfred isn't pleased. Alfred, of course, *ought* to be our principal suspect. He had by far the strongest motive. However, to get on, Harry comes along next. Is in boisterous spirits. Has got the old man just where he wants him. But *before* those two interviews Simeon Lee has discovered the loss of the diamonds and has telephoned to me. He doesn't mention his loss to either of his two sons. Why? In my opinion because he was quite sure neither of them had anything to do with it. Neither of them were under suspicion. I believe, as I've said all along, that the old man suspected Horbury and *one other person*. And I'm pretty sure of what he meant to do. Remember, he said definitely he didn't want anyone to come and sit with him that evening. Why? Because he was preparing the way for two things. First, my visit, and second, *the visit of that other suspected person*. He did ask *someone* to come and see him immediately after dinner. Now who was that person likely to be? Might have been George Lee. Much more likely to have been his wife. And there's another person who comes back into the picture here. Pilar Estravados. He'd shown her the diamonds. He'd told her their value. How do we know that girl isn't a thief? Remember these mysterious hints about the disgraceful behaviour of her father. Perhaps *he* was a professional thief and finally went to prison for it."

Poirot said slowly:

"And so, as you say, Pilar Estravados comes back into the picture. . . ."

"Yes—as a *thief*. No other way. She *may* have lost her head when she was found out. She *may* have flown at her grandfather and attacked him."

108

Poirot said slowly:

"It is possible—yes. . . ."

Superintendent Sugden looked at him keenly.

"But that's not *your* idea? Come, Mr. Poirot, what *is* your idea?"

Poirot said:

"I go back always to the same thing—*the character of the dead man*. What manner of a man was Simeon Lee?"

"There isn't much mystery about that," said Sugden, staring.

"Tell me then. That is to say, tell me from the local point of view what was known of the man."

Superintendent Sugden drew a doubtful finger along his jawbone. He looked perplexed. He said:

"I'm not a local man myself. I come from Reeveshire, over the border—next county. But of course old Mr. Lee was a well-known figure in these parts. I know all about him by hearsay."

"Yes? And that hearsay was—what?"

Sugden said:

"Well, he was a sharp customer—there weren't many who could get the better of him. But he was generous with his money. Open-handed as they make 'em. Beats me how Mr. George Lee can be the exact opposite and he his father's son."

"Ah! but there are two distinct strains in the family. Alfred, George and David resemble—superficially at least—their mother's side of the family. I have been looking at some portraits in the gallery this morning."

"He was hot-tempered," continued Superintendent Sugden, "and of course he had a bad reputation with women—that was in his younger days. He's been an invalid for many years now. But even there he always behaved generously. If there was trouble, he always paid up handsomely and got the girl married off as often as not. He may have been a bad lot, but he wasn't mean. He treated his wife badly, ran after other women and neglected her. She died of a broken heart, so they say. It's a convenient term, but I believe she was really very unhappy, poor lady. She was always sickly and never went about much. There's no doubt that Mr. Lee was an odd character. Had a revengeful streak in him, too. If anyone did him a nasty turn he always paid it back, so they say, and didn't mind how long he had to wait to do it."

"*The mills of God grind slowly, yet they grind exceeding small,*" murmured Poirot.

Superintendent Sugden said heavily:

"Mills of the devil, more likely! Nothing saintly about Simeon Lee. The kind of man you might say had sold his soul to the devil and enjoyed the bargain! And he was proud, too, proud as Lucifer."

"Proud as Lucifer!" said Poirot. "It is suggestive, what you say there."

Superintendent Sugden said, looking puzzled:

"You don't mean that he was murdered because he was proud?"

"I mean," said Poirot, "that there is such a thing as inheritance. Simeon Lee transmitted that pride to his sons—"

He broke off. Hilda Lee had come out of the house and was standing looking along the terrace.

III

Hilda Lee said simply:

"I wanted to find you, Mr. Poirot."

Superintendent Sugden had excused himself and gone back into the house. Looking after him, Hilda said:

"I didn't know he was with you. I thought he was with Pilar. He seems a nice man, quite considerate."

Her voice was pleasant, a low soothing cadence to it.

Poirot asked:

"You wanted to see me, you say?"

She inclined her head.

"Yes. I think you can help me."

"I shall be delighted to do so, madam."

She said:

"You are a very intelligent man, Mr. Poirot. I saw that last night. There are things which you will, I think, find out quite easily. I want you to understand my husband."

"Yes, madam?"

"I shouldn't talk like this to Superintendent Sugden. He wouldn't understand. But you will."

Poirot bowed.

"You honour me, madam."

Hilda went calmly on:

"My husband, for many years, ever since I married him, has been what I can only describe as a mental cripple."

"Ah!"

"When one suffers some great hurt physically, it causes shock and pain, but slowly it mends, the flesh heals, the bone knits. There may be, perhaps, a little weakness, a slight scar, but nothing more. My husband, Mr. Poirot, suffered a great hurt *mentally* at his most susceptible age. He adored his mother and he saw her die. He believed that his father was morally responsible for that death. From that shock he has never quite recovered. His resentment against is father never died down. It was I who persuaded David to come here this Christmas, to be reconciled to his father. I wanted it—for *his* sake—I wanted that mental wound to heal. I realize now that coming here was a mistake. Simeon Lee amused himself by probing into that old wound. It was—a very dangerous thing to do. . . ."

Poirot said:

"Are you telling me, madam, that your husband killed his father?"

"I am telling you, Mr. Poirot, that he easily *might* have done so. . . . And I will also tell you this—that he did *not!* When Simeon Lee was killed, his son David was playing the *Dead March.* The wish to kill was in his heart. It passed out through his fingers and died in waves of sound. . . . That is the truth."

Poirot was silent for a minute or two, then he said:

"And you, madam, what is your verdict on that past drama?"

"You mean the death of Simeon Lee's wife?"

"Yes."

Hilda said slowly:

"I know enough of life to know that you can never judge any case on its outside merits. To all seeming, Simeon Lee was entirely to blame and his wife was abominably treated. At the same time I honestly believe that there is a kind of meekness, a predisposition to martyrdom which does arouse the worst instincts in men of a certain type. Simeon Lee would have admired, I think, spirit and force of character. He was merely irritated by patience and tears."

Poirot nodded. He said:

"Your husband said last night, 'My mother never complained.' Is that true?"

Hilda Lee said impatiently:

"Of course it isn't! She complained the whole time to David! She laid the whole burden of her unhappiness on his shoulders. He was too young—far too young to bear all she gave him to bear!"

Poirot looked thoughtfully at her. She flushed under his gaze and bit her lip.

He said:

"I see."

She said sharply:

"What do you see?"

He answered:

"I see that you have had to be a mother to your husband when you would have preferred to be a wife."

She turned away.

At that moment David Lee came out of the house and

along the terrace towards them. He said, and his voice had a clear joyful note in it:

"Hilda, isn't it a glorious day? Almost like spring instead of winter."

He came nearer. His head was thrown back, a lock of fair hair fell across his forehead, his blue eyes shone. He looked amazingly young and boyish. There was about him a youthful eagerness, a carefree radiance. Hercule Poirot caught his breath. . . .

David said:

"Let's go down to the lake, Hilda."

She smiled, put her arm through his and they moved off together.

As Poirot watched them go, he saw her turn and give him a rapid glance. He caught a momentary glimpse of swift anxiety—or was it, he wondered, fear?

Slowly Hercule Poirot walked to the other end of the terrace.

He murmured to himself:

"As I have always said, me, I am the father confessor! And since women come to confession more frequently than men, it is women who have come to me this morning. Will there, I wonder, be another very shortly?"

As he turned at the end of the terrace and paced back again, he knew that his question was answered. Lydia Lee was coming towards him.

IV

Lydia said:

"Good-morning, Mr. Poirot. Tressilian told me I should find you out here with Harry but I am glad to find you alone. My husband has been speaking about you. I know he is very anxious to talk to you."

"Ah! yes? Shall I go and see him now?"

"Not just yet. He got hardly any sleep last night. In the end I gave him a strong sleeping draught. He is still asleep, and I don't want to disturb him."

"I quite understand. That was very wise. I could see last night that the shock had been very great."

She said seriously:

"You see, Mr. Poirot, he really *cared*—much more than the others."

"I understand."

She asked:

"Have you—has the Superintendent—any idea of who can have done this awful thing?"

112

Poirot said deliberately:

"We have certain ideas, madam, as to who did *not* do it."

Lydia said, almost impatiently:

"It's like a nightmare—so fantastic—I can't believe it's real!"

She added:

"What about Horbury? Was he really at the pictures as he said?"

"Yes, madam, his story has been checked. He was speaking the truth."

Lydia stopped and plucked at a bit of yew. Her face went a little paler. She said:

"But that's *awful!* It only leaves—the family!"

"Exactly."

"Mr. Poirot, I *can't* believe it!"

"Madam, you *can* and you *do* believe it!"

She seemed about to protest. Then suddenly she smiled ruefully.

She said:

"What a hypocrite one is!"

He nodded.

"If you were to be frank with me, madam," he said, "you would admit that to you it seems quite natural that one of his family should murder your father-in-law!"

Lydia said sharply:

"That's really a fantastic thing to say, Mr. Poirot!"

"Yes, it is. But your father-in-law was a fantastic person!"

Lydia said:

"Poor old man. I can feel sorry for him now. When he was alive, he just annoyed me unspeakably!"

Poirot said:

"So I should imagine!"

He bent over one of the stone sinks.

"They are very ingenious, these. Very pleasing."

"I'm glad you like them. It's one of my hobbies. Do you like this Arctic one with the penguins and the ice?"

"Charming. And this, what is this?"

"Oh, that's the Dead Sea—or going to be. It isn't finished yet. You mustn't look at it. Now this one is supposed to be Piana in Corsica. The rocks there, you know, are quite pink and too lovely where they go down into the blue sea. This desert scene is rather fun, don't you think?"

She led him along. When they had reached the further end she glanced at her wrist-watch.

"I must go and see if Alfred is awake."

When she had gone Poirot went slowly back again to the garden representing the Dead Sea. He looked at it with a good deal of interest. Then he scooped up a few of the pebbles and let them run through his fingers.

Suddenly his face changed. He held up the pebbles close to his face.

"*Sapristi!*" he said. "This is a surprise! Now what exactly does this mean?"

Part V ======DECEMBER 26TH

I

THE CHIEF Constable and Superintendent Sugden stared at Poirot incredulously. The latter returned a stream of small pebbles carefully into a small cardboard box and pushed it across to the Chief Constable.

"Oh, yes," he said. "They are the diamonds all right."

"And you found them, where did you say? In the garden?"

"In one of the small gardens constructed by Madam Alfred Lee."

"Mrs. Alfred?" Sugden shook his head. "Doesn't seem likely."

Poirot said:

"You mean, I presume, that you do not consider it likely that Mrs. Alfred cut her father-in-law's throat?"

Sugden said quickly:

"We know she didn't do that. I meant it seemed unlikely that she pinched these diamonds."

Poirot said:

"One would not easily believe her a thief—no."

Sugden said:

"Anybody could have hidden them there."

"That is true. It was convenient that in that particular garden—the Dead Sea as it represents—there happened to be pebbles very similar in shape and appearance."

Sugden said:

"You mean she fixed it like that beforehand? Ready?"

Colonel Johnson said warmly:

114

"I don't believe it for a moment. Not for a moment. Why should she take the diamonds in the first place?"

"Well, as to that—" Sugden said slowly.

Poirot nipped in quickly:

"There is a possible answer to that. She took the diamonds to suggest a motive for the murder. That is to say she knew that murder was going to be done though she herself took no active part in it."

Johnson frowned.

"That won't hold water for a minute. You're making her out to be an accomplice—but whose accomplice would she be likely to be? Only her husband's. But as we know that he, too, had nothing to do with the murder, the whole theory falls to the ground."

Sugden stroked his jaw reflectively.

"Yes," he said, "that's so. No, if Mrs. Lee took the diamonds—and it's a big if—it was just plain robbery, and it's true she might have prepared that garden specially as a hiding place for them till the hue and cry had died down. Another possibility is that of *coincidence*. That garden, with its similarity of pebbles, struck the thief, whoever he or she was, as an ideal hiding place."

Poirot said:

"That is quite possible. I am always prepared to admit *one* coincidence."

Superintendent Sugden shook his head dubiously.

Poirot said:

"What is your opinion, Superintendent?"

The Superintendent said cautiously:

"Mrs. Lee's a very nice lady. Doesn't seem likely that she'd be mixed up in any business that was fishy. But, of course, one never knows."

Colonel Johnson said testily:

"In any case, whatever the truth is about the diamonds, her being mixed up in the murder is out of the question. The butler saw her in the drawing-room at the actual time of the crime. You remember that, Poirot?"

Poirot said:

"I had not forgotten that."

The Chief Constable turned to his subordinate.

"We'd better get on. What have you got to report? Anything fresh?"

"Yes, sir. I've got hold of some new information. To start with—Horbury. There's a reason why he might be scared of the police."

"Robbery? Eh?"

"No, sir. Extorting money under threats. Modified blackmail. The case couldn't be proved so he got off, but I rather fancy he's got away with a thing or two in that line. Having a guilty conscience he probably thought we were on to something of that kind when Tressilian mentioned a police officer last night and it made him get the wind up."

The Chief Constable said:

"H'm, so much for Horbury! What else?"

The Superintendent coughed:

"Er—Mrs. George Lee, sir. We've got a line on her before her marriage. Was living with a Commander Jones. Passed as his daughter—but she *wasn't* his daughter. . . . I think from what we've been told, that old Mr. Lee summed her up pretty correctly—he was smart where women were concerned, knew a bad lot when he saw one—and was just amusing himself by taking a shot in the dark. *And* he got her on the raw!"

Colonel Johnson said thoughtfully:

"That gives her another possible motive—apart from the money angle. She may have thought he knew something definite and was going to give her away to her husband. That telephone story of hers is pretty fishy. She *didn't* telephone."

Sugden suggested:

"Why not have them in together, sir, and get that telephone business straight? See what we get."

Colonel Johnson said:

"Good idea."

He rang the bell. Tressilian answered it.

"Ask Mr. and Mrs. George Lee to come here."

"Very good, sir."

As the old man turned away Poirot said:

"The date on that wall calendar, has it remained like it is since the murder?"

Tressilian turned back.

"Which calendar, sir?"

"The one on the wall over there."

The three men were sitting once more in Alfred Lee's small sitting-room. The calendar in question was a large one with tear off leaves, a bold date on each leaf.

Tressilian peered across the room, then shuffled slowly across till he was a foot or two away.

He said:

"Excuse me, sir, it has been torn off. It's the twenty-sixth to-day."

"Ah, pardon. Who would have been the person to tear it off?"

"Mr. Lee does, sir, every morning. Mr. Alfred, he's a very methodical gentleman."

"I see. Thank you."

Tressilian went out. Sugden said, puzzled:

"Is there anything fishy about that calendar, Mr. Poirot? Have I missed something there?"

With a shrug of his shoulders, Poirot said:

"The calendar is of no importance. It was just a little experiment I was making."

Colonel Johnson said:

"Inquest to-morrow. There'll be an adjournment, of course."

Sugden said:

"Yes, sir, I've seen the Coroner and it's all arranged for."

II

George Lee came into the room accompanied by his wife. Colonel Johnson said:

"Good-morning. Sit down, will you? There are a few questions I want to ask you both. Something I'm not quite clear about."

"I shall be glad to give you any assistance I can," said George, somewhat pompously.

Magdalene said faintly:

"Of course!"

The Chief Constable gave a slight nod to Sugden. The latter said:

"About those telephone calls on the night of the crime? You put through a call to Westeringham, I think you said, Mr. Lee?"

George said coldly:

"Yes, I did. To my agent in the constituency. I can refer you to him and—"

Superintendent Sugden held up his hand to stem the flow.

"Quite so—quite so, Mr. Lee. We're not disputing that point. Your call went through at 8:59 exactly."

"Well—I—er—couldn't say as to the exact time."

"Ah," said Sugden. "But we can! We always check up on these things very carefully. Very carefully indeed. The call was put through at 8:59 and it was terminated at 9:04. Your father, Mr. Lee, was killed about 9:15. I must ask you once more for an account of your movements."

"I've told you—I was telephoning!"

"No, Mr. Lee, you weren't."

"Nonsense—you must have made a mistake! Well, I may perhaps have just finished telephoning—I think I debated making another call—was just considering whether it was—

er—worth—the expense—when I heard the noise upstairs."

"You would hardly debate whether or not to make a telephone call for ten minutes."

George went purple. He began to splutter.

"What do you mean? What the devil do you mean? Damned impudence! Are you doubting my word? Doubting the word of a man of my position? I—er—why should I have to account for every minute of my time?"

Superintendent Sugden said with a stolidness that Poirot admired:

"It's usual."

George turned angrily on the Chief Constable.

"Colonel Johnson. Do you countenance this—this unprecedented attitude?"

The Chief Constable said crisply:

"In a murder case, Mr. Lee, these questions must be asked —and answered."

"I have answered them! I had finished telephoning and was—er—deliberating a further call."

"You were in this room when the alarm was raised upstairs?"

"I was—yes, I was."

Johnson turned to Magdalene.

"I think, Mrs. Lee," he said, "that you stated that *you* were telephoning when the alarm broke out, and that at the time you were alone in this room?"

Magdalene was flustered. She caught her breath, looked sideways at George—at Sugden, then appealingly at Colonel Johnson. She said:

"Oh, really—I don't know—I don't remember what I said. . . . I was so *upset.* . . ."

Sugden said:

"We've got it all written down, you know."

She turned her batteries on him—wide appealing eyes— quivering mouth. But she met in return the rigid aloofness of a man of stern respectability who didn't approve of her type.

She said uncertainly:

"I—I—of course I telephoned. I can't be quite sure just *when*—"

She stopped.

George said:

"What's all this? Where did you telephone from? Not in here."

Superintendent Sugden said:

"I suggest, Mrs. Lee, that *you didn't telephone at all.* In that case, where were you and what were you doing?"

Magdalene glanced distractedly about her and burst into tears. She sobbed:

"George, don't let them bully me! You know that if anyone frightens me and thunders questions at me, I can't remember anything *at all!* I—I didn't know *what* I was saying that night —it was all so horrible—and I was so upset—and they're being so beastly to me. . . ."

She jumped up and ran sobbing out of the room.

Springing up, George Lee blustered:

"What d'you mean? I won't have my wife bullied and frightened out of her life! She's very sensitive. It's disgraceful! I shall have a question asked in the House about the disgraceful bullying methods of the police. It's absolutely disgraceful!"

He strode out of the room and banged the door.

Superintendent Sugden threw his head back and laughed. He said:

"We've got them going properly! Now we'll see!"

Johnson said, frowning:

"Extraordinary business! Looks fishy. We must get a further statement out of her."

Sugden said easily:

"Oh! she'll be back in a minute or two. When she's decided what to say. Eh, Mr. Poirot?"

Poirot, who had been sitting in a dream, gave a start.

"Pardon?"

"I said she'll be back."

"Probably—yes, possibly. Oh, yes!"

Sugden said, staring at him:

"What's the matter, Mr. Poirot? Seen a ghost?"

Poirot said slowly:

"You know—I am not sure that I have not done *just exactly that.*"

Colonel Johnson said impatiently:

"Well, Sugden, anything else?"

Sugden said:

"I've been trying to check up on the order in which everyone arrived on the scene of the murder. It's quite clear what must have happened. The murderer slipped out, locked the door with pliers, or something of that kind, and a moment or two later became one of the people hurrying *to* the scene of the crime. Unfortunately it's not easy to check exactly whom everyone has seen because people's memories aren't very accurate on a point like that. Tressilian says he saw Harry and Alfred Lee cross the hall from the dining-room and race upstairs. That lets them out, but we don't suspect them anyway. As far as I can make out Miss Estravados got there late —one of the last. The general idea seems to be that Farr, Mrs. George and Mrs. David were the first. Each of those three says one of the others was just ahead of them. That's what's so difficult, you can't distinguish between a deliberate lie and a genuine haziness of recollection. Everybody ran there—that's agreed—but in what order they ran isn't so easy to get at."

Poirot said slowly:

"You think that important?"

Sugden said:

"It's the time element. The time, remember, was incredibly short."

Poirot said:

"I agree with you that the time element is very important in this case."

Sugden went on:

"What makes it more difficult is that there are two stair-cases. There's the main one in the hall here about equidistant from the dining-room and the drawing-room doors. Then there's one the other end of the house. Stephen Farr came up by the latter. Miss Estravados came along the upper landing from that end of the house (her room is right at the other end). The others say they went up by this one."

Poirot said:

"It is a confusion, yes."

The door opened and Magdalene came quickly in. She was breathing fast and had a bright spot of colour in each cheek. She came up to the table and said quietly:

"My husband thinks I'm lying down. I slipped out of my room quietly. Colonel Johnson," she appealed to him with wide, distressed eyes, "if I tell you the truth you *will* keep quiet about it, won't you? I mean you don't have to make *everything* public?"

Colonel Johnson said:

"You mean, I take it, Mrs. Lee, something that has no connection with the crime?"

"Yes, no connection at all. Just something in my—my private life."

The Chief Constable said:

"You'd better make a clean breast of it, Mrs. Lee, and leave us to judge."

Magdalene said, her eyes swimming:

"Yes, I will trust you. I know I can. You look so kind. You see it's like this. There's somebody—" She stopped.

"Yes, Mrs. Lee?"

"I wanted to telephone to somebody last night—a man— a friend of mine, and I didn't want George to know about it. I know it was very wrong of me—but, well, it was like that. So I went to telephone after dinner when I thought George would be safely in the dining-room. But when I got here I heard him telephoning, so I waited."

"Where did you wait, madam?" asked Poirot.

"There's a place for coats and things behind the stairs. It's dark there. I slipped back there where I could see George come out from this room. But he didn't come out and then all the noise happened and Mr. Lee screamed and I ran upstairs."

"So your husband did not leave this room until the moment of the murder?"

"No."

The Chief Constable said:

"And you yourself from nine o'clock to nine-fifteen were waiting in the recess behind the stairs?"

"Yes, but I couldn't *say* so, you see! They'd want to know what I was doing there. It's been very, very awkward for me, you *do* see that, *don't* you?"

Johnson said drily:

"It was certainly awkward."

She smiled at him sweetly.

"I'm *so* relieved to have told you the truth. And you *won't* tell my husband, will you? No, I'm sure you won't! I can trust you, all of you."

She included them all in her final pleading look, then she slipped quickly out of the room.

Colonel Johnson drew a deep breath.

"Well," he said. "It *might* be like that! It's a perfectly plausible story. On the other hand——"

"It might not," finished Sugden. "That's just it. We don't know."

III

Lydia Lee stood by the far window of the drawing-room looking out. Her figure was half hidden by the heavy window curtain. A sound in the room made her turn with a start to see Hercule Poirot standing by the door.

She said:

"You startled me, Mr. Poirot."

"I apologize, madam. I walk softly."

She said:

"I thought it was Horbury."

Hercule Poirot nodded.

"It is true, he steps softly, that one—like a cat—or a *thief*."

He paused a minute, watching her.

Her face showed nothing, but she made a slight grimace of distaste as she said:

"I have never cared for that man. I shall be glad to get rid of him."

"I think you will be wise to do so, madam."

She looked at him quickly. She said:

"What do you mean? Do you know anything against him?"
Poirot said:

"He is a man who collects secrets—and uses them to his advantage."

She said sharply:

"Do you think he knows anything—about the murder?"

Poirot shrugged his shoulders. He said:

"He has quiet feet and long ears. He may have overheard something that he is keeping to himself."

Lydia said clearly:

"Do you mean that he may try to blackmail one of us?"

"It is within the bounds of possibility. But that is not what I came here to say."

"What did you come to say?"

Poirot said slowly:

"I have been talking with Mr. Alfred Lee. He has made to me a proposition, and I wished to discuss it with you before accepting or declining it. But I was so struck by the picture you made—the charming pattern of your jumper against the deep red of the curtains—that I paused to admire."

Lydia said sharply:

"Really, Mr. Poirot, must we waste time in compliments?"

"I beg your pardon, madam. So few English ladies understand *la toilette*. The dress you were wearing the first night I saw you, its bold but simple pattern, it had grace—distinction."

Lydia said impatiently:

"What was it you wanted to see me about?"

Poirot became grave.

"Just this, madam. Your husband, he wishes me to take up the investigation very seriously. He demands that I stay here, in the house, and do my utmost to get to the bottom of the matter."

Lydia said sharply:

"Well?"

Poirot said slowly:

"I would not wish to accept an invitation that was not endorsed by the lady of the house."

She said coldly:

"Naturally I endorse my husband's invitation."

"Yes, madam, but I need more than that. Do you really *want* me to come here?"

"Why not?"

"Let us be more frank. What I ask you is this: do you want the truth to come out, or not?"

"Naturally."

Poirot sighed.

122

"Must you return me these conventional replies?"

Lydia said:

"I am a conventional woman."

Then she bit her lip, hesitated, and said:

"Perhaps it is better to speak frankly. Of course I understand you! The position is not a pleasant one. My father-in-law has been brutally murdered, and unless a case can be made out against the most likely suspect—Horbury—for robbery and murder—and it seems that it cannot—then it comes to this—*one of his own family killed him.* To bring that person to justice will mean bringing shame and disgrace on us all. . . . If I am to speak honestly I must say that I do *not* want this to happen."

Poirot said:

"You are content for the murderer to escape unpunished?"

"There are probably several undiscovered murderers at large in the world."

"That, I grant you."

"Does one more matter, then?"

Poirot said:

"And what about the other members of the family? The innocent?"

She stared.

"What about them?"

"Do you realize that if it turns out as you hope, *no one will ever know.* The shadow will remain on all alike. . . ."

She said uncertainly:

"I hadn't thought of that. . . ."

Poirot said:

"*No one will ever know who the guilty person is. . . .*"

He added softly:

"Unless *you* already know, madam?"

She cried out:

"You have no business to say that! It's not true! Oh! if only it could be a stranger—not a member of the family."

Poirot said:

"It might be both."

She stared at him.

"What do you mean?"

"It might be a member of the family—and at the same time a stranger . . . you do not see what I mean? *Eh bien,* it is an idea that has occurred to the mind of Hercule Poirot."

He looked at her.

"Well, madam, what am I to say to Mr. Lee?"

Lydia raised her hands and let them fall in a sudden, helpless gesture.

She said:

"Of course—you must accept."

Pilar stood in the centre of the music room. She stood very straight, her eyes darting from side to side like an animal who fears an attack.

She said:

"I want to get away from here!"

Stephen Farr said gently:

"You're not the only one who feels like that. But they won't let us go, my dear."

"You mean—the police?"

"Yes."

Pilar said very seriously:

"It is not nice to be mixed up with the police. It is a thing that should not happen to respectable people."

Stephen said with a faint smile:

"Meaning yourself?"

Pilar said:

"No, I mean Alfred and Lydia and David and George and Hilda and—yes—Magdalene, too."

Stephen lit a cigarette. He puffed at it for a moment or two before saying:

"Why the exception?"

"What is that, please?"

Stephen said:

"Why leave out brother Harry?"

Pilar laughed, her teeth showing white and even.

"Oh, Harry is different! I think he knows very well what it is to be mixed up with the police."

"Perhaps you are right. He certainly is a little too picturesque to blend well into the domestic picture."

He went on:

"Do you like your English relations, Pilar?"

Pilar said doubtfully:

"They are kind—they are all very kind. But they do not laugh much, they are not gay."

"My dear girl, there's just been a murder in the house!"

"Y-es," said Pilar doubtfully.

"A murder," said Stephen instructively, "is not such an everyday occurrence as your nonchalance seems to imply. In England they take their murders seriously, whatever they may do in Spain."

Pilar said:

"You are laughing at me. . . ."

Stephen said:

"You're wrong. I'm not in a laughing mood."

Pilar looked at him and said:

"Because you, too, wish to get away from here?"

"Yes."

"And the big handsome policeman will not let you go?"

"I haven't asked him. But if I did, I've no doubt he'd say no. I've got to watch my step, Pilar, and be very, very careful."

"That is tiresome," said Pilar, nodding her head.

"It's just a little bit more than tiresome, my dear. Then there's that lunatic foreigner prowling about. I don't suppose he's any good but he makes me feel jumpy."

Pilar was frowning. She said:

"My grandfather was very, very rich, was he not?"

"I should imagine so."

"Where does his money go to now? To Alfred and the others?"

"Depends on his will."

Pilar said thoughtfully:

"He might have left me some money, but I am afraid that perhaps he did not."

Stephen said kindly:

"You'll be all right. After all, you're one of the family. You belong here. They'll have to look after you."

Pilar said with a sigh:

"I—belong here. It is very funny, that. And yet it is not funny at all."

"I can see that you mightn't find it very humorous."

Pilar sighed again. She said:

"Do you think if we put on the gramophone, we could dance?"

Stephen said dubiously:

"It wouldn't look any too good. This is a house of mourning, you callous Spanish baggage."

Pilar said, her big eyes opening very wide:

"But I do not feel sad at all. Because I did not really know my grandfather, and though I liked to talk to him, I do not want to cry and be unhappy because he is dead. It is very silly to pretend."

Stephen said:

"You're adorable!"

Pilar said coaxingly:

"We could put some stockings and some gloves in the gramophone, and then it would not make much noise, and no one would hear."

"Come along then, temptress."

She laughed happily and ran out of the room, going along towards the ballroom at the far end of the house.

Then, as she reached the side passage which led to the

garden door she stopped dead. Stephen caught up with her and stopped also.

Hercule Poirot had unhooked a portrait from the wall and was studying it by the light from the terrace. He looked up and saw them.

"Aha!" he said. "You arrive at an opportune moment."

Pilar said:

"What are you doing?"

She came and stood beside him.

Poirot said gravely:

"I am studying something very important, the face of Simeon Lee when he was a young man."

"Oh, is that my grandfather?"

"Yes, mademoiselle."

She stared at the painted face. She said slowly:

"How different--how very different . . . he was so old, so shriveled up. Here he is like Harry, like Harry might have been ten years ago."

Hercule Poirot nodded.

"Yes, mademoiselle. Harry Lee is very much the son of his father. Now here"--he led her a little way along the gallery--"here is madam, your grandmother—a long gentle face, very blond hair, mild blue eyes."

Pilar said:

"Like David."

Stephen said:

"Just a look of Alfred, too."

Poirot said:

"The heredity, it is very interesting. Mr. Lee and his wife were diametrically opposite types. On the whole the children of the marriage took after the mother. See here, mademoiselle."

He pointed to a picture of a girl of nineteen or so, with hair like spun gold and wide, laughing blue eyes. The colouring was that of Simeon Lee's wife, but there was a spirit, a vivacity that those mild blue eyes and placid features had never known.

"Oh!" said Pilar.

The colour came up in her face.

Her hand went to her neck. She drew out a locket on a long gold chain. She pressed the catch and it flew open. The same laughing face looked up at Poirot.

"My mother," said Pilar.

Poirot nodded. On the opposite side of the locket was the portrait of a man. He was young and handsome, with black hair and dark blue eyes.

Poirot said:

126

"Your father?"

Pilar said:

"Yes, my father. He is very beautiful, is he not?"

"Yes, indeed. Few Spaniards have blue eyes, have they, señorita?"

"Sometimes, in the north. Besides, my father's mother was Irish."

Poirot said thoughtfully:

"So you have Spanish blood, and Irish and English and a touch of gypsy too. Do you know what I think, mademoiselle? With that inheritance, you should make a bad enemy."

Stephen said, laughing:

"Remember what you said in the train, Pilar? That your way of dealing with your enemies would be to cut their throats. Oh!"

He stopped—suddenly realizing the import of his words.

Hercule Poirot was quick to lead the conversation away. He said:

"Ah, yes, there was something, señorita, I had to ask you. Your passport. It is needed by my friend the Superintendent. There are, you know, police regulations—very stupid, very tiresome, but necessary—for a foreigner in this country. And of course by law you are a foreigner."

Pilar's eyebrows rose.

"My passport? Yes, I will get it. It is in my room."

Poirot said apologetically as he walked by her side:

"I am most sorry to trouble you. I am indeed."

They had reached the end of the long gallery. Here was a flight of stairs. Pilar ran up and Poirot followed. Stephen came too. Pilar's bedroom was just at the head of the stairs.

She said as she reached the door:

"I will get it for you."

She went in. Poirot and Stephen Farr remained waiting outside.

Stephen said remorsefully:

"Damn silly of me to say a thing like that. I don't think she noticed, though, do you?"

Poirot did not answer. He held his head a little on one side as though listening.

He said:

"The English are extraordinarily fond of fresh air. Miss Estravados must have inherited that characteristic."

Stephen said, staring:

"Why?"

Poirot said softly:

"Because though it is to-day extremely cold—the black

frost you call it (not like yesterday so mild and sunny)—Miss Estravados has just flung up her lower window sash. Amazing to love so much the fresh air."

Suddenly there was an exclamation in Spanish from inside the room and Pilar reappeared laughingly dismayed.

"Ah!" she cried. "But I am stupid—and clumsy. My little case it was on the window-sill, and I was sorting through it so quickly and very stupidly I knock my passport out of the window. It is down on the flower bed below. I will get it."

"I'll get it," said Stephen, but Pilar had flown past him and cried back over her shoulder.

"No, it was my stupidity. You go to the drawing-room with Mr. Poirot and I will bring it to you there."

Stephen Farr seemed inclined to go after her, but Poirot's hand fell gently on his arm and Poirot's voice said:

"Let us go this way."

They went along the corridor towards the other end of the house until they got to the head of the main staircase. Here Poirot said:

"Let us not go down for a minute. If you will come with me to the room of the crime there is something I want to ask you."

They went along the corridor which led to Simeon Lee's room. On their left they passed an alcove which contained two marble statues, stalwart nymphs clasping their draperies in an agony of Victorian propriety.

Stephen Farr glanced at them and murmured:

"Pretty frightful by daylight. I thought there were three of them when I came along the other night, but thank goodness there are only two!"

"They are not what is admired nowadays," admitted Poirot. "But no doubt they cost much money in their time. They look better by night, I think."

"Yes, one sees only a white glimmering figure."

Poirot murmured:

"All cats are grey in the dark!"

They found Superintendent Sugden in the room. He was kneeling by the safe and examining it with a magnifying glass. He looked up as they entered.

"This was opened with the key all right," he said. "By some-one who knew the combination. No sign of anything else."

Poirot went up to him, drew him aside and whispered something. The Superintendent nodded and left the room.

Poirot turned to Stephen Farr, who was standing staring at the armchair in which Simeon Lee always sat. His brows were drawn together and the veins showed in his forehead. Poirot looked at him for a minute or two in silence, then he said:

128

"You have the memories—yes?"

Stephen said slowly:

"Two days ago he sat here alive—and now . . ."

Then, shaking off his absorption, he said:

"Yes, Mr. Poirot, you brought me here to ask me something?"

"Ah, yes. You were, I think, the first person to arrive on the scene that night?"

"Was I? I don't remember. No, I think one of the ladies was here before me."

"Which lady?"

"One of the wives—George's wife or David's—I know they were both here pretty soon."

"You did not hear the scream, I think you said?"

"I don't think I did. I can't quite remember. Somebody did cry out but that may have been someone downstairs."

Poirot said:

"You did not hear a noise like this?"

He threw his head back and suddenly gave vent to a piercing yell.

It was so unexpected that Stephen started backwards and nearly fell over. He said angrily:

"For the Lord's sake, do you want to scare the whole house? No, I didn't hear anything in the least like that! You'll have the whole place by the ears again! They'll think another murder has happened!"

Poirot looked crestfallen. He murmured:

"True . . . it was foolish . . . we must go at once."

He hurried out of the room. Lydia and Alfred were at the foot of the stairs peering up—George came out of the library to join them and Pilar came running, a passport held in her hand.

Poirot cried:

"It is nothing—nothing. Do not be alarmed. A little experiment that I make. That was all."

Alfred looked annoyed and George indignant. Poirot left Stephen to explain and he hurriedly slipped away along the passage to the other end of the house.

At the end of the passage, Superintendent Sugden came quietly out of Pilar's door and met Poirot.

"*Eh bien?*" asked Poirot.

The Superintendent shook his head.

"Not a sound."

His eyes met Poirot's appreciatively and he nodded.

Alfred Lee said:

"Then you accept, Mr. Poirot?"

His hand, as it went to his mouth, shook slightly. His mild, brown eyes were alight with a new and feverish expression. He stammered slightly in his speech. Lydia, standing silently by, looked at him with some anxiety.

Alfred said:

"You don't know—you c-c-can't imagine—what it m-m-means to me . . . my father's murderer *must* be f-f-found."

Poirot said:

"Since you have assured me that you have reflected long and carefully—yes, I accept. But you comprehend, Mr. Lee, there can be no drawing back. I am not the dog one sets on to hunt and then recalls because you do not like the game he puts up!"

"Of course . . . of course . . . everything is ready. Your bedroom is prepared. Stay as long as you like—"

Poirot said gravely:

"It will not be long."

"Eh? What's that?"

"I said it will not be long. There is in this crime such a restricted circle that it cannot possibly take long to arrive at the truth. Already, I think, the end draws near."

Alfred stared at him.

"Impossible!" he said.

"Not at all. The facts all point more or less clearly in one direction. There is just some irrelevant matter to be cleared out of the way. When that is done the truth will appear."

Alfred said incredulously:

"You mean you *know?*"

Poirot smiled.

"Oh, yes," he said. "I know."

Alfred said:

"My father—my father—" He turned away.

Poirot said briskly:

"There are, Mr. Lee, two requests that I have to make."

Alfred said in a muffled voice:

"Anything—anything."

"Then, in the first place, I would like the portrait of Mr. Lee as a young man placed in the bedroom you are good enough to allot to me."

Alfred and Lydia stared at him.

The former said:

"My father's portrait—but why?"

Poirot said with a wave of the hand:

"It will—how shall I say—inspire me?"

Lydia said sharply:

"Do you propose, Mr. Poirot, to solve a crime by clairvoyance?"

"Let us say, madam, that I intend to use not only the eyes of the body, but the eyes of the mind."

She shrugged her shoulders.

Poirot continued:

"Next, Mr. Lee, I should like to know of the true circumstances attending the death of your sister's husband, Juan Estravados."

Lydia said:

"Is that necessary?"

"I want all the facts, madam."

Alfred said:

"Juan Estravados, as the result of a quarrel about a woman, killed another man in a café."

"How did he kill him?"

Alfred looked appealingly at Lydia. She said evenly:

"He stabbed him. Juan Estravados was not condemned to death, as there had been provocation. He was sentenced to a term of imprisonment and died in prison."

"Does his daughter know about her father?"

"I think not."

Alfred said:

"No, Jennifer never told her."

"Thank you."

Lydia said:

"You don't think that Pilar— Oh, it's absurd!"

Poirot said:

"Now, Mr. Lee, will you give me some facts about your brother, M. Harry Lee?"

"What do you want to know?"

"I understand that he was considered somewhat of a disgrace to the family. Why?"

Lydia said:

"It is so long ago. . . ."

Alfred said, the colour coming up in his face:

"If you want to know, Mr. Poirot, he stole a large sum of money by forging my father's name to a check. Naturally my father didn't prosecute. Harry's always been crooked. He's been in trouble all over the world. Always cabling for money to get out of a scrape. He's been in and out of gaol here, there and everywhere."

Lydia said:

"You don't really *know* all this, Alfred."

Alfred said angrily, his hands shaking:

"Harry's no good—no good whatever! He never has been!"

Poirot said:

"There is, I see, no love lost between you?"

Alfred said:

"He victimized my father—victimized him shamefully!"

Lydia sighed—a quick, impatient sigh. Poirot heard it and gave her a sharp glance.

She said:

"If only those diamonds could be found. I'm sure the solution lies there."

Poirot said:

"They have been found, madam."

"What?"

Poirot said gently:

"They were found in your little garden of the Dead Sea. . . ."

Lydia cried:

"In my garden? How—how extraordinary!"

Poirot said softly:

"Is it not, madam?"

Part VI ━━━━━ DECEMBER 27TH

I

ALFRED LEE said with a sigh:

"That was better than I feared!"

They had just returned from the inquest.

Mr. Charlton, an old-fashioned type of solicitor with a cautious blue eye, had been present and had returned with them. He said:

"Ah—I told you the proceedings would be purely formal —purely formal—there was bound to be an adjournment— to enable the police to gather up additional evidence."

George Lee said vexedly:

"It is all most unpleasant—really *most* unpleasant—a ter-

132

rible position in which to be placed! I myself am quite convinced that this crime was done by a maniac who somehow or other gained admittance to the house. That man Sugden is obstinate as a mule. Colonel Johnson should enlist the aid of Scotland Yard. These local police are no good. Thickheaded. What about this man Horbury, for instance? I hear his past is definitely unsatisfactory but the police do nothing whatever about it."

Mr. Charlton said:

"Ah—I believe the man Horbury has a satisfactory alibi covering the period of time in question. The police have accepted it."

"Why should they?" George fumed. "If I were they, I should accept such an alibi with reserve—with great reserve. Naturally a criminal always provides himself with an alibi! It is the duty of the police to break down the alibi—that is, if they know their job."

"Well, well," said Mr. Charlton. "I don't think it's quite our business to teach the police their jobs, eh? Pretty competent body of men on the whole."

George shook his head darkly.

"Scotland Yard should be called in. I'm not at all satisfied with Superintendent Sugden—he may be painstaking—but he is certainly far from brilliant."

Mr. Charlton said:

"I don't agree with you, you know. Sugden's a good man. Doesn't throw his weight about, but he gets there."

Lydia said:

"I'm sure the police are doing their best. Mr. Charlton, will you have a glass of sherry?"

Mr. Charlton thanked her politely, but declined. Then, clearing his throat, he proceeded to the reading of the will, all members of the family being assembled.

He read it with a certain relish, lingering over its more obscure phraseology, and savouring its legal technicalities.

He came to the end, took off his glasses, wiped them and looked round on the assembled company inquiringly.

Harry Lee said:

"All this legal stuff's a bit hard to follow. Give us the bare bones of it, will you?"

"Really," said Mr. Charlton. "It's a perfectly simple will."

Harry said:

"My God, what's a difficult will like then?"

Mr. Charlton rebuked him with a cold glance. He said:

"The main provisions of the will are quite simple. Half Mr. Lee's property goes to his son, Mr. Alfred Lee, the remainder is divided among his other children."

Harry laughed unpleasantly. He said:

"As usual, Alfred's struck lucky! Half my father's fortune! Lucky dog, aren't you, Alfred?"

Alfred flushed. Lydia said sharply:

"Alfred was a loyal and devoted son to his father. He's managed the works for years and has had all the responsibility."

Harry said:

"Oh, yes. Alfred was always the good boy."

Alfred said sharply:

"You may consider *yourself* lucky, I think, Harry, that my father left you anything at all!"

Harry laughed, throwing his head back, and said:

"You'd have liked it better if he'd cut me right out, wouldn't you? You've always disliked me."

Mr. Charlton coughed. He was used—only too well used—to the painful scenes that succeeded the reading of a will. He was anxious to get away before the usual family quarrel got too well under way.

He murmured:

"I think—er—that that is all that I need—er—"

Harry said sharply:

"What about Pilar?"

Mr. Charlton coughed again, this time apologetically.

"Er— Miss Estravados is not mentioned in the will."

Harry said:

"Doesn't she get her mother's share?"

Mr. Charlton explained.

"Señora Estravados, if she had lived, would of course have received an equal share with the rest of you, but as she is dead, the portion that would have been hers goes back into the estate to be shared out among you."

Pilar said slowly in her rich Southern voice:

"Then—I—have—nothing?"

Lydia said quickly:

"My dear, the family will see to that, of course."

George Lee said:

"You will be able to make your home here with Alfred—eh, Alfred? We—er—you are our niece—it is our duty to look after you."

Hilda said:

"We shall always be glad to have Pilar with us."

Harry said:

"She ought to have her proper share. She ought to have Jennifer's whack."

Mr. Charlton murmured:

"Must really—er—be going. Good-bye, Mrs. Lee—anything I can do—er—consult me at any time. . . ."

134

He escaped quickly. His experience enabled him to predict that all the ingredients for a family row were present.

As the door shut behind him Lydia said in her clear voice:

"I agree with Harry. I think Pilar is entitled to a definite share. This will was made many years before Jennifer's death."

"Nonsense," said George. "Very slipshod and illegal way of thinking, Lydia. The law's the law. We must abide by it."

Magdalene said:

"It's hard luck, of course, and we're all very sorry for Pilar, but George is right. As he says, the law is the law."

Lydia got up. She took Pilar by the hand.

"My dear," she said. "This must be very unpleasant for you. Will you please leave us while we discuss the question?"

She led the girl to the door.

"Don't worry, Pilar, dear," she said. "Leave it to me."

Pilar went slowly out of the room. Lydia shut the door behind her and turned back.

There was a moment's pause while everyone drew breath and in another moment the battle was in full swing.

Harry said:

"You've always been a damned skinflint, George."

George retorted:

"At any rate I've not been a sponge and a rotter!"

"You've been just as much of a sponge as I have! You've battened on Father all these years."

"You seem to forget that I hold a responsible and arduous position which—"

Harry said:

"Responsible and arduous my foot! You're only an inflated gas bag!"

Magdalene screamed.

"How dare you?"

Hilda's calm voice, slightly raised, said:

"Couldn't we just discuss this *quietly?*"

Lydia threw her a grateful glance.

David said with sudden violence:

"Must we have all this disgraceful fuss over *money!*"

Magdalene said venomously to him:

"It's all very well to be so high-minded. You're not going to refuse your legacy, are you? *You* want money just as much as the rest of us do! All this unworldliness is just a pose!"

David said in a strangled voice:

"You think I ought to refuse it? I wonder—"

Hilda said sharply:

"Of course you oughtn't. Must we all behave like children? Alfred, you're the head of the family—"

Alfred seemed to wake out of a dream. He said:

"I beg your pardon. All of you shouting at once. It—it confuses me."

Lydia said:

"As Hilda has just pointed out, why must we behave like greedy children? Let us discuss this thing quietly and sanely and—" she added this quickly—"one at a time. Alfred shall speak first because he is the eldest. What do you think, Alfred, we should do about Pilar?"

He said slowly:

"She must make her home here, certainly. And we should make her an allowance. I do not see that she has any legal claim to the money which would have gone to her mother. She's not a Lee, remember. She's a Spanish subject."

"No legal claim, no," said Lydia. "But I think she has a *moral* claim. As I see it, your father, although his daughter had married a Spaniard against his wishes, recognized her to have an equal claim upon him. George, Harry, David and Jennifer were to share equally. Jennifer only died last year. I am sure that when he sent for Mr. Charlton, he meant to make ample provision for Pilar in a new will. He would have allotted her at least her mother's share. It is possible that he might have done much more than that. She was the only grandchild, remember. I think the least *we* can do is to endeavour to remedy an injustice that your father himself was preparing to remedy."

Alfred said warmly:

"Well put, Lydia! I was wrong. I agree with you that Pilar must be given Jennifer's share of my father's fortune."

Lydia said:

"Your turn, Harry."

Harry said:

"As you know, I agree. I think Lydia has put the case very well, and I'd like to say I admire her for it."

Lydia said:

"George?"

George was red in the face. He spluttered:

"Certainly not! Whole thing's preposterous! Give her a home and a decent dress allowance. Quite enough for her!"

"Then you refuse to cooperate?" asked Alfred.

"Yes, I do."

"And he's quite right," said Magdalene. "It's disgraceful to suggest he should do anything of the kind! Considering that George is the *only* member of the family who has done *anything* in the world, I think it's a shame his father left him so little!"

Lydia said:

"David?"

136

David said vaguely:

"Oh, I think you're right. It's a pity there's got to be so much ugliness and disputing about it all."

Hilda said:

"You're quite right, Lydia. It's only justice!"

Harry looked round. He said:

"Well, that's clear. Of the family, Alfred, David and myself are in favour of the motion. George is against it. The ayes have it."

George said sharply:

"There is no question of ayes or noes. My share of my father's estate is mine absolutely. I shall not part with a penny of it."

"No, indeed," said Magdalene.

Lydia said sharply:

"If you like to stand out, that is your business. The rest of us will make up your share of the total."

She looked round for assent and the others nodded.

Harry said:

"Alfred's got the lion's share. He ought to stand most of the racket."

Alfred said:

"I see that your original disinterested suggestion will soon break down."

Hilda said firmly:

"Don't let's start again! Lydia shall tell Pilar what we've decided. We can settle details later." She added in the hope of making a diversion. "I wonder where Mr. Farr is and Mr. Poirot?"

Alfred said:

"We dropped Poirot in the village on our way to the inquest. He said he had an important purchase to make."

Harry said:

"Why didn't *he* go to the inquest? Surely he ought to have done so."

Lydia said:

"Perhaps he knew it was not going to be important. Who's that our there in the garden? Superintendent Sugden, or Mr. Farr?"

The efforts of the two women were successful. The family conclave broke up.

Lydia said to Hilda privately:

"Thank you, Hilda. It was nice of you to back me up. You know, you really *have* been a comfort in all this."

Hilda said thoughtfully:

"Queer how money upsets people."

The others had all left the room. The two women were alone.

Lydia said:

"Yes—even Harry—although it was his suggestion! And my poor Alfred—he is so British—he doesn't really like Lee money going to a Spanish subject."

Hilda said, smiling:

"Do you think we women are more unworldly?"

Lydia said with a shrug of her graceful shoulders:

"Well, you know, it isn't really our money—not our *own!* That may make a difference."

Hilda said thoughtfully:

"She is a strange child—Pilar, I mean. I wonder what will become of her?"

Lydia sighed.

"I'm glad that she will be independent. To live here, to be given a home and a dress allowance, would not, I think, be very satisfactory to her. She's too proud and, I think, too—too—alien."

She added musingly:

"I once brought some beautiful blue lapis home from Egypt. Out there, against the sun and the sand it was a glorious colour—a brilliant, warm blue. But when I got it home, the blue of it hardly showed any more. It was just a dull, darkish string of beads."

Hilda said:

"Yes, I see. . . ."

Lydia said gently:

"I am so glad to come to know you and David at last. I'm glad you both came here."

Hilda sighed:

"How often I've wished in the last few days that we hadn't!"

"I know. You must have done . . . but you know, Hilda, the shock hasn't affected David nearly as badly as it might have done. I mean he is so sensitive that it might have upset him completely. Actually, since the murder, he's seemed ever so much better—"

Hilda looked slightly disturbed. She said:

"So you've noticed that? It's rather dreadful in a way . . . but, oh! Lydia, it's undoubtedly so!"

She was silent a minute recollecting words that her husband had spoken only the night before. He had said to her, eagerly, his fair hair tossed back from his forehead.

"Hilda, you remember in *Tosca*—when Scarpia is dead and Tosca lights the candles at his head and feet? Do you remember what she says: '*Now* I can forgive him.' That is what I feel—about Father. I see now that all these years I couldn't forgive him and yet I really wanted to. . . . But now—*now*—there's no rancour any more. It's all wiped away.

138

And I feel—oh, I feel as though a great load had been lifted from my back."

She had said, striving to fight back a sudden fear:

"Because he's dead?"

He had answered quickly, stammering in his eagerness:

"No, no, you don't understand. Not because *he* is dead, but because my childish, stupid hate of him is dead. . . ."

Hilda thought of those words now. . . .

She would have liked to repeat them to the woman at her side, but she felt instinctively that it was wiser not.

She followed Lydia out of the drawing-room into the hall.

Magdalene was there standing by the hall table with a little parcel in her hand. She jumped when she saw them. She said:

"Oh, this must be Mr. Poirot's important purchase. I saw him put it down here just now. I wonder what it is."

She looked from one to the other of them, giggling a little, but her eyes were sharp and anxious, belying the affected gaiety of her words.

Lydia's eyebrows rose. She said:

"I must go and get ready for lunch."

Magdalene said, still with that affectation of childishness, but unable to keep the desperate note out of her voice:

"I must just *peep!*"

She unrolled the piece of paper and gave a sharp exclamation. She stared at the thing in her hand.

Lydia stopped and Hilda too. Both women stared.

Magdalene said in a puzzled voice:

"It's a false moustache. But—but—why—?"

Hilda said doubtfully:

"Disguise? But—"

Lydia finished the sentence for her.

"But Mr. Poirot has a very fine moustache of his own!"

Magdalene was wrapping the parcel up again. She said:

"I don't understand. It's—it's *mad. Why* does Mr. Piorot buy a false moustache?"

II

When Pilar left the drawing-room she walked slowly along the hall. Stephen Farr was coming in through the garden door. He said:

"Well? Is the family conclave over? Has the will been read?"

Pilar said, her breath coming fast:

"I have got nothing—nothing at all! It was a will made many years ago. My grandfather left money to my mother, but because she is dead it does not go to me but goes back to *them*."

Stephen said:

"That seems rather hard lines."

Pilar said:

"If that old man had lived, he would have made another will. He would have left money to *me*—a lot of money! Perhaps in time, he would have left me *all* the money!"

Stephen said, smiling:

"That wouldn't have been very fair either, would it?"

"Why not? He would have liked me best, that is all."

Stephen said:

"What a greedy child you are. A real little gold digger."

Pilar said soberly:

"The world is very cruel to women. They must do what they can for themselves—while they are young. When they are old and ugly no one will help them."

Stephen said slowly:

"That's more true than I like to think. But it isn't *quite* true. Alfred Lee, for instance, was genuinely fond of his father in spite of the old man being thoroughly trying and exacting."

Pilar's chin went up.

"Alfred," she said, "is rather a fool."

Stephen laughed.

Then he said:

"Well, don't worry, lovely Pilar. The Lees are bound to look after you, you know."

Pilar said disconsolately:

"It will not be very amusing, that."

Stephen said slowly:

"No, I'm afraid it won't. I can't see you living here, Pilar. Would you like to come to South Africa?"

Pilar nodded.

Stephen said:

"There's sun there, and space. There's hard work, too. Are you good at work, Pilar?"

Pilar said doubtfully:

"I do not know."

He said:

"You'd rather sit on a balcony and eat sweets all day long? And grow enormously fat and have three double chins?"

Pilar laughed and Stephen said:

"That's better. I've made you laugh."

Pilar said:

"I thought I should laugh this Christmas! In books I have read that an English Christmas is very gay, that one eats burning raisins and there is a plum pudding all in flames and something that is called a Yule log."

Stephen said:

"Ah, but you must have a Christmas uncomplicated by murder. Come in here a minute. Lydia took me in here yesterday. It's her storeroom."

He led her into a small room little bigger than a cupboard.

"Look, Pilar, boxes and boxes of crackers, and preserved fruits and oranges and dates and nuts. And here——"

"Oh!" Pilar clasped her hands. "They are pretty, these gold and silver balls."

"Those were to hang on a tree, with presents for the servants. And here are little snow men all glittering with frost to put on the dinner table. And here are balloons of every colour all ready to blow up!"

"Oh!" Pilar's eyes shone. "Oh! can we blow up one? Lydia would not mind. I do love balloons."

Stephen said:

"Baby! Here, which will you have?"

Pilar said: "I will have a red one."

They selected their balloons and blew, their cheeks distended. Pilar stopped blowing to laugh and her balloon went down again.

She said:

"You look so funny—blowing—with your cheeks puffed out."

Her laugh rang out. Then she fell to, blowing industriously. They tied up their balloons carefully and began to play with them, patting them upwards, sending them to and fro.

Pilar said:

"Out in the hall, there would be more room."

They were sending the balloons to each other and laughing when Poirot came along the hall. He regarded them indulgently.

"So you play *les jeux d'enfants?* It is pretty, that!"

Pilar said breathlessly:

"Mine is the red one. It is bigger than his. Much bigger. If we took it outside it would go right up in the sky."

"Let's send them up and wish," said Stephen.

"Oh, yes, that is a good idea."

Pilar ran to the garden door, Stephen followed. Poirot came behind, still looking indulgent.

"I will wish for a great deal of money," announced Pilar.

She stood on tiptoe, holding the string of the balloon. It tugged gently as a puff of wind came. Pilar let go and it floated along, taken by the breeze.

141

Stephen laughed:

"You mustn't tell your wish."

"No, why not?"

"Because it doesn't come true. Now, I'm going to wish."

He released his balloon. But he was not so lucky. It floated sideways, caught on a holly bush and expired with a bang.

Pilar ran to it.

She announced tragically:

"It is gone. . . ."

Then, as she stirred the little limp wisp of rubber with her toe, she said:

"So that was what I picked up in grandfather's room. He, too, had had a balloon, only his was a pink one."

Poirot gave a sharp exclamation. Pilar turned inquiringly.

Poirot said:

"It is nothing. I stabbed—no, stubbed—the toe."

He wheeled round and looked at the house.

He said:

"So many windows! A house, mademoiselle, has its eyes —and its ears. It is indeed regrettable that the English are so fond of open windows."

Lydia came out on the terrace.

She said:

"Lunch is just ready. Pilar, my dear, everything has been settled quite satisfactorily. Alfred will explain the exact details to you after lunch. Shall we come in?"

They went into the house. Poirot came last. He was looking grave.

III

Lunch was over.

As they came out of the dining-room, Alfred said to Pilar:

"Will you come into my room? There is something I want to talk over with you."

He led her across the hall and into his study, shutting the door after him. The others went on into the drawing-room. Only Hercule Poirot remained in the hall, looking thoughtfully at the closed study door.

He was aware suddenly of the old butler hovering uneasily near him.

Poirot said:

"Yes, Tressilian, what is it?"

The old man seemed troubled. He said:

"I wanted to speak to Mr. Lee. But I don't like to disturb him now."

Poirot said:

142

"Something has occurred?"

Tressilian said slowly:

"It's such a queer thing. It doesn't make sense."

"Tell me," said Hercule Poirot.

Tressilian hesitated. Then he said:

"Well, it's this, sir. You may have noticed that each side of the front door there was a cannon ball. Big heavy stone things. Well, sir, *one of them's gone.*"

Hercule Poirot's eyebrows rose. He said:

"Since when?"

"They were both there this morning, sir. I'll take my oath on that."

"Let us see."

Together they went outside the front door. Poirot bent and examined the remaining cannon ball. When he straightened himself, his face was very grave.

Tressilian quavered.

"Who'd want to steal a thing like that, sir? It doesn't make *sense.*"

Poirot said:

"I do not like it. I do not like it at all. . . ."

Tressilian was watching him anxiously. He said slowly:

"What's come to the house, sir? Ever since the master was murdered it doesn't seem like the same place. I feel the whole time as though I am going about in a dream. I mix things up, and I sometimes feel I can't trust my own eyes."

Hercule Poirot shook his head. He said:

"You are wrong. Your own eyes are just what you must trust."

Tressilian said, shaking his head:

"My sight's bad—I can't see like I used to do. I get things mixed up—and people. I'm getting too old for my work."

Hercule Poirot clapped him on the shoulder and said:

"Courage."

"Thank you, sir. You mean it kindly, I know. But there it is, I am too old. I'm always going back to the old days and the old faces. Miss Jenny and Master David and Master Alfred. I'm always seeing them as young gentlemen and ladies. Ever since that night when Mr. Harry came home—"

Poirot nodded.

"Yes," he said, "that is what I thought. You said just now 'ever since the master was murdered'—but it began before that. It is *ever since Mr. Harry came home,* is it not, that things have altered and seemed unreal?"

The butler said:

"You're quite right, sir. It was then. Mr. Harry always brought trouble into the house, even in the old days."

His eyes wandered back to the empty stone base.

"Who can have taken it, sir?" he whispered. "And why? It's—it's like a madhouse."

Hercule Poirot said:

"It is not madness I am afraid of. It is sanity! Somebody, Tressilian, is in great danger."

He turned and reentered the house.

At that moment Pilar came out from the study. A red spot shone on either cheek. She held her head high and her eyes glittered.

As Poirot came up to her, she suddenly stamped her foot and said:

"I will not take it."

Poirot raised his eyebrows. He said:

"What is this that you will not take, mademoiselle?"

Pilar said:

"Alfred has just told me that I am to have my mother's share of the money my grandfather left."

"Well?"

"I could not get it by law, he said. But he and Lydia and the others consider it should be mine. They say it is a matter of justice. And so they will hand it over to me."

Poirot said again:

"Well?"

Pilar stamped once more with her foot.

"Do you not understand? They are giving it to me—*giving* it to me."

"Need that hurt your pride? Since what they say is true— that it should in justice be yours?"

Pilar said:

"You do not understand. . . ."

Poirot said:

"On the contrary—I understand very well."

"Oh! . . ." She turned away pettishly.

There was a ring at the bell. Poirot glanced over his shoulder. He saw the silhouette of Superintendent Sugden outside the door. He said hurriedly to Pilar:

"Where are you going?"

She said sulkily:

"To the drawing-room. To the others."

Poirot said quickly:

"Good. Stay with them there. Do not wander about the house alone, especially after dark. Be on your guard. You are in great danger, mademoiselle. You will never be in greater danger than you are to-day."

He turned away from her and went to meet Sugden.

The latter waited till Tressilian had gone back into his pantry.

Then he shoved a cable form under Poirot's nose.

"Now we've got it!" he said. "Read that. It's from the South African Police."

The cable said:

"Ebenezer Farr's only son died two years ago."

Sugden said:

"So now we know! Funny—I was on a different tack altogether. . . ."

IV

Pilar marched into the drawing-room, her head held high.

She went straight up to Lydia, who was standing in the window with some knitting.

Pilar said:

"Lydia, I have come to tell you that I will not take that money. I am going away—at once. . . ."

Lydia looked astonished. She laid down her knitting.

She said:

"My dear child, Alfred must have explained very badly! It is not in the least a matter of charity, if that is what you feel. Really, it is not a question of kindness or generosity on our part. It is a plain matter of right and wrong. In the ordinary course of events your mother would have inherited this money, and you would have come into it from her. It is your right—your blood right. It is a matter, not of charity, but of *justice!*"

Pilar said fiercely:

"And that is why I cannot do it—not when you speak like that—not when you are like that! I enjoyed coming here. It was fun! It was an adventure, but now you have spoiled it all! I am going away now, at once—you will never be bothered by me again. . . ."

Tears choked her voice. She turned and ran blindly out of the room.

Lydia stared. She said helplessly:

"I'd no idea she would take it like that!"

Hilda said:

"The child seems quite upset. . . ."

George cleared his throat and said portentously:

"Er—as I pointed out this morning—the principle involved is wrong. Pilar has the wit to see that for herself. She refuses to accept charity—"

Lydia said sharply:

"It is *not* charity. It is her right!"

George said:

"She does not seem to think so!"

Superintendent Sugden and Hercule Poirot came in. The former looked round and asked:

"Where's Mr. Farr? I want a word with him."

Before anyone had time to answer, Hercule Poirot said sharply:

"Where is the señorita Estravados?"

George Lee said with a trace of malicious satisfaction:

"Going to clear out, so she says. Apparently she has had enough of her English relations."

Poirot wheeled round.

He said to Sugden:

"Come!"

As the two men emerged into the hall, there was the sound of a heavy crash and a faraway shriek.

Poirot cried:

"Quick . . . come. . . ."

They raced along the hall and up the far staircase. The door of Pilar's room was open and a man stood in the doorway. He turned his head as they ran up. It was Stephen Farr.

He said:

"She's alive. . . ."

Pilar stood crouched against the wall of her room. She was staring at the floor where a big stone cannon ball was lying.

She said breathlessly:

"It was on top of my door, balanced there. It would have crashed down on my head when I came in, but my skirt caught on a nail and jerked me back just as I was coming in."

Poirot knelt down and examined the nail. On it was a threat of purple tweed. He looked up and nodded gravely:

"That nail, mademoiselle," he said, "saved your life."

The Superintendent said, bewildered:

"Look here, what's the meaning of all this?"

Pilar said:

"Someone tried to kill me!"

She nodded her head several times.

Superintendent Sugden glanced up at the door.

"Booby trap," he said. "An old-fashioned booby trap—and its purpose was murder! That's the second murder planned in this house. But this time it didn't come off!"

Stephen Farr said huskily:

"Thank God you're safe."

Pilar flung out her hands in a wide, appealing gesture.

"Madre de Dios!" she cried. "Why should anyone wish to kill *me?* What have I done?"

Hercule Poirot said slowly:

"You should rather ask, mademoiselle, *what do I know?*"

She stared.

"Know? I do not know anything."

Hercule Poirot said:

"That is where you are wrong. Tell me, Mademoiselle Pilar, where were you at the time of the murder? You were not in this room."

"I was. I have told you so!"

Superintendent Sugden said with deceptive mildness:

"Yes, but you weren't speaking the truth when you said that, you know. You told us you heard your grandfather scream—you couldn't have heard that if you were in here—Mr. Poirot and I tested that yesterday."

"Oh!" Pilar caught her breath.

Poirot said:

"You were somewhere very much nearer his room. I will tell you where you were, mademoiselle. You were in the recess with the statues quite close to your grandfather's door."

Pilar said, startled:

"Oh . . . how did you know?"

Poirot said with a faint smile:

"Mr. Farr saw you there."

Stephen said sharply:

"I did not. That's an absolute lie!"

Poirot said:

"I ask your pardon, Mr. Farr, but you *did* see her. Remember your impression that there were *three* statues in that recess, not *two*. Only one person wore a white dress that night, Mademoiselle Estravados. *She* was the third white figure you saw. That is so, is it not, mademoiselle?"

Pilar said after a moment's hesitation:

"Yes, it is true."

Poirot said gently:

"Now tell us, mademoiselle, the whole truth. *Why* were you there?"

Pilar said:

"I left the drawing-room after dinner and I thought I would go and see my grandfather. I thought he would be pleased. But when I turned into the passage I saw someone else was there at his door. I did not want to be seen because I knew my grandfather had said he did not want to see anyone that night. I slipped into the recess in case the person at the door turned round.

"Then, all at once, I heard the most terrible sounds—tables—chairs—" she waved her hands—"everything falling and crashing. I did not move. I do not know why. I was

147

frightened. And then there was a terrible scream—" she crossed herself—"and my heart, it stopped beating, and I said: '*Someone is dead. . . .*'"

"And then?"

"And then people began coming running along the passage and I came out at the end and joined them."

Superintendent Sugden said sharply:

"You said nothing of all this when we first questioned you. Why not?"

Pilar shook her head. She said with an air of wisdom:

"It is not good to tell too much to the police. I thought, you see, that if I said I was near there, you might think that *I* had killed him. So I said I was in my room."

Sugden said sharply:

"If you tell deliberate lies all that it ends in is that you're bound to come under suspicion."

Stephen Farr said:

"Pilar?"

"Yes."

"*Who did you see standing at the door* when you turned into the passage? Tell us."

Sugden said:

"Yes—tell us."

For a moment the girl hesitated. Her eyes opened, then narrowed. She said slowly:

"I don't know who it was. It was too dimly lit to see. But it was a woman. . . ."

V

Superintendent Sugden looked round at the circle of faces. He said with something as near irritation as he had yet shown:

"This is very irregular, Mr. Poirot."

Poirot said:

"It is a little idea of mine. I wish to share with everyone the knowledge that I have acquired. I shall then invite their cooperation, and so we shall get at the truth."

Sugden murmured under his breath:

"Monkey tricks."

He leaned back in his chair.

Poirot said:

"To begin with, you have, I think, an explanation to ask of Mr. Farr."

Sugden's mouth tightened.

"I should have chosen a less public moment," he said.

"However, I've no objection." He handed the cable to Stephen Farr. "Now, Mr. *Farr*, as you call yourself, perhaps you can explain *this?*"

Stephen Farr took it. Raising his eyebrows, he read it slowly out loud. Then, with a bow, he handed it back to the Superintendent.

"Yes," he said. "It's pretty damning, isn't it?"

Sugden said:

"Is that all you've got to say about it? You quite understand there is no obligation on you to make a statement—"

Stephen Farr interrupted. He said:

"You needn't caution me, Superintendent. I can see it trembling on your tongue! Yes, I'll give you an explanation. It's not a very good one, but it's the truth."

He paused. Then he began:

"I'm not Ebenezer Farr's son. But I knew both father and son quite well. Now try and put yourself in my place—(my name is Stephen Grant, by the way). I arrived in this country for the first time in my life. I was disappointed. Everything and everybody seemed drab and lifeless. Then I was traveling by train and I saw a girl. I've got to say it straight out! I fell for that girl! She was the loveliest and most unlikely creature in the world! I talked to her for a while in the train and I made up my mind then and there not to lose sight of her. As I was leaving the compartment I caught sight of the label on her suitcase. Her name meant nothing to me, but the address to which she was traveling did. I'd heard of Gorston Hall and I knew all about its owner. He was Ebenezer Farr's one-time partner and old Eb often talked about him and said what a personality he was.

"Well, the idea came to me to go to Gorston Hall and pretend I was Eb's son. He had died, as this cable says, two years ago, but I remembered old Eb saying that he had not heard from Simeon Lee now for many years and I judged that Lee would not know of the death of Eb's son. Anyway, I felt it was worth trying."

Sugden said:

"You didn't try it on at once, though. You stayed in the King's Arms at Addlesfield for two days."

Stephen said:

"I was thinking it over—whether to try it or not. At last I made up my mind I would. It appealed to me as a bit of an adventure. Well, it worked like a charm! The old man greeted me in the friendliest manner and at once asked me to come and stay in the house. I accepted. There you are, Superintendent, there's my explanation. If you don't fancy it, cast your mind back to your courting days and see if you don't remember some bit of foolishness you indulged in then. As for my real name, as I say, it's Stephen Grant. You can cable to South Africa and check up on me, but I'll tell you this, you'll find I'm a perfectly respectable citizen. I'm not a crook or a jewel thief."

Poirot said softly:

"I never believed you were."

Superintendent Sugden stroked his jaw cautiously.

He said:

"I'll have to check up on that story. What I'd like to know is this: Why didn't you come clean after the murder instead of telling us a pack of lies?"

Stephen said disarmingly:

"Because I was a fool! I thought I could get away with it! I thought it would look fishy if I admitted to being here under a false name. If I hadn't been a complete idiot I would have realized you were bound to cable to Jo'-burg."

Sugden said:

"Well, Mr. Farr—er—Grant—I'm not saying I disbelieve your story. It will be proved or disproved soon enough."

He looked across inquiringly at Poirot. The latter said:

"I think Miss Estravados has something to say."

Pilar had gone very white. She said in a breathless voice:

"It is true. I would never have told you, but for Lydia and the money. To come here and pretend and cheat and act —that was fun, but when Lydia said the money was mine and that it was only justice, that was different. It was not fun any longer."

Alfred Lee said with a puzzled face:

"I do not understand, my dear, what you are talking about?"

Pilar said:

"You think I am your niece, Pilar Estravados? But that is not so! Pilar was killed when I was traveling with her in a car in Spain. A bomb came and it hit the car and she was killed, but I was not touched. I did not know her very well, but she had told me all about herself and how her grandfather had sent for her to England and that he was very rich. And I had no money at all and I did not know where to go or what to do. And I thought suddenly: 'Why should not I take Pilar's passport and go to England and become very rich?'" Her face lit up with its sudden wide smile. "Oh, it was fun wondering if I could get away with it! Our faces on the photograph were not unlike. But when they wanted my passport here I opened the window and threw it out and ran down to get it, and then I rubbed some earth just over the face a little because at a barrier traveling they do not look very closely, but here they might—"

Alfred Lee said angrily:

"Do you mean to say that you represented yourself to my father as his granddaughter, and played on his affection for you?"

Pilar nodded. She said complacently:

"Yes, I saw at once I could make him like me very much."

George Lee broke out:

"Preposterous!" he spluttered. "Criminal! Attempting to get money by false pretences."

Harry Lee said:

"She didn't get any from *you*, old boy! Pilar, I'm on your side! I've got a profound admiration for your daring. And, thank goodness, I'm not your uncle any more! That gives me a much freer hand."

Pilar said to Poirot:

"*You* knew? When did you know?"

Poirot smiled.

"Mademoiselle, if you had studied the laws of Mendel you would know that two blue-eyed people are not likely to have a brown-eyed child. Your mother was, I was sure, a most chaste and respectable lady. It followed then, that you were not Pilar Estravados at all. When you did your trick with the passport, I was quite sure of it. It was ingenious, but not, you understand, quite ingenious enough."

Superintendent Sugden said unpleasantly:

"The whole thing's not quite ingenious enough."

Pilar stared at him. She said:

"I don't understand. . . ."

Sugden said:

"You've told us a story—but I think there's a good deal more you haven't told."

Stephen said:

"You leave her alone!"

Superintendent Sugden took no notice. He went on:

"You've told us that you went up to your grandfather's room after dinner. You said it was an impulse on your part. I'm going to suggest something else. It was you who stole those diamonds. You'd handled them. On occasion, perhaps, you'd put them away in the safe and the old man hadn't watched you do it! When he found the stones were missing, he saw at once that only two people could have taken them. One was Horbury, who might have got to know the combination and have crept in and stolen them during the night. The other person was *you*.

"Well, Mr. Lee at once took measures. He rang me up and had me come to see him. Then he sent word to you to come and see him immediately after dinner. You did so and he

151

accused you of the theft. You denied it, he pressed the charge. I don't know what happened next—perhaps he tumbled to the fact that you weren't his granddaughter but a very clever little professional thief. Anyway the game was up, exposure loomed over you and you slashed at him with a knife. There was a struggle and he screamed. You were properly up against it then. You hurried out of the room, turned the key from the outside and then, knowing you could not get away, before the others came, *you slipped into the recess by the statues.*"

Pilar cried shrilly:

"It is not true! It is not true! I did not steal the diamonds! I did not kill him. I swear it by the Blessed Virgin."

Sugden said sharply:

"*Then who did?* You say you saw a figure standing outside Mr. Lee's door. According to your story, *that person must have been the murderer. No one else* passed the recess! But we've only *your* word for it *that there was a figure there at all.* In other words, *you made that up* to exculpate yourself!"

George Lee said sharply:

"Of course she's guilty! It's all clear enough! I always *said* an outsider killed my father! Preposterous nonsense to pretend one of his family would do a thing like that! It—it wouldn't be natural!"

Poirot stirred in his seat. He said:

"I disagree with you. Taking into consideration the character of Simeon Lee, it would be a very natural thing to happen."

"Eh?" George's jaw dropped. He stared at Poirot.

Poirot went on:

"And in my opinion that very thing *did* happen. Simeon Lee was killed by his own flesh and blood, for what seemed to the murderer a very good and sufficient reason."

George cried:

"One of us? I deny—"

Poirot's voice broke in hard as steel.

"There is a case against every person here. We will, Mr. George Lee, begin with the case against *you. You* had no love for your father! You kept on good terms with him for the sake of money. On the day of his death *he threatened to cut down your allowance.* You knew that on his death you would probably inherit a very substantial sum. There is the motive. After dinner you went, as you say, to telephone. You *did* telephone—but the call lasted only *five minutes.* After that, you could easily have gone to your father's room, chatted with him, and then attacked him and killed him. You left the room and turned the key from outside, for you hoped the affair would be put down to a burglar. You omitted, in your panic, to make sure that the window was fully open so as to support the burglar theory. That was stupid, but you are, if you will pardon my saying so, rather a stupid man!

"However," said Poirot, after a brief pause during which George tried to speak and failed, "many stupid men have been criminals!"

He turned his eyes on Magdalene.

"Madam, too, she also had a motive. She is, I think, in debt, and the tone of certain of your father's remarks may—have caused her uneasiness. She, too, has no alibi. She went to telephone, but she did *not* telephone, and we have *only her word for* what she did do. . . .

"Then"—he paused—"there is Mr. David Lee. We have heard, not once but many times of the revengeful tempers and long memories that went with the Lee blood. Mr. David Lee did not forgive or forget the way his father had treated his mother. A final jibe directed at the dead lady may have been the last straw. David Lee is said to have been playing the piano at the time of the murder. By a coincidence he was playing the *Dead March*. But suppose *somebody else* was playing that *Dead March*, somebody who knew what he was going to do and who approved his action."

Hilda Lee said quietly:

"That is an infamous suggestion."

Poirot turned to her.

"I will offer you another, madam. It was *your* hand that did the deed. It was *you* who crept upstairs to execute judgment on a man you considered beyond human forgiveness. You are of those, madam, who can be terrible in anger. . . ."

Hilda said:

"I did not kill him."

Superintendent Sugden said brusquely:

"Mr. Poirot's quite right. There is a possible case against everyone except Mr. Alfred Lee, Mr. Harry Lee and Mrs. Alfred Lee."

Poirot said gently:

"I should not even except those three. . . ."

The Superintendent protested.

"Oh, come now, Mr. Poirot!"

Lydia Lee said:

"And what is the case against me, Mr. Poirot?"

She smiled a little as she spoke, her brows raised ironically.

Poirot bowed. He said:

"Your motive, madam, I pass over. It is sufficiently obvious. As to the rest, you were wearing last night a flowered taffeta dress of a very distinctive pattern with a cape. I will remind you of the fact that Tressilian, the butler, is shortsighted. Objects at a distance are dim and vague to him. I will also point out that your drawing-room is big and lighted by heavily shaded lamps. On that night, a minute or two before the cries were heard, Tressilian came into the drawing-room to take away the coffee cups. He saw you, *as he thought*, in a familiar attitude by the far window half concealed by the heavy curtains."

Lydia Lee said:

"He did see me."

Poirot went on:

"I suggest that it is possible that *what Tressilian saw was the cape of your dress,* arranged to show by the window curtain, as though you yourself were standing there."

Lydia said:

"I was standing there. . . ."

Alfred said:

"How dare you suggest——"

Harry interrupted him.

"Let him go on, Alfred. It's our turn next. How do you suggest that dear Alfred killed his beloved father since we were both together in the dining-room at the time?"

Poirot beamed at him.

"That," he said, "is very simple. An alibi gains in force accordingly as it is unwillingly given. You and your brother are on bad terms. It is well known. *You* jibe at *him* in public. *He* has not a good word to say for *you!* But *supposing that were all part of a very clever plot.* Supposing that Alfred Lee is tired of dancing attendance upon an exacting taskmaster. Supposing that you and he have got together some time ago. Your plan is laid. You come home. Alfred appears to resent your presence. He shows jealousy and dislike of you. You show contempt for him. And then comes the night of the murder you have so cleverly planned together. One of you remains in the dining-room, talking and perhaps quarreling aloud as though two people were there. *The other goes upstairs and commits the crime. . . .*"

Alfred sprang to his feet.

"You devil," he said. His voice was inarticulate. "You inhuman devil. . . ."

Sugden was staring at Poirot. He said:

"Do you really mean——?"

Poirot said, with a sudden ring of authority in his voice:

"I have had to show you the *possibilities!* These are the things that *might* have happened! Which of them actually *did*

154

happen we can only tell by passing from the outside appearance to the inside reality. . . ."

He paused and then said slowly:

"We must come back, as I said before, to the character of Simeon Lee himself. . . ."

VI

There was a momentary pause. Strangely enough, all indignation and all rancour had died down. Hercule Poirot held his audience under the spell of his personality. They watched him, fascinated, as he began slowly to speak.

"It is all there, you see. The dead man is the focus and centre of the mystery! We must probe deep into the heart and mind of Simeon Lee and see what we find there. For a man does not live and die to himself alone. That which he has, he hands on—to those who come after him. . . .

"What had Simeon Lee to bequeath to his sons and daughter? Pride, to begin with—a pride which in the old man was frustrated in his disappointment over his children. Then there was the quality of patience. We have been told that Simeon Lee waited patiently for years in order to revenge himself upon someone who had done him an injury. We see that that aspect of his temperament was inherited by the son who resembled him least in face. David Lee also could remember and continue to harbour resentment through long years. In *face,* Harry Lee was the only one of his children who closely resembled him. That resemblance is quite striking when we examine the portrait of Simeon Lee as a young man. There is the same high-bridged aquiline nose, the long sharp line of the jaw, the backward poise of the head. I think, too, that Harry inherited many of his father's mannerisms—that habit, for instance, of throwing back his head and laughing and another habit of drawing his finger along the line of his jaw.

"Bearing all these things in mind and being convinced that the murder was committed by a person closely connected with the dead man, I studied the family from the psychological standpoint. That is, I tried to decide which of them were *psychologically possible criminals*. And in my judgment only two persons qualified in that respect. They were Alfred Lee and Hilda Lee, David's wife. David himself I rejected as a possible murderer. I do not think a person of his delicate susceptibilities could have faced the actual bloodshed of a cut throat. George Lee and his wife I likewise rejected. Whatever their desires I did not think they had the temperament to take a *risk*. They were both essentially cautious. Mrs. Alfred Lee I felt sure was quite incapable of an act of violence. She has too much irony in her nature. About Harry Lee I hesitated. He had a certain coarse truculence of aspect, but I was nearly sure that Harry Lee, in spite of his bluff and his bluster, was essentially a weakling. That, I now know, was also his father's opinion. Harry, he said, was worth no more than the rest. That left me with the two people I have already mentioned. Alfred Lee was a person capable of a great deal of selfless devotion. He was a man who had controlled and subordinated himself to the will of another person for many long years. It is always possible under these conditions for something to snap. Moreover he might quite possibly have harboured a secret grudge against his father which might gradually have grown in force through never being expressed in any way. It is the quietest and meekest people who are often capable of the most sudden and unexpected violences for the reason that when their control does snap, it goes entirely! The other person I considered was capable of the crime was Hilda Lee. She is the kind of individual who is capable on occasions of taking the law into her own hands—though never through selfish motives. Such people judge and also execute. Many Old Testament characters are of this type. Jael and Judith for example.

"And now having got so far I examined the circumstances of the crime itself. And the first thing that arises—that strikes one in the face as it were—is the extraordinary conditions under which that crime took place! Take your minds back to that room where Simeon Lee lay dead. If you remember, there was both a heavy table and a heavy chair overturned, a lamp, crockery, glasses, etc. But the chair and the table were especially surprising. They were of solid mahogany. It was hard to see how *any* struggle between that frail old man and his opponent could result in so much solid furniture being overturned and knocked down. The whole thing seemed *unreal*. And yet surely no one in their senses would stage such an effect if it had not really occurred—unless possibly Simeon Lee had been killed by a powerful man and the idea was to suggest that the assailant was a woman or somebody of weak physique.

"But such an idea was unconvincing in the extreme since the noise of the furniture falling would give the alarm and the murderer would thereby have very little time to make his exit. It would surely be to *anyone's* advantage to cut Simeon Lee's throat as *quietly* as possible.

"Another extraordinary point was the turning of the key in the lock from the outside. Again there seemed no *reason* for such a proceeding. It could not suggest suicide, since nothing in the death itself accorded with suicide. It was not to suggest escape through the windows—for those windows were so arranged that escape that way was impossible! Moreover, once again, it involved *time*. Time which *must* be precious to the murderer!

"There was one other incomprehensible thing—a piece of rubber cut from Simeon Lee's sponge bag and a small wooden peg shown to me by Superintendent Sugden. These had been picked up from the floor by one of the persons who first entered that room. There again—*these things did not make sense!* They meant exactly nothing at all! Yet they had been there.

"The crime, you perceive, is becoming increasingly incomprehensible. It has no order, no method—*enfin*, it is not *reasonable!*

"And now we come to a further difficulty. Superintendent Sugden was sent for by the dead man—a robbery was reported to him and he was asked to return an hour and a half later. *Why?* If it is because Simeon Lee suspected his granddaughter or some other member of his family, why does he not ask Superintendent Sugden to wait downstairs while he has his interview straightaway with the suspected party? With the Superintendent actually in the house, his lever over the guilty person would have been much stronger.

"So now we arrive at the point where not only the behaviour of the murder is extraordinary but the behaviour of Simeon Lee also is extraordinary!

"And I say to myself: 'This thing is all wrong!' Why? Because we are looking at it *from the wrong angle*. We are looking at it *from the angle that the murderer wants us to look at it* . . . .

"We have three things that do not make sense—the struggle, the turned key, and the snip of rubber. But there *must* be some way of looking at those three things which *would* make sense! And I empty my mind blank and forget the circumstances of the crime and take these things *on their own merits*. I say—a *struggle*—what does *that* suggest? Violence —breakage—noise. . . . The *key? Why* does one turn a key? So that no one shall enter? But the key did not prevent that since the door was broken down almost immediately. To keep someone *in?* To keep someone *out?* A snip of rubber? I say to myself: 'A little piece of a sponge bag is a little piece of a sponge bag and that is all!'

"So you would say there is nothing there—and yet that is not strictly true, for three impressions remain. Noise—seclusion—blankness. . . .

"Do they fit with either of my two possibles? No, they do not. To both Alfred Lee and Hilda Lee a *quiet* murder would

157

have been infinitely preferable, to have wasted time in locking the door from the outside is absurd, and the little piece of sponge bag means yet once more—nothing at all!

"And yet I have very strongly the feeling that there is nothing absurd about this crime—that it is on the contrary very well planned and admirably executed. That it has, in fact, *succeeded!* Therefore that everything that has happened was *meant*. . . .

"And then, going over it again, I got my first glimmer of light. . . .

"Blood—*so much blood*—blood everywhere. . . . An insistence on blood—fresh wet gleaming blood . . . so much blood—*too much blood.* . . .

"And a second thought comes with that. This is a crime of *blood*—it is *in* the blood. *It is Simeon Lee's own blood that rises up against him.* . . ."

Hercule Poirot leaned forward.

"The two most valuable clues in this case were uttered quite unconsciously by two different people. The first was when Mrs. Alfred Lee quoted a line from Macbeth: *Who would have thought the old man to have had so much blood in him?* The other was a phrase uttered by Tressilian, the butler. He described how he felt dazed and things seemed to be happening that had happened before. It was a very simple occurrence that gave him that strange feeling. He heard a ring at the bell and went to open the door to Harry Lee, and the next day he did the same thing to Stephen Farr.

"Now *why* did he have that feeling? Look at Harry Lee and Stephen Farr *and you will see why.* They are astoundingly alike! *That* was why *opening the door to Stephen Farr was just like opening the door to Harry Lee.* It might almost have been the same man standing there. And then, only to-day, Tressilian mentioned that he was always getting muddled between people. No wonder! Stephen Farr has a high-bridged nose, a habit of throwing his head back when he laughs and a trick of stroking his jaw with his forefinger. Look long and earnestly at the portrait of Simeon Lee as a young man and you see *not only Harry Lee, but Stephen Farr.* . . .

Stephen moved. His chair creaked. Poirot said:

"Remember that outburst of Simeon Lee's, his tirade against his family. He said, if you remember, that he would swear he had better sons *born the wrong side of the blanket.* We are back again at the character of Simeon Lee. Simeon Lee who was successful with women and who broke his wife's heart! Simeon Lee who boasted to Pilar that he might have a bodyguard of sons almost the same age! So I came to this conclusion. Simeon Lee had not only his legitimate family in the house *but an unacknowledged and unrecognized son of his own blood.*"

Stephen got to his feet. Poirot said:

"That was your real reason, wasn't it? Not that pretty romance of the girl you met in the train! You were coming here *before you met her.* Coming to see *what kind of a man your father was.* . . ."

Stephen had gone dead white. He said, and his voice was broken and husky:

"Yes, I've always wondered. . . . Mother spoke about him sometimes. It grew into a kind of obsession with me—to see what he was like! I made a bit of money and I came to England. I wasn't going to let him know who I was. I pretended to be old Eb's son. I came here for one reason only—to see the man who was my father. . . ."

Superintendent Sugden said in almost a whisper:

"Lord, I've been blind. . . . I can see it now. Twice I've taken you for Mr. Harry Lee and then seen my mistake, and yet I never guessed!"

He turned on Pilar:

"That was it, wasn't it? It was Stephen Farr you saw standing outside that door? You hesitated, I remember, and looked at him before you said it was a woman. It was Farr you saw, *and you weren't going to give him away.*"

There was a gentle rustle. Hilda Lee's deep voice spoke.

"No," she said. "You're wrong. It was *I* whom Pilar saw. . . ."

Poirot said:

"You, madam? Yes, I thought so. . . ."

Hilda said quietly:

"Self-preservation is a curious thing. I wouldn't believe I could be such a coward. To keep silence just because I was afraid!"

Poirot said:

"You will tell us now?"

She nodded.

"I was with David in the music room. He was playing. He was in a very queer mood. I was a little frightened and I felt my responsibility very keenly because it was I who had insisted on coming here. David began to play the *Dead March* and suddenly I made up my mind. However odd it might seem, I determined that we would both leave at once—that night. I went quietly out of the music room and upstairs. I meant to go to old Mr. Lee and tell him quite plainly why we were going. I went along the corridor to his room and knocked on the door. There was no answer. I knocked again a little louder. There was still no answer. Then I tried the door-handle. The door was locked. And then, as I stood hesitating, *I heard a sound inside the room—*"

She stopped.

"You won't believe me, but it's true! *Someone was in there* —assaulting Mr. Lee. I heard tables and chairs overturned and the crash of glass and china and then I heard that one last horrible cry that died away to nothing and then silence.

"I stood there paralyzed! I couldn't move! And then Mr. Farr came running along and Magdalene and all the others and Mr. Farr and Harry began to batter on the door. It went down and we saw the room *and there was no one in it*—except Mr. Lee lying dead in all that blood."

Her quiet voice rose higher. She cried:

"*There was no one else there—no one,* you understand! And *no one had come out of the room. . . .*"

VII

Superintendent Sugden drew a deep breath. He said:

"Either I'm going mad or everybody else is! What you've said, Mrs. Lee, is just plumb impossible. It's crazy!"

Hilda Lee cried:

"I tell you I heard them fighting in there and I heard the old man scream when his throat was cut—and no one came out and no one was in the room!"

Hercule Poirot said:

"And all this time you have said nothing?"

Hilda Lee's face was white, but she said steadily:

"No, because if I told you what had happened there's only one thing you could say or think—that it was *I* who killed him. . . ."

Poirot shook his head.

"No," he said. "You did not kill him. His son killed him."

Stephen Farr said:

"I swear before God I never touched him!"

"Not you," said Poirot. "He had other sons!"

Harry said:

"What the Hell—"

George stared. David drew his hand across his eyes. Alfred blinked twice.

Poirot said:

"The very first night I was here—the night of the murder I saw a ghost. *It was the ghost of the dead man.* When I first saw Harry Lee I was puzzled. I felt I had seen him before. Then I noted his features carefully and I realized how like his father he was, and I told myself that that was what caused the feeling of familiarity.

"But yesterday a man sitting opposite me threw back his head and laughed—*and I knew who it was Harry Lee reminded me of*. And I traced again, in another face, the features of the dead man.

"No wonder poor old Tressilian felt confused when he had answered the door not to two, but to *three* men who resembled each other closely. No wonder he confessed to getting muddled about people when there were three men in the house who, at a little distance, could pass for each other! The same build, the same gestures (one in particular, a trick of stroking the jaw), the same habit of laughing with the head thrown back, the same distinctive high-bridged nose. Yet the similarity was not always easy to see—*for the third man had a moustache*."

He leaned forward.

"One forgets sometimes that police officers are men, that they have wives and children, mothers"—he paused—"and *fathers*. . . . Remember Simeon Lee's local reputation: A man who broke his wife's heart because of his affairs with women. A son, born on the wrong side of the blanket, may inherit many things. He may inherit his father's features and even his gestures. He may inherit his pride and his patience and his revengeful spirit!"

His voice rose.

"All your life, Sugden, you've resented the wrong your father did you. I think you determined long ago to kill him. You come from the next county, not very far away. Doubtless your mother, with the money Simeon Lee so generously gave her, was able to find a husband who would stand father to her child. Easy for you to enter the Middleshire Police Force and wait your opportunity. A Police Superintendent has a grand opportunity of committing a murder and getting away with it."

Sugden's face had gone white as paper.

He said:

"You're mad! I was outside the house when he was killed."

Poirot shook his head.

"No, you killed him before you left the house the first time. No one saw him alive after you left. It was all so easy for you. Simeon Lee expected you, yes, *but he never sent for you*. It was *you* who rang him up and spoke vaguely about an attempt at robbery. You said you would call upon him just before eight that night and would pretend to be collecting for a Police Charity. Simeon Lee had no suspicions. He did not know you were his son. You came and told him a tale of substituted diamonds. He opened the safe to show you that the real diamonds were safe in his possession. You apologized, came back to the hearth with him, and catching him unawares you cut his throat, holding your hand over his mouth so that he shouldn't cry out. Child's play to a man of your powerful physique.

"Then you set the scene. You took the diamonds. You piled up tables and chairs, lamps and glasses, and twined a very thin rope or cord which you had brought in coiled round your body, in and out between them. You had with you a bottle of some freshly killed animal's blood to which you had added a quantity of sodium citrate. You sprinkled this about freely and added more sodium citrate to the pool of blood which flowed from Simeon Lee's wound. You made up the fire so that the body should keep its warmth. Then you passed the two ends of the cord out through the narrow slit at the bottom of the window and let them hang down the wall. You left the room and turned the key from the outside. That was vital, *since no one must by any chance enter that room.*

"Then you went out and hid the diamonds in the stone sink garden. If, sooner or later, they were discovered there, they would only focus suspicion more strongly where you wanted it—on the members of Simeon Lee's legitimate family. A little before nine-fifteen you returned and going up to the wall underneath the window you pulled on the cord. That dislodged the carefully piled up structure you had arranged. Furniture and china fell with a crash. You pulled on one end of the cord and rewound it round your body under your coat and waistcoat.

"You had one further device!"

He turned to the others.

"Do you remember, all of you, how each of you described the dying scream of Mr. Lee in a different way. You, Mr. Lee, described it as the cry of a man in mortal agony. Your wife and David Lee both used the expression, a soul in Hell. Mrs. David Lee, on the contrary, said it was the cry of someone who had *no* soul. She said it was inhuman like a beast. It was Harry Lee who came nearest to the truth. He said it sounded like killing a pig.

"Do you know those long pink bladders that are sold at fairs with faces painted on them called 'Dying Pigs'? As the air rushes out they give forth an inhuman wail. That, Sugden, was your final touch. You arranged one of those in the room. The mouth of it was stopped up with a peg, but that peg was connected to the cord. When you pulled on the cord the peg came out and the pig began to deflate. On top of the falling furniture came the scream of the Dying Pig."

He turned once more to the others.

"You see now what it was that Pilar Estravados picked up? The Superintendent had hoped to get there in time to retrieve that little wisp of rubber before anyone noticed it. However, he took it from Pilar quickly enough in his most official manner. But remember *he never mentioned that incident to anyone.* In itself that was a singularly suspicious fact. I heard of it from Magdalene Lee and tackled him about it. He was prepared for that eventuality. He had snipped a piece from Mr. Lee's rubber sponge bag and produced that together with a wooden peg. Superficially it answered to the same description—a fragment of rubber and a piece of wood. It meant, as I realized at the time, absolutely nothing! But fool that I was, I did not at once say: 'This means nothing, *so it cannot have been there and Superintendent Sugden is lying.* . . .' No, I foolishly went on trying to find an explanation for it. It was not until Mademoiselle Estravados was playing with a balloon that burst, and she cried out that it must have been a burst balloon she picked up in Simeon Lee's room, that I saw the truth.

"You see now how everything fits in? The improbable struggle *which is necessary to establish a false time of death.* The locked door—so that nobody shall find the body too soon. The dying man's scream. The crime is now logical and reasonable.

"But from the moment that Pilar Estravados cried aloud her discovery about the balloon, she was a source of danger to the murderer. And if that remark had been heard by him from the house (which it well might, for her voice was high and clear and the windows were open) she herself was in considerable danger. Already she had given the murderer one very nasty moment. She had said, speaking of old Mr. Lee: 'He must have been very good-looking when he was young.' And had added, speaking directly to Sugden— '*like you.*' She meant that literally and Sugden knew it. No wonder Sugden went purple in the face and nearly choked. It was so unexpected and so deadly dangerous. He hoped after that to fix the guilt on her but it proved unexpectedly difficult, since as the old man's granddaughter she had obviously no motive for the crime. Later, when he overheard from the house, her clear high voice calling out its remark about the balloon, he decided on desperate measures. He set that booby trap when we were at lunch. Luckily, almost by a miracle, it failed. . . ."

There was dead silence. Then Sugden said quietly:

"When were you sure?"

Poirot said:

"I was not quite sure till I brought home a false moustache and tried it on Simeon Lee's picture. Then—the face that looked at me was yours."

Sugden said:

"God rot his soul in Hell! I'm glad I did it!"

Part VII ------DECEMBER 28TH

I

LYDIA LEE said:

"Pilar, I think you had better stay with us until we can arrange something definite for you."

Pilar said meekly:

"You are very good, Lydia. You are nice. You forgive people quite easily without making a fuss about it."

Lydia said, smiling:

"I still call you Pilar, though I know your name is something else."

"Yes, I am really Conchita Lopez."

"Conchita is a pretty name, too."

"You are really almost too nice, Lydia. But you don't need to be bothered by me. I am going to marry Stephen and we are going to South Africa."

Lydia said, smiling:

"Well, that rounds off things very nicely."

Pilar said timidly:

"Since you have been so kind, do you think, Lydia, that one day we might come back and stay with you—perhaps for Christmas and then we could have the crackers and the burning raisins and those shiny things on a tree and the little snow men?"

"Certainly you shall come and have a real English Christmas."

"That will be lovely. You see, Lydia, I feel that this year it was not a nice Christmas at all."

Lydia caught her breath. She said:

"No, it was not a nice Christmas. . . ."

II

Harry said:

"Well, good-bye, Alfred. Don't suppose you'll be troubled by seeing much of me. I'm off to Hawaii. Always meant to live there if I had a bit of money."

Alfred said:

"Good-bye, Harry. I expect you'll enjoy yourself. I hope so."

Harry said rather awkwardly:

"Sorry I riled you so much, old man. Rotten sense of humour I've got. Can't help trying to pull a fellow's leg."

Alfred said with an effort:

"Suppose I must learn to take a joke."

Harry said with relief:

"Well—so long."

III

Alfred said:

"David, Lydia and I have decided to sell up this place. I thought perhaps you'd like some of the things that were our mothers'—her chair and that footstool. You were always her favourite."

David hesitated a minute. Then he said slowly:

"Thanks for the thought, Alfred, but do you know, I don't think I will. I don't want anything out of the house. I feel it's better to break with the past altogether."

Alfred said:

"Yes, I understand. Maybe you're right."

IV

George said:

"Well, good-bye, Alfred. Good-bye, Lydia. What a terrible time we have been through. There's the trial coming on, too. I suppose the whole disgraceful story is bound to come out? Sugden being—er—my father's son. One couldn't arrange for it to be put to him, I suppose, that it would be better if he pleaded advanced Communist views and dislike of my father as a Capitalist—something of that kind?"

Lydia said:

"My dear George, do you really imagine that a man like Sugden would tell lies to soothe *our* feelings?"

George said:

"Er—perhaps not. No, I see your point. All the same, the man must be mad. Well, good-bye again."

Magdalene said:

"*Good*-bye. Next year do let's all go to the Riviera or somewhere for Christmas and be really gay."

George said:

"Depends on the Exchange."

Magdalene said:

"Darling, don't be *mean*."

V

Alfred came out on the terrace. Lydia was bending over a stone sink. She straightened up when she saw him.

He said with a sigh:

"Well—they've all gone."

Lydia said:

"Yes—what a blessing."

"It is rather."

Alfred said:

"You'll be glad to leave here."

She asked:

"Will you mind very much?"

"No, I shall be glad. There are so many interesting things we can do together. To live on here would be to be constantly reminded of that nightmare. Thank God, it's all over!"

Lydia said:

"Thanks to Hercule Poirot."

"Yes. You know, it was really amazing the way everything fell into place when he explained it."

"I know. Like when you finish a jig-saw puzzle and all the queer shaped bits you swear won't fit in anywhere find their places quite naturally."

Alfred said:

"There's one little thing that never fitted in. What *was* George doing *after* he telephoned. Why wouldn't he say?"

Lydia laughed.

"Don't you know? I knew all the time. He was having a look through your papers on your desk."

"Oh! no, Lydia, no one would do a thing like that!"

"George would. He's frightfully curious about money matters. But of course he couldn't say so. He'd have had to be actually in the dock before he'd have owned up to that."

Alfred said:

"Are you making another garden?"

166

"Yes."

"What is it this time?"

"I think," said Lydia, "it's an attempt at the Garden of Eden. A new version—without any serpent—and Adam and Eve are definitely middle-aged."

Alfred said gently:

"Dear Lydia, how patient you have been all these years. You have been very good to me."

Lydia said:

"But you see, Alfred, I love you. . . ."

VI

Colonel Johnson said:

"God bless my soul!" Then he said: "Upon my word!" and finally once more, "God bless my soul!"

He leaned back in his chair and stared at Poirot. He said plaintively:

"My best man! What's the police coming to?"

Poirot said:

"Even policemen have private lives! Sugden was a very proud man."

Colonel Johnson shook his head.

To relieve his feelings he kicked at the logs in the grate. He said jerkily:

"I always say—nothing like a wood fire."

Hercule Poirot, conscious of the draughts round his neck, thought to himself:

"*Pour moi*, every time the central heating. . . ."

EUROPE, YOUR WAY!

These three helpful, matter-of-fact guides give you everything you need to know **before** you go! Whether it's your first trip or your fifty-first, these three guides tell you how to get the most out of Europe, your way!

THE REAL EUROPE AND THE MEDITERRANEAN (B7724/$2.25)
From what to see to where to shop, from where to sleep to what to eat, this is the MOST COMPREHENSIVE, UP-TO-DATE, all-inclusive guide to Europe and the Mediterranean, 1973!

THE REAL ECONOMY GUIDE TO EUROPE (Y7721/$1.95)
From how to stay in London for less than $5.00 a night to how to live in an Italian villa absolutely FREE! Here are hundreds of money-saving secrets to seeing Europe on **your** budget!

THE REAL RESTAURANT GUIDE TO EUROPE (Y7723/$1.95)
From the most elegant Parisian restaurants to enchanting inexpensive hideaways—here is the handiest, most complete guide to more than 200 great restaurants.

Buy them at your local bookstore or use this handy coupon for ordering:

SMALL
COMFORTS

❖

Also by Tom Bodett

AS FAR AS YOU CAN GO WITHOUT A PASSPORT
The View from the End of the Road

SMALL
COMFORTS

More Comments and Comic Pieces

TOM BODETT

Addison-Wesley Publishing Company, Inc.

*Reading, Massachusetts Menlo Park, California New York
Don Mills, Ontario Wokingham, England Amsterdam Bonn Sydney
Singapore Tokyo Madrid Bogotá Santiago San Juan*

Grateful acknowledgment is made to Harper & Row, Publishers, Inc., for permission to reprint two passages from the foreword to *Essays of E. B. White,* copyright © 1977 by E. B. White.

Many of the designations used by manufacturers and sellers to distinguish their products are claimed as trademarks. Where those designations appear in this book and Addison-Wesley was aware of a trademark claim, the designations have been printed in initial capital letters (e.g., Brylcreem).

Library of Congress Cataloging-in-Publication Data

Bodett, Tom.
  Small comforts.

  I. Title.
AC8.B563   1987   081   87-12804
ISBN 0-201-13417-9

Cover illustration by Leslie Evans, from a sketch of the
  Bodett family hearth by Debi Bodett
Text design by Copenhaver Cumpston
Set in 11-point Galliard by Compset, Inc., Beverly, MA

ABCDEFGHIJ-DO-8987
First printing, July 1987

To Debi

My first editor, my best friend,
my lover, the mother of our child,
and, as luck would have it,
my wife

ACKNOWLEDGMENTS

I continue to thank Eileen Hughes and Joe Gallagher at KBBI, public radio for Homer, Alaska, for putting my stuff on the air in the first place. The folks at the Alaska Public Radio Network and National Public Radio's "All Things Considered" also deserve special credit for helping perpetuate much of the work on the following pages.

I'd like to thank Kathleen McCoy, my editor at the *Anchorage Daily News,* for letting me do whatever I wanted. Thanks also to Christopher Carduff and George Gibson, my editors at Addison-Wesley, for *not* letting me do whatever I wanted.

My wife, Debi, once again earns my undying love and gratitude for living with me through this project, and special thanks to my two-year-old son, Courtney, who, with time and a little luck, won't remember anything about it.

And last but never least, thanks to all my dear friends and cohorts around this little town who give me my ideas, keep me honest, and continue to let me believe I know what I'm talking about.

T.B., Homer, Alaska

CONTENTS

ix

INTRODUCTION

The essayist is a self-liberated man, sustained by the childish belief that everything he thinks about, everything that happens to him, is of general interest. He is a fellow who thoroughly enjoys his work, just as people who take bird walks enjoy theirs. Each new excursion of the essayist, each new "attempt," differs from the last and takes him into new country. This delights him. Only a person who is congenitally self-centered has the effrontery and the stamina to write essays.

I think some people find the essay the last resort of the egoist, a much too self-conscious and self-serving form for their taste; they feel that it is presumptuous of a writer to assume that his little excursions or his small observations will interest the reader. There is some justice in their complaint. I have always been aware that I am by nature self-absorbed and egoistical; to write of myself to the extent I have done indicates a too great attention to my own life, not enough to the lives of others.

It is always a great joy for me to stumble across insights and admissions by other writers, like those above by E. B. White, which spark instant identification. It's especially comforting to find certain familiar emotions and experiences expressed across time and social barriers with perfect authenticity. We've all had our moments when reading, at the theater, or listening to a gifted storyteller when we've stopped to say to ourselves, "Yeah, it's just like that." Such moments serve, for a time, to take a bit of the loneliness out of being human. This sharing of experience seems to me the only real purpose to produce or consume art of any kind.

Not having been trained as either an artist or a writer, I am all too aware of the audacity involved in presenting this collection of my thoughts on the world at large. I am not well educated or even particularly experienced in the wider scope of things. I've yet to commit an idea to paper that I didn't read later and think, "Who really cares?" I'm always pleasantly surprised when anyone does. It helps keep me going despite my lack of credentials.

By far the most striking characteristic of the life I write about is its bone-chilling normalcy. I'm a generic American. Reading a list of national averages is like leafing through my résumé. I'm of medium height and build, was raised in the Midwest, and assume more and more middle-of-the-road views as I approach midlife. I have one of those faces that reminds people of a brother or old roommate. I take some satisfaction from all this, but am also painfully aware of being ordinary. We ordinary people lead ordinary lives full of ordinary things while we peer through windshields and TV screens at interesting surroundings. We're in the middle of the curve and haul around our 2.6 children in our

1.8 cars doing the best we can on average incomes. It's not a bad life. It is simply life as we know it.

We seem to spend a lot of time hungering after the details of the lives of the rich and famous, the up and coming, and just about everyone else we view as exceptional people. Most of us know more about Elizabeth Taylor than we do about our next-door neighbors. We celebrate our eccentrics at the expense of ourselves. This has always rubbed me a little in the wrong direction. I'm of the mind that there are no exceptional people. There are only normal people who sometimes do exceptional things.

Most of the exceptional things we do never hit the papers. Every once in a while we'll read of the local hero who drags the neighbors' kids from a burning building, or the poverty-stricken old widow who turns in the bag of cash she found on the street. These certainly are exceptional deeds and worthy of attention, but few of us will have the opportunity to imitate them.

The less newsworthy but every bit as exceptional things we do, we do in private. Quitting cigarettes is one of the toughest roads a person can ever travel. Letting your baby girl out the door on her first date is probably one of the most painful and selfless acts on record. Saving a failing marriage with patience and love deserves no less than the highest honors. There should be a Hall of Fame for these sorts of things.

There is also a flip side to all of this, one we're all too familiar with. Even though we mostly want to, and frequently intend to, we don't always do the right thing. The good intentions of ordinary people are constantly at odds with the world around them. We have our selfish desires, and our unreasonable fears. We make mistakes and are forced to look back on lives fraught with stupid remarks, cruel gestures, and sad regrets. We live with this guilt, and that is the price of being human. This, too, is life as we know it.

My only expertise in these matters is being a card-carrying member of this life as we know it. I don't expect that you out there will learn much from what you read in here. In fact, you'll probably come away reminded of an old friend or roommate. But that's all I really ask out of this deal. That and if at least once during the reading you stop to think, "Yeah, it's just like that."

I'm always comforted when a writer does that for me. I've tried to pay a little of it back with this collection, and hope you'll find some of that same sort of comfort on your way through.

TAKING
POTLUCK

❖

Mood Piece

I had kind of a mood on lately. It lasted nearly a week before I snapped out of it. I was absolutely miserable and so was everyone around me. Bad moods are strange things. They seem to compound themselves and look for dark events to add to the gloom. Mysteriously, they can even cause them to happen. Some religions call this karma, others a loss of grace, but whatever it is, it stinks.

The bad mood scenario goes typically like this.

You wake up late, bound out of bed, and jam your foot under the closet door. This dislodges the big toenail from its setting, which hurts worse than if you'd taken the whole leg off at the knee. Recovering through rapid breathing, you throw on some clothes and fire up the coffeepot. While urging the brew cycle to its conclusion you sift through a stack of yesterday's mail and find a piece you'd overlooked, an official envelope from the City. It's one of those "Hold firmly here, grasp and snap" deals that never work. You put your fingers at the indicated points and give it a stiff pull, neatly tearing the entire packet in two. It turns out to have been your personal property tax statement, and the rip went precisely through the amount due, rendering it unreadable.

Your temples start to throb, so you pour a fresh cup of coffee and turn on the radio to try and settle down. A little music usually soothes, but instead of music you're met with a barrage of incomprehensible jazz being forced through a saxophone at a pressure of ninety pounds per square inch. It's about as soothing as listening to an aircraft engine seize up in a small room, so you snap off the radio with a finality that sends the volume knob rolling under the stove. You figure it's time to stop screwing around and go to work.

There is just the tiniest ball of rust bouncing around in your fuel filter. It's remained there harmlessly for months, biding its time for a morning such as this. Halfway to town, which is exactly as far as you can get from both home and a qualified mechanic at the same time, this little ball of rust decides to head north and lodge itself inside the opening of the main fuel jet. This shuts the engine off quicker than if you'd used the key, leaving you with absolutely no clue as to what went wrong.

After forty-five minutes of dinking around with a stripped-out crescent wrench, you throw up your hands and decide to thumb a ride to town for help. As you slam the hood shut on your shirttail, you think you hear the unmistakable snicker of a rust ball buried deep within the bowels of a disabled wonder of modern engineering.

Your gray mood has turned a deep charcoal, and walking into an auto repair shop is never a good way to cheer up. There's always some grim mechanic who's the hottest thing since the magnetic screwdriver and thinks you're the worst thing that could ever happen to an internal combustion engine, rust notwithstanding. No matter what the problem turns out to be, it's always something you did wrong, and he'll inconvenience his entire day to get you back on the road out of the goodness of his heart and a nominal fee plus tax.

As far as bad moods go, this one is getting downright dangerous, so you head back home to start over. Pulling into the driveway you accidentally flatten the sleeping cat that you never liked anyway, and feel just awful about it. When your wife sees the mood you're in, she thinks you did it on purpose, and you wonder why you didn't do it a long time ago if you're going to get blamed for it anyway. It starts to look like this string of bad luck is just never going to quit.

I saw a logger I once worked with get so mad about something he tore his clothes off, sat down in them, and cried. He looked so silly that everybody laughed, which made him so much madder he started throwing dirt and rocks at us. We laughed even harder at that and were doubled over with cramps and tears by the time he caught on and started laughing himself. We laughed ourselves out, he put his clothes back on, and we went back to work. After that, anytime a guy got really upset about something, he'd pretend to be tearing his clothes off, and everybody'd laugh. That would be the end of it.

I lost my ability to blow it off somewhere along the line, and have to make myself remember those logging days when ill-fortune settles in for one of its marathon visits. They say all humor is rooted in tragedy and it's our capacity to laugh that sustains us. Humans are the only critters who have this ability, and it's a good thing we do. It wouldn't look very good for the tourists if we all had to rip our clothes to pieces every time the truck broke down.

Mechanical Inclinations

Machinery and I have an understanding: we hate each other. I just have a hard time when it comes to fixing things. This, along with my inability to spit very far, is the most disappointing aspect of my life as a man. I do have some mechanical inclination. It's an attribute of my gender. There's a certain amount of knowledge about things mechanical that is passed on genetically from man to boy. Even my little son, when presented with a toy tractor, knew that blowing air through his flapping lips is what a tractor sounds like. He'd never seen a tractor until that day, but innately knew as much about them as I do. When tractors don't sound like flapping lips, they're broken. Of course, knowing when something is broken and knowing how to fix it are two separate fruits altogether.

It is something of a tribal custom among the males of our species to hold forth on what we know about twirly things with gears and springs. If you want to entertain the menfolk on a slow Sunday, throw a broken lawnmower at their feet.

"Must be the spark. She ain't gettin' no spark."

"No, it ain't got fuel. Look, the plug's bone-dry."

"Gotta be a stuck valve, you can feel there's no compression."

"No spark, no fuel, no compression. That 'bout covers it. What do ya figure, Bubba?"

"This is one broke lawnmower."

If the afternoon progresses according to custom, the guys will completely disassemble the thing, find nothing wrong, put it back together, and it'll run like a top. They won't have the foggiest notion what they did to fix it, but they'll all take the credit.

"Musta been that hunk of dirt grounding out the magneto."

"No, was a piece of grit in the carburetor fell out when Bubba dropped it."

"All the bangin' around unstuck the valve. That's all it was, I tell ya."

I'm always the guy that runs for more beer.

My first inclination when faced with a piece of broken equipment is to pick it up and shake it. It works well on toasters, waffle irons, and sometimes lawnmowers, but it's a stupid thing to try with a pickup truck.

With a broken car or truck it's best to open up the hood, remove the air cleaner, shrug your shoulders in bewilderment, and try turning 'er over again. She'll start more often than not, and this supports my theory that most of the time machines break down they're only looking for attention.

I had the privilege and the horror some years ago of owning a small crane. I say "small" because there are bigger cranes, but I still had to climb a ladder to get into the thing. The reason I bring this up is that among all the devices on this earth craving attention, heavy equipment is by far the most starved for it. The general rule with large, dangerous machines is that you work *on* them just about as much as you work *with* them.

For this reason I owe what little I've learned about mechanics to that crane. I used it to drive pilings in Petersburg. My pile driver at the time consisted of a 1,200-pound weight I would pick twenty feet in the air then drop on a piling. As scientific as this sounds, you'd be surprised how hard it was on the equipment. What it finally came down to was this: I'd drive a piling, bolt everything back together, drive a piling, and so on.

It's when things actually did break that I ran into trouble. It so happens this crane was built in 1945 by a company that's been bankrupt since before the Korean War. I'd rather look for a hot date in a convent than try to find a replacement part for that thing. This led to what we'll call "creative mechanics," more commonly known as jury-rigging, and my only formal goodwrench schooling to date.

I'd won the Rube Goldberg award for improvisational tinkering three years in a row by the time I handed that sorry mess of cable and gears over to some other poor soul. My driving lesson to the new owner went something like this:

"That wire hanging out of the dash is your air brake 'cause the pedal linkage broke. It works good, but don't pull too hard. It's only a wire, ya know. If you want second gear, put it in third and then wind 'er out. Double-clutch and go back to second for fourth. She don't have third gear anymore, but don't worry, I got all the pieces out of the transmission. On the swing knob here, left is right and right is left, and don't try to boom down until you shove this block of wood up under the hoist. I guess that's about it. If the engine catches fire, just jump outa there and hang back for a while. It usually goes out all on its own."

I've never really wondered what became of that crane. I only worry what's become of me because of it. I'm pretty careful about most of the things I do. My woodwork fits, my pants fit, and I habitually look up words I don't know how to spell. It's only machines that bring out the hack in me. If the glove compartment latch quits working, my solution is to wedge a folded-up matchbook in the crack. I spray WD-40 like it was bug spray at funny noises wherever they occur. If that doesn't fix them, I get used to the noise.

My tool box contains two hammers (one large, one small), a pliers, and three different gauges of baling wire. This is the combat gear I employ against all my broken gadgets. Come dangling muffler, flapping fender, or dead snow blower, there's nothing that a couple hammers and a little wire won't fix.

It's not something I'm terribly proud of. I win my little battles but ultimately lose the war. My mechanically inclined friends shake sorrowful heads at my contraptions, then shake them at me. I try not to take it personally, but this deficiency of mine does get on my nerves. Sometimes it makes me mad enough to spit — but not very darned far, I'm afraid.

Wood: You Can Count on It

I had an opportunity to become intimate with my wood-pile this morning thanks to our recent storm. If it's true what they say about comets being dirty snowballs of ice and rocks, then I had sort of a homemade Halley's laying in my front yard, with wood where the rocks should have been. First the wind blew the covers off the pile, then it injection-molded snow into every little nook and cranny of it. As woodpiles are well known for their nooks and crannies, I was faced with the engaging task of prying up each piece of wood, knocking the snow off it, and putting it down some-place else. I threw myself at this brainless endeavor with high abandon and let my mind lapse into a little woodpile reminiscence.

The pieces that were pretty small I knew must have been split early on the day I had the hydraulic splitter up here. As that day wore on and one cord led to another and another, the pieces of split wood grew decidedly bigger. By the fourth cord I was considering buying a wood-fired blast furnace and just leaving the logs in the round.

I remembered wondering the day I started the pile what happens if you lay your wood right on the ground instead of putting it up on pallets. As I beat it from the frozen earth with big hunks of turf stuck all over it, I decided it wasn't an experiment worth repeating.

I worked my way through the pile piece by piece. I admired some nicely shaped dry specimens, and snarled at others with knots protruding from them and wispy hairs of grain, evidence that a struggle was had on the wood splitter.

"Ah, wood," I thought, obviously drunk with the tedium. "What a wonderful way to stay warm." It's an *alive* heat. You can hear wood heat, but not like you hear an old furnace or the creak of an electric baseboard. It's an unpredictable noise. A pop in the night will sometimes wake you; you realize it's only the wood stove sounding off and curl back into the blankets, assured of your warmth. Heating with wood is finding a red-hot bed of coals in the morning and coming in from the porch shivering with a log in each hand. It's letting 'er roar for a while just to take the chill off while you contemplate the day ahead. It's also looking out the window at the neatly stacked pile of wood, knowing you've got a whole bunch of warm days out there all bought and paid for.

Nobody's going to send you a gas bill if you use it. There's no calculating kilowatt-hours every time you turn up the thermostat, no staying intentionally cool because you're too cheap to toast. It's one big pile of comfort without price or definition. We gauge our wood reserves in *cords,* a loose quantity at best, and think in terms of seasons instead of monthly billings. It's all very romantic and countryesque, and I'm behind it all the way. At least I was until I moved the woodpile.

I have this really stupid habit. I count things. I don't know how it started. It could be a genetic defect. I just find myself counting things when faced with any dull, repetitive task. I count cars when I drive on highways. I count plates and cups when I do dishes. Sometimes I count steps when I walk. It drives me crazy mostly, but I keep on counting and look at it as a way of pacing myself for lack of a better excuse.

So as I moved my woodpile, the least interesting thing I've done all year, there I was: " . . . three hundred and fifty-eight . . . three hundred and fifty-nine . . ." In the end I was faced with the reality of having one thousand one hundred and eighty-seven pieces of wood left. You wouldn't think that would bother a person. It sounds like a lot. But I also happen to count pieces of wood as I haul them up to the wood box every morning. Nineteen. Nineteen pieces of wood, more or less, every day.

What this means is I have exactly sixty-two and a half days of wood going for me. That means about two in the afternoon on February 7 I'm going to have a problem.

So much for the big pile of comfort without price or definition.

Every day, now, I'll count off nineteen pieces and brood as I take all that hard work, bring it up to the house, and set it on fire. I get a little crabby thinking about it. Now when I walk in the house with wood, I'll chuck it in the stove with ill-concealed spite: "Here ya go, have this one! Want another? Here! Here, take it all!" I'll slam down the lid. "Must think this stuff grows on trees!"

This afternoon I took a walk around the place and discovered the same storm that forced me to take inventory of my wood supply had also blown over about the nicest spruce on the lot. On any other day I'd have been a little heartbroken over this. I'd have kicked at the stump, shrugged my shoulders, and gone to tell my wife, "We lost the big one," like the dog just died.

But this didn't happen. I started to drool as I walked up and down its length: ". . . twenty-four . . . twenty-five . . . twenty-six. . ." My spirits were picking up for sure: ". . . forty-two . . . forty-three. . ."

The way I have it figured, I can get enough wood out of that spruce to take us through March if we burn the branches too, and by God, that tree next to it is looking a little sick itself. Probably fall down all on its own and leave a big mess. So let's see what we got here: ". . . sixty-eight . . . sixty nine. . ."

Old Friend Guilt

There's something funny going on around here. I'm ready for winter. No kidding. All the firewood I'll need for this year and part of next is put away. The house is buttoned up and the snow tires are on the truck. I'm not bragging about it, I'm worried about it. This has never happened to me before, and I'm not so sure I can handle it. My winter income is secured, and there's little more I can do but chew on the lip of my coffee mug and watch that gloomy southwesterly pad through the hills like a big gray cat. Oh good God, *poetry,* I'm even writing poetry. What's going on here? That "fog comes on little cat feet" routine is for pampered poets of other places, not for me. I'm supposed to be out in a forty-knot driven rain trying to get a chainsaw started over a log that's going to be too wet to burn until June.

I should be outside inspecting window caulk, or up on the roof with frozen fingers gluing down wind-damaged shingles. But it's a new house. All that stuff's done. There's not another place for a bead of caulk anywhere on it. The skirting is tight, the pipes are insulated, even the truck's got enough antifreeze in it to make a polar expedition. It's driving me crazy.

My good ol' "I'm too busy to talk now" stride has fallen away to a "Wanna play some cribbage?" shuffle, and it's only October. That's not supposed to happen until February when we all run out of money and can't afford to move around a lot.

All my friends are too preoccupied with their own preparations to be of any use right now. I think maybe I should go help them with their wood and general battening down of the hatches, but then they'd be in the same boat I'm in. I'd just hate to do that to them. Hanging around, reading novels, writing letters, throwing darts. Gag me with a *TV Guide*. Give me thirty feet of heat tape and a damp crawl space any ol' day of the week.

I've never been a big one for self-motivation. It takes a certain amount of guilt in the air to get me to plant both feet next to the bed each morning. Last winter I was fortunate and had a half-finished addition stuck on the front of the house to worry about. Every day I'd get up intending to do something about it, but then it'd rain, or snow, or blow, or I'd run out of nails and have to give it up. Boy, those were the days. Each morning waking up to stare at the ceiling and say to myself, "Get going, you lazy slob. Your wife's pregnant, the house is cold, and nothing's going to get done if you don't do it." So I went and did it. Now I wake up to stare at the ceiling and stay that way.

Like many Alaskans, I think I'm mistaking contentment for boredom. Maybe it's because of the antagonistic relationship we keep with our weather. It's like an ongoing friendly argument that we miss when it's over. You say, "I think I'll patch the roof today," and the freezing rain says, "Oh no you won't." You think, "I'll just sit and read my paper this morning," then the wind comes through the front door and asks, "Why don't you fix this rotten threshold instead?" We come to rely on that after a while. We get trained not to count on anything. It's a spooky, lonesome feeling to say to yourself, "I'm going to watch Donahue, write for a couple hours, then take a nap," and have the elements agree, "Good idea." What do you do in a case like that?

I think I know what I'm going to do. I've got about a gallon of paint here that will get half of one side of the garage covered. If I start now, I'll run out of paint by dark, and by the time I get around to buying some more, it will be too cold to finish the job.

Every day I'll be able to look out the living room window at the half-painted wall. My wife will say, "I can't believe you started that and didn't finish." I'll shrug my shoulders in a familiar way, and smile at the return of my dear old sweet friend, Guilt.

Ditch
Diving

T he graceful winter sports of skiing, skating, and dog-
sledding get a lot of attention around Alaska, but
there's another winter activity that nobody seems to appreciate for the art that it actually is — ditch diving. We all
become practitioners of this art at one time or another, but
none of us seems to hold proper appreciation of what we're
doing, perhaps because its aesthetics have never been fully
defined for us. Allow me.

To dive you need a road, a ditch, some snow on the
ground, and any licensed highway vehicle or its equivalent.
Nothing else is required, but a good freezing rain will speed
up the process.

The art of the dive is in the elegance with which you
perform three distinct actions. The first one, of course, is
that you and your car *leave the roadway.* Not so fast there,
hotshot — remember, this is an art. The manner and theme
of your dive are weighed heavily in this maneuver.

For instance, the "I wasn't looking and drove into the ditch" dive will gain you nothing with the critics. The "He wasn't looking and drove me into the ditch" dive is slightly better, but lacks character. The "It sucked me into the ditch" dive shows real imagination, and the "We spun around three times, hit the ditch going backwards, and thought we were all going to die" dive will earn you credits for sheer drama. The "I drove in the ditch rather than slide past the school bus" dive might win the humanitarian award, but only if you can explain to the police why you were going that fast in the first place.

Okay, so now you've left the road. Your second challenge is to *place the vehicle*. Any dumbbell can put a car in a ditch, but it takes an artist to put one there with panache. The overall appeal of your installation is gauged by how much the traffic slows down to gawk at it.

Nosed-in within ten degrees of level won't even turn a head. Burrowed into a snowbank with one door buried shut is better, and if you're actually caught in the act of climbing out a window, you're really getting somewhere. Letting your car sit overnight so the snowplows can bury it is a good way of gaining points with the morning commuter traffic. Any wheel left visibly off the ground is good for fifty points each, with a hundred-point bonus for all four. Caution: Only master-class ditch divers should endeavor to achieve this bonus positioning.

All right, there you are, nicely featured alongside your favorite roadway. The third part of your mission is to *ask for assistance*. Simply walking to a phone and calling a tow truck will prove you a piker and not an artist at all. Hit the showers, friend. The grace and creativity you display getting back on the road must at least equal those you employed while leaving it.

Let's say you were forced into the ditch and are neatly enshrined with one rear wheel off the ground and the hood buried in the berm. Wait until any truck bigger than your bathroom happens along and start walking in that direction with a pronounced limp. Look angry but not defeated, as if you'd walk all night to find the guy who ran you off the road. Look the driver in the eye like it would have been him if he'd been there sooner. This is a risky move, but it's been proven effective. If the truck has personalized license plates and lights mounted all over it, you're in good shape. Those guys love to show how hard their trucks can pull on things.

I prefer, however, to rely on the softer side of human nature. Addle-brained people hold a special place in our hearts, and I like to play on these protective instincts. If my car is buried beyond hope, I'll display my tongue in the corner of my mouth and begin frantically digging at the snow drift with my hands until someone stops to talk me out of it. If my hands get cold and still nobody's stopped, I'll crawl head-first into the hole I've dug and flail my legs around like I was thrown clear of the wreck. This works every time and has won me many a ditch-diving exhibition over the years.

I certainly hope I've enlarged your appreciation of this undervalued creative medium. I warn against exercising this art to excess, but when the opportunity arises, remember: Hit 'er hard, sink 'er deep, get 'er out, and please, dive carefully.

Sixty-Four-Dollar
Questions

Deep thinkers throughout the centuries have dedicated themselves to solving the great mysteries of life. Why are we here? What is death? How many angels can dance on the head of a pin? Who's in charge of all this? They've come out long on opinions, short on answers, and only served to muck things up worse than they already were. So I'd like to propose that these guys back off from the eternal questions for a while and put their heads together on some of the puzzles we face every day. Having solutions to even a few of these could go a long way toward quelling a lot of the fear and anxiety that make up our stay on this strange planet.

Take those little colored stickers that turn up on some of my mail, those fluorescent green and orange labels with the single letters on them, *C, D,* or *F.* Who puts them there? What do they mean? It makes me a little nervous to receive a letter and find that I'm an *F.* I don't like being classified in a system I know nothing about. Is this a contest I haven't heard of? Am I supposed to save them? If I get enough to spell out the name of the state I live in, do I win something? Put your mind to that, Plato. I want to know what's up here.

As long as we're on the subject of the postal service, who decides what goes on stamps, and why do we have seashells on ours? Have we run out of important people to commemorate and now have to use these mollusks to keep from issuing blank ones? The Canadians get Queen Elizabeth, and we get the frilled dogwinkle. What does this mean, and is it something I'm supposed to worry about?

After they've explained away those, I hope they'll have a go at this one: How do grocery shopping carts escape, and why do they end up where they do? More important, why aren't we surprised to see them there? When we find one in the middle of a field or overturned on an exit ramp, we never say, "What's that shopping cart doing way out here?" We just think "Oh, there's another one," and go on about our business. I swear if there'd been a shopping cart waiting at the foot of the ladder when Neil Armstrong climbed out of the *Eagle,* nobody would have paid any attention to it. We're so used to seeing them in strange places they've become invisible to us. What causes this? Could it have military applications?

And as long as we're in the mood, let's pose a few more questions. Why did they stop making the '64 Chevy pickup? There was nothing wrong with it. Where did all this oil come from? I thought we were supposed to be out. If they've stopped creating "Star Trek" episodes, how come I keep seeing new ones after watching it for fifteen years? Same goes for "M*A*S*H" and Ernest Hemingway novels. Can we look forward to any more Steinbeck in the near future?

Forget about the chicken and the egg, how far is up, and where does the time go. Just tell me where the lids to all my trash cans went, and can I find my missing socks there too?

Come on, all you poets and philosophers, preachers and professors. Earn your keep. These are simple riddles with undoubtedly simple solutions. People need to know these things. Take care of us on this and we'll let you get back to the eternal mysteries. And while you're at it, tell me this: Just what *is* the sixty-four-dollar question, and why does it cost so much?

Bad Signs

As one of the most modern and well-educated citizenries in the world, you'd think we could take pretty good care of ourselves, that we could drive cars, shop in stores, and heat up a can of beans without a lot of supervision. That doesn't seem to be the case. Every place you look we are warned about things that we shouldn't need to be warned about, and reminded of things that should go without saying. Either we've all gone soft in the head, or we were among some of God's dimmer creations in the first place.

It begins as soon as you get in the car. Bells and whistles go off, lights flash, and the simple matter of starting the engine takes on the feel of an emergency dive in an attack submarine. You sit back dumbly as a four-wheeled hunk of chrome and plastic orders you around. FASTEN YOUR SEAT BELTS! CLOSE THE DOOR! CHECK MY OIL! AND FOR GOD'S SAKE PUT SOME GAS IN ME!

After that bawling out, you drive to the store and are greeted by yet another command, PULL. But it's useless. We always push, then pull. Except on the way out, when we pull, then push. We don't need these signs on doors because we don't read them.

Once inside, you wander through the aisles and come upon a little stairway. STEP UP, it says. Oh, so *that's* how you work those things. You'd think a person who can shower, shave, dress himself, and drive to town wouldn't need to be told how to operate stairs. Maybe STEP UP is a coy sales tactic urging you to buy something beyond your means and boost your social position.

Back home while putting up the groceries, you really get a talking-to. STORE IN WARM DRY PLACE. DO NOT FREEZE. DO NOT BOIL. OPEN CAN, PLACE PAN OVER OPEN FLAME OR HEAT SOURCE, SEASON TO TASTE. An old favorite of mine, DO NOT LITTER, has lately been replaced. I have a bottle here I'm asked to DISPOSE OF THOUGHTFULLY. It's a kindly-worded phrase, but it doesn't make sense. I can meet the requirements of DISPOSE OF THOUGHTFULLY by heaving it in the river, then pausing to reflect on what a rotten thing that was to do. They should have stuck to DO NOT LITTER. It's less confusing.

Some commands are downright insulting. I was in a taxicab once that had a sign behind the driver's seat which read NO SPITTING, as if I looked like the kind of person that would spit in a taxi. People that would spit in a taxi probably couldn't read the sign, and would ignore it if they could. That sign should go.

NO SMOKING signs on self-serve gas pumps are the ultimate insult. Although there may be some individuals who don't understand the principles of octane, anyone who'd light up in a cloud of gas fumes would probably deserve everything he got. Mother Nature's cute little way of weeding out the bad apples.

Dumb signs like this are there only to protect the businesses that put them up. It's a sad commentary, but sooner or later some twit will blow himself up at a gas pump. A lawsuit will follow, with the family of the man begging the judge for sixty million dollars in pain-and-suffering compensation.

"Your Honor, he was a kind but simple man. He should have been warned that gasoline explodes." Case closed.

It occurs to me that if we all took more responsibility for ourselves, we could replace all these mindless instructions with reminders of real importance. DON'T WALK ON ICE WITH YOUR HANDS IN YOUR POCKETS. WRITE YOUR MOTHER. DON'T GO OUTSIDE WITH WET HAIR. Those are the sorts of things we do forget about.

But even those things, like all the others, could be covered with a single stern command. It's something my third-grade teacher used to use on me a lot.

"Mr. Bodett!" she'd snap.

"Yes, ma'am?"

"SHUT UP AND PAY ATTENTION!"

"Yes, ma'aaaam!"

Command
Performance

U p until a few days ago I was one of those people who didn't know a megabyte from an overbite, but that's all history now. I've joined the technocrats, that global group of future-minded individuals who embrace advanced technology and use it to their utmost advantage. I bought a personal computer.

Now, a personal computer is unlike all those other kinds in that, like a checking account or deodorant stick, you have it all to yourself. Other people can't just bop in and use it even if the spirit did move them to. This one is all mine, so keep your hands off while I run you through the details.

Like most new technology, computers can be a little scary to the uninitiated. The cavemen who first discovered fire no doubt circled around it cautiously, poking at it with sticks while daring each other to touch it. New computer owners do much the same with their machines. Once our cavemen finally did break down and touch the fire, they quickly got an idea of its basic properties. Technological advancement can be a very real and moving experience. Fortunately, most of the name-brand computers won't singe the hair off your knuckles. In fact, we don't even have hair on our knuckles anymore. You can see we've come a long way since fire was discovered.

Unlike fire, computers are what they call "user-friendly." Now, what I think that means is that those little boxes of microchips *like* you and want to hang around with you. Like dogs do. Just like our dogs, they are happiest when they're doing things for us. They want us to give them commands. So let's try a command here.

>SIT<

Let's see what it does with that.

<BAD COMMAND — TRY AGAIN>

You know, it's right. "Sit" is a bad command. It has domineering overtones and doesn't really suggest the friendship we're trying to develop here. Let's try this, then:

>PLEASE TAKE A SEAT<

That's better.

<BAD COMMAND — TRY AGAIN>

Oops. There it goes again. Obviously it either doesn't feel like sitting, knows it already is sitting, or considers it too elementary a command to deal with. Maybe it's looking for something a little more complex. Probably wants to impress me and win my undying friendship. Let me find a more advanced function. Here's a key that says SEARCH on it. Let's see what that does.

```
>SEARCH<
<SEARCH FOR WHAT?>
```

Now we're getting somewhere.

```
>NORTHWEST PASSAGE<
```

That should keep it busy. Oh good, it's making little noises. Must be working on it.

```
<NOT FOUND>
```

Not found? It sure couldn't have looked very hard. That's all right. I know where it is anyway, and it's a stupid route to take. Let's have it look around for something a little more practical and closer to home. I'll have it search for my lug-nut wrench. I haven't been able to find it all summer. Here goes nothing:

```
>LUG WRENCH<
<NOT FOUND>
```

There it is again. What good is this thing? How about this:

```
>SEARCH FOR YOUR PLASTIC BUTT WITH
BOTH HANDS<
```

<NOT FOUND>

I knew it. Either I've got a real lemon of a computer here, or an exceptionally lazy one. How about this MOVE key:

<MOVE WHAT?>
>MOVE YOU!<

That oughta burn its brain box.

<MOVE WHERE?>

Oh, how easily it fell into my trap. Let it flop this around its disk drive for a while:

>SEATTLE! HOUSTON! BACK TO SILICON VALLEY! I DON'T CARE JUST GO!<
<BAD COMMAND — TRY AGAIN>

A mutiny, is it? I might not be able to move this over-rated high-tech stick-in-the-mud to do a darn thing for me, but I'll tell you one function I know how to use. It's this big red switch on the side of it that says OFF.

<   >

There, that worked.

So, as you can tell, these computers are nothing to be afraid of. Now you know as much about them as I do. If you have any questions, just give me a call. I'd be happy to walk you through this last procedure.

See and
Be Seen

E yeglasses have come a long way since that regrettable day twenty years ago when I got my first pair. It didn't seem that so many people wore glasses then. What a horrible injustice to serve on a kid. There were two basic styles to choose from, boys' and girls'. A boy got plain black frames, big or small, thick or thin, depending on how big a deal he wanted to make of it. A girl got plain, small, thick black frames with little wings on them, to which optional paste jewels might be added for style. As a boy, wearing glasses put you into that class of kids who were good at science but couldn't do very many chin-ups. Since the nose doesn't develop until well into puberty, elastic straps had to be worn to keep the frames on your face. This gave your friends something to fiddle with in the lunch line, and ultimately led to some customized repair work with a variety of tape and wires. Things got a little better later on.

John Lennon ushered in the era of wire-rimmed

frames, and many a young four-eye was able to recover any hipness he may have lost a few years earlier. But of course it was all for show, and private suffering endured behind those fashionable frames. Little did the sharp-sighted abstainers realize those wires constantly sawed away at the fleshy spot where the ears attach to the head and left huge pink pits on the sides of the nose where all the weight of the glasses bore down on two tiny spots. The nose pads left the tender young schnoz permanently furrowed, lending a whole new meaning to the term "groovy."

It's been blamed on everything from color television to self-abuse, but over the years more and more people began wearing glasses. The eyewear industry rose to the challenge of pleasing them all. Optometrists' walls are now lined with choices, and what's a modern shopping center without an eyeglass boutique? What once were purely functional gizmos to prop corrective lenses in front of our eyes are now nearly a fashion accessory. You can get the most delicate little wafers of glass set in gold designs as fine as any jewelry. There are sweeping multicolored plastic frames holding lenses the size of windshields. You can make statements with smiley faces, hearts, or butterflies etched into the extra glass, or have them tinted in a variety of ways to become a person of mystery.

The age of the eyesore eyeglass is dead. All the old black frames have been either made into safety goggles for machine shops or given to auto industry executives to wear in car commercials to make them look like on-the-job sorts of guys.

There are even those more plain of face among us who wear noncorrective lenses and use glasses only to enhance their features. Vanity aside, that is the craziest thing I ever heard of. I can't for the life of me think of a single reason to wear glasses other than to see things.

Although I'm sure they're not as bad as false teeth, crutches, or hearing aids, I think glasses fall into the same category of inconvenience. In the winter they fog up when you walk indoors. In the summer little bugs stroll around on them to appear as large dogs on the optic nerve, while sweat and gravity team up to slide them off the tip of your nose. Small children love to yank them from your face, taking tiny pieces of ear flesh along with them. When they get misplaced they are bound to turn up exactly where you decide to sit down and think about where you left them.

This is not the only time they become a pain in that general vicinity. After several months of wiping dust and fingerprints on shirtsleeves, restroom paper towels, and seat cushions, the subtlest little lines become etched in the lenses. These serve to provide you with a mind-bending light show every time you go to a movie or watch TV in the dark.

Contact lenses might offer a release from all of this, but not for me. I tried them once on a whim, and the act of installing them endeared itself to me as much as sticking poker chips under my eyelids would. The enemy could learn anything they wanted from me by making me wear contacts.

I guess I'll learn how to live with the foggy view, scarred nose bridge, and sore ears, but I won't have to like it. My secret fantasy (way before a Pulitzer, Cybill Shepherd, or Cybill Shepherd's sister if she has one) is to wake up one morning and see things clearly. You'd think that after twenty years of wearing glasses I'd be used to them and wouldn't think about it so much. Well, I just can't help it. Every place I look, there they are.

Taking
Potluck

O f all the wonderful distractions that summer has to
offer, none is quite as wonderful as the potluck. I
know it isn't strictly a summer event, but a potluck takes on
much broader dimensions in the warmer months. It's held
outdoors, usually accompanied by horseshoes or volleyball.
The children run circles around each other, and the fish is
fresh.

Fish is a staple of the Alaskan potluck, and I've never
been to one that didn't have at least three species of it on
hand in one form or another. Back in the Midwest where I
first sat down to one, you could ruin a good potluck by
bringing fish to it. People are suspicious of fish back there,
and I'm sure the expression "smells fishy to me" originated
at a community feed somewhere in northern Indiana. Fried
chicken is the heart of the Great Plains foodfest, but outside
the entrée, the ingredients of a good potluck are pretty
universal.

Start with a large folding table on an uneven lawn and invite a bunch of people over. No matter what happens someone always brings too much fish, so there's no need to worry about the main course. Then wanders in a pot of beans and weenies and a relish tray with rolled-up cold cuts splayed around a radish-and-celery arrangement. Someone always brings marshmallows so the kids have something to get stuck in their hair, and a bachelor or two will show up with a six-pack and a bag of Doritos.

No fewer than five potato salads will appear in rapid succession. You have to like potato salad if you're going to like potlucks. In fact, I think the "pot" in "potluck" is an abbreviation for "potato salad", and the luck refers to those few fortunate individuals who can get through the meal and not wear some of it home.

Everything is served up on paper plates with the constitution of flour tortillas and eaten with little plastic forks that couldn't pry a bone from a cooked cod let alone penetrate your neighbor's lasagna.

Potlucks are hardest on those who do the cooking. They hover around the food table to see what's going over the best. "Now, no one has touched the three-bean salad. What's the matter with you people?" The builder of the salad turns the color of the red-cabbage clam dip and slinks toward the beer cooler. The hero of any potluck is the one who brings the deviled eggs. They are usually devoured before the other folks can even get the tin foil off their casseroles.

After one or two courses your plate has become something of a trough folded in the palm of one hand. An amazing blend of flavors is then inevitable. The juice from the fruit-and-nut salad seeps in under your uncle's world-famous beef-and-bean burritos, and the hot sauce from that makes an interesting topping for the fresh apple crumb cake you discovered while going back for one more bratwurst.

In a while most folks will have had their fill and will wander off sleepily in small groups to toss horseshoes or slap mosquitoes. There's always one or two guys who linger to graze at the table, but their picking has no real spirit behind it. A survey of the ravaged spread will reveal a half-dozen potato salads with one scoop out of each and a large basket of wholly untouched fruit.

I got an idea from this. You see, in this season of multiple potlucks it's not unusual to be invited to more than one on a single day. You can't make a different dish for each of them, so I recommend you make a potato salad and take the paprika shaker along with you. When you leave the first party, just smooth over your salad with a spoon and put some fresh paprika on top. No one will know the difference, and you'll be able to gracefully enter potluck after potluck.

To be prepared for the improbable — like if someone actually eats all your salad — keep a basket of plastic fruit in the car at all times. This will get you into the next party and it's perfectly safe, as no one ever eats the fruit. I glue them all together in case those lingering grazers get nosy and try to get them out of the basket. They usually give up after a few dispirited tugs and wander off to test the potato salads.

Of course, I don't recommend everyone follow my advice on this. *Somebody's* gotta bring the fish.

Off the Top
of My Head

There's something about a haircut that gets on the wrong side of me. I don't know quite what to make of it, but like most things, it can probably be traced back to an impressionable youth. Even in those innocent days when short hair was not only acceptable but stridently enforced, nothing was more humiliating than to show up somewhere sporting a new haircut. Girls would giggle and boys would mess it up with their hands while a blush worked its way into a freshly raised hairline. Of course, not all of this was without reason.

I used to get haircuts from my dad. When my brothers and I started to get a little shaggy — shaggy being defined as having hair that actually laid down on our heads — he'd line us up in the kitchen on a Saturday night. He had a haircutting kit made up of electric shears, a soft brush, and a scissors. I still don't know what the brush and scissors were for. He went at us with those shears in much the same way a rancher goes at sheep, except sheep don't put up near the fuss that we did. By the time he was done with us, we'd all be in tears and rubbing heads that felt like the passive side of a Velcro fastener. Well-worn Little League caps that were perfect fits just the day before now slid around uselessly, even though we'd fight within an inch of our lives to keep them on our scalps to hide the damage.

As we got older Dad gave in to our protests and let us have our way with a new hairstyle called the Pineapple. Now, the Pineapple was a haircut ridiculous enough to rival anything I've seen on the head of an eighties punker. It consisted mostly of no hair anywhere except right in front. A little knot was left on the forehead for no reason I can think of now other than to demonstrate what color your hair would be if given a chance to show itself. Of course we all looked like highway accident casualties, and my dad finally gave up on the shears altogether. Probably a kind word from a close friend like, "God-darn, Pete, those kids are ugly," helped to persuade him.

When left to grow our hair out to lengths we could actually pinch between our fingers, the first thing we did was smear it with grease. Brylcreem, Vitalis, Butchwax. We could've stayed afloat in heavy seas standing on our heads the whole time. Those were the days. Peel the pillow case off our hair in the morning and head right down to the bathroom mirror to try and make it look just like the guys on "Route 66."

Then the Beatles came along and screwed up everything. I think I was fashionable once for about twenty minutes when I was twelve, then it was off to the barber. They used to call them barbers. Now they're hair stylists, hair sculptors, and tonsorial artists. Back then they used to cut your hair and talk about the weather. Now they cut your hair and talk about hair. I think I liked it better the old way. Except it wasn't any fun to be a kid in a barber shop. Barber shops were where men went to look at magazines and tell rancid jokes. They had to stop telling their jokes when I showed up, and all the really interesting magazines disappeared under their smocks. There were no redeeming qualities to a trip to the barber. Just when I thought I was a dead ringer for Paul McCartney, I'd be reduced to looking like a fourth-grader at a parochial school. Which wasn't too far from the truth, seeing as I was in the sixth grade at the time.

Still later it became fashionable to look like Jesus Christ with a bad attitude, and by then I was old enough to pursue the look, attitude and all. I let my hair grow in all its gnarled-up glory for many years. I resisted going to barbers to stay with the trend of the day, but now I go to hair stylists to resist the trend of the day. All the hairstyles I would have sold my sister for twenty years ago are once again the fashion, and I'd buy her back to keep away from them. The only magazines I find at the hair places are full of androgynous men with eye shadow, who get paid to look like Liza Minelli. I won't get paid if I look like Liza Minelli, and I refuse to do it.

I'm a big disappointment to my hair stylist, and it bothers me a little. I sound just like the old guys who used to hide their magazines from me at the barber shops. "Just take a little off the back and sides, and don't mess with my part." They always fluff me up on the sly, but it's nothing that a hat won't fix.

Like I say, I never got along very well with haircuts, but I try not to dwell on it. I remember something else those old guys used to say. They'd see my little heart breaking as my hard-earned Beatle locks hit the floor and tell me, "You know what the difference is between a good haircut and a bad haircut?"

"What's that?" I'd moan.

"Two weeks, boy. Just two weeks."

Shake
<u>What</u> Thing?

O f all the peculiar things we find ourselves doing with each other in this world, dancing is the one that I've always had the most trouble with. It's not that I think it's immoral, nonproductive, or uncivilized. It's just that it's nigh on to impossible for me to do.

Oh, like most people I've done my little share of shuffling over the years. Back in my rutting days I'd appear on schedule every Saturday night at one hot spot or another to prey on available females. I'd compete with the other young bucks screaming their invitations over impossibly loud music. This most unnatural of rituals always made me feel ridiculous with no little help from my own natural awkwardness.

If the band played a tune I felt I could plausibly move to, I'd muster the courage to approach someone for a dance. Typically, as soon as I opened my mouth to shout my proposition, the band would abruptly stop. The room would become suddenly quiet except for my "WANNA DANCE?" hollered a half-second too late. My foiled prospect would giggle into her Tequila Sunrise as I returned to the perimeter to do my wall-paneling impersonation.

I'd hoped marriage would save me from all this humiliation, but I was sorely mistaken. Just because I don't go to the hot spots alone anymore doesn't get me off the hook. From time to time I still find myself in the unpleasant process of trying to dance.

I say "trying" because to this day I've yet to feel like I ever actually succeeded. I like music as much as the next person, but it doesn't seem to get very far past my eardrums. It just won't penetrate down into my bones and ligaments where it needs to be if you're going to dance with any kind of credibility. A really hot band on a really good night might find me making little squares out of cocktail straws while tapping one or occasionally both feet under the table. I'm having a perfectly fine time of it, but my partner is not impressed. She'll be led out to the dance floor by one or another handsome stranger until I can stand no more and plunge headlong into the fray.

This is where the real trouble starts. The only dance step I've perfected to date is jumping up and down and wagging my arms around. I lean over and ask my partner, "What do I do?," and she smiles, "Do what comes natural." I tell her, naturally, I'd like to go back to the table and finish my beer, and she says, "Don't be so self-conscious. Just do what everyone else is doing." So I look it over. I see someone swivel his hips; I swivel my hips. Some gal puts her arms up in the air; I put my arms up. If there's some shoulder jive goin' on, I try that. The overall effect is that I'm hung from the ceiling by my collarbone and being shook around like one of those cardboard Halloween skeletons. It's exhausting and embarrassing, and this bothers me.

I understand that dance is supposed to be celebration, a communal tribute to our love of life, each other, and our kinship with ancient rhythm. It's supposed to be expressive, revealing, even suggestive of inner desires. And there I am floppin' around like a cat on a clothesline. I don't like what this has to say about me and my link to ancestral harmony. The only thing ancient about my sense of rhythm is that it does get old after a while.

I boogie when I oughta woogie, rock where I oughta roll, and mambo all over a good tango. I don't know, maybe I just haven't found my niche yet. I've heard of this stuff called "square" dancing. I'll have to look into it. I hope it's something you do with cocktail straws.

Pet Peeves

I t's been said that people who keep pets live longer. I hope
that means they live longer than their pets. At least longer than *my* pets. It's a terrible thing to say and I'll probably
end up in that circle of doggie hell where all the legless yap
dogs go because of it, but I can't help it. I want to wring
the necks of both my animals, and I don't know what to do
about it.

I've had pets for as long as I can remember, but each
of them found some way to die quietly before there were
any serious rifts in our relationship. A string of hamsters,
stunned birds, and chapped frogs worked in and out of a
joyful childhood. Then of course there were the more durable breeds of the canine persuasion.

My folks kept wonderful dogs, the kind of exceptional
animals that become part of the family. They could be spoken to in plain English, would fret dutifully when a kid was
ill, and put up with all the degradations a houseful of sadis-

tic children could engineer. They were never a problem and are still dearly missed.

Now I have a dog and cat of my very own, and I can't stand either one of them. I'm a little torn up about it. The cat, especially, has earned a certain amount of tenure around here — I've had him for ten years. He came into my life as a Christmas gift. (Oh. How nice. You shouldn't have.) I initially named him Shark Bait because that's what I had him figured as, but we soon became fast friends. I was a lonely young bachelor living in an unfamiliar Alaskan town, and having something soft and warm around the place was a real asset. His companionship was welcome, and he was a pretty good cat as far as cats go.

He'd do his business outside, was an accomplished hunter, and could swat the snot out of most dogs that messed with him. I guess what we had was a masculine bond. He tangled with a mink one time and got his face ripped off. I had to send him in an airplane to another town to have it fixed, and it cost me a hundred and fifty dollars. That says a lot about the way I used to feel about him.

After I married, he took to my wife more than me and turned into, well, a cat. Cream and egg yolks. He got bitchy and lazy, and I lost interest. I started thinking of him as a piece of furniture, and I guess I have for a long time now. At least until he started to lose control of himself. I've never had a piece of furniture make a mess like that before.

I'm sure it's just old age, but I can't forgive him for it. I mean he's not suffering. He sleeps in his own chair, goes outside when he's good and ready, comes in to eat dinner, then craps on the new rug. It wouldn't be so bad if he'd show some remorse, but instead he lies back in his chair with that "You should have known I was ready to go out" look on his face, the smug little face I once went to great effort to have re-secured to his skullcap. I just don't know what to do about it. I have a pest in my house. If he were a rat or a cockroach I would know what to do, but he's not. He's a pet. You can't exterminate pets, you have to murder them. I'm not a murderer.

The situation might not bother me so much if it wasn't compounded by the dog. I'm using the term "dog" pretty loosely. A wheelbarrow full of common garden vegetables would offer just as much companionship on a walk.

He's three years old and a beautiful specimen of a black Lab. All except for one thing. He was born with a head of solid bone. You could say he's a good-natured animal, but that's what they always say about stupid dogs. We have to keep him tied up all the time because he'll follow anything that moves. He's never been in much trouble with the neighbor's chickens or anything, but that's because the chickens can outsmart him. The trouble is that he's big and scary-looking, and nobody wants a big, scary-looking dog running around without a brain in its head. So he stays tied up, and we give him huge amounts of food for the pleasure of watching him lie in the sun and bark at clouds.

It's driving me crazy. When a terminal patient stops producing brain waves, he's declared legally dead. My dog's EEG is flatter than Kansas, but he's healthy as a horse and happy as a clam. We had him fixed a couple years back to see if he'd calm down and pay attention. All it did was calm him down. Now we have a cabbage on a chain in the front yard that eats its weight in Purina every month. Again, I don't know what to do about it. I harbored some hope for a while that he might redeem himself by eating the cat, but gave that up when I noticed the cat kicks him out of the doghouse whenever he feels like it.

I know I'm responsible for these animals. In fact, I can't stand people who mistreat or abandon their pets just because they've become an inconvenience. It's not their fault they drive me nuts, and it's not their fault they're mine. I can't do them in just because I screwed up. They might have been adopted by someone who likes stupid, lazy pets if I hadn't come along.

I could take them to the pound, but that'd just be letting someone else do the dirty work for me. I suppose if I tried hard enough I could find a benevolent soul to take them off my hands, but I can't bring myself to do it. It'd be like asking someone to take a beating for me. Even if they agreed, I'd feel lousy about it later.

What it boils down to is that I can only hope to outlive them. I look forward to maybe a handful of pet-free years before I take the big sleep myself, the sleep not even the bark of a one-hundred-pound dog could jerk me out of. I've buttered my bread and now I'll just have to eat it.

There's a lesson here someplace but I'm not sure what it is. I'll have to sort it out. I've heard of cats that live for twenty years or more, and as healthy as that dog looks, I'm going to have plenty of time to think about it.

Wait
Divisions

I read somewhere that we spend a full third of our lives waiting. I've also read where we spend a third of our lives sleeping, a third working, and a third at our leisure. Now either somebody's lying, or we're spending all our leisure time waiting to go to work or sleep. That can't be true or league softball and Winnebagos never would have caught on.

So where are we doing all of this waiting and what does it mean to an impatient society like ours? Could this unseen waiting be the source of all our problems? A shrinking economy? The staggering deficit? Declining mental health and moral apathy? Probably not, but let's take a look at some of the more classic "waits" anyway.

The very purest form of waiting is what we'll call the *Watched-Pot Wait*. This type of wait is without a doubt the most annoying of all. Take filling up the kitchen sink. There is absolutely nothing you can do while this is going on but keep both eyes glued to the sink until it's full. If you try to cram in some extracurricular activity, you're asking for it. So you stand there, your hands on the faucets, and wait. A temporary suspension of duties. During these waits it's common for your eyes to lapse out of focus. The brain disengages from the body and wanders around the imagination in search of distraction. It finds none and springs back into action only when the water runs over the edge of the counter and onto your socks.

The phrase "A watched pot never boils" comes of this experience. Pots don't care whether they are watched or not; the problem is that nobody has ever seen a pot actually come to a boil. While they are waiting, their brains turn off.

Other forms of the Watched-Pot Wait would include waiting for your drier to quit at the laundromat, waiting for your toast to pop out of the toaster, or waiting for a decent idea to come to mind at a typewriter. What they all have in common is that they render the waiter helpless and mindless.

A cousin to the Watched-Pot Wait is the *Forced Wait*. Not for the weak of will, this one requires a bit of discipline. The classic Forced Wait is starting your car in the winter and letting it slowly idle up to temperature before engaging the clutch. This is every bit as uninteresting as watching a pot, but with one big difference. You have a choice. There is nothing keeping you from racing to work behind a stone-cold engine save the thought of the early demise of several thousand dollars' worth of equipment you haven't paid for yet. Thoughts like that will help you get through a Forced Wait.

Properly preparing packaged soup mixes also requires a Forced Wait. Directions are very specific on these mixes. "Bring three cups water to boil, add mix, simmer three minutes, remove from heat, let stand five minutes." I have my doubts that anyone has ever actually done this. I'm fairly spineless when it comes to instant soups and usually just boil the bejeezus out of them until the noodles sink. Some things just aren't worth a Forced Wait.

All in all Forced Waiting requires a lot of a thing called *patience,* which is a virtue. Once we get into virtues I'm out of my element, and can't expound on the virtues of virtue, or even lie about them. So let's move on to some of the more far-reaching varieties of waiting.

The *Payday Wait* is certainly a leader in the long-term anticipation field. The problem with waits that last more than a few minutes is that you have to actually do other things in the meantime. Like go to work. By far the most aggravating feature of the Payday Wait is that even though you must keep functioning in the interludes, there is less and less you are able to do as the big day draws near. For some of us the last few days are best spent alone in a dark room for fear we'll accidentally do something that costs money. With the Payday Wait comes a certain amount of hope that we'll make it, and faith that everything will be all right once we do.

With the introduction of faith and hope, I've ushered in the most potent wait class of all, the *Lucky-Break Wait,* or the *Wait for One's Ship to Come In.* This type of wait is unusual in that it is for the most part voluntary. Unlike the Forced Wait, which is also voluntary, waiting for your lucky break does not necessarily mean that it will happen.

Turning one's life into a waiting game of these proportions requires gobs of the aforementioned faith and hope, and is strictly for the optimists among us. For these people life is the thing that happens to them while they're waiting for something to happen to them. On the surface it seems as ridiculous as following the directions on soup mixes, but the Lucky-Break Wait performs an outstanding service to those who take it upon themselves to do it. As long as one doesn't come to rely on it, wishing for a few good things to happen never hurt anybody.

In the end it is obvious that we certainly do spend a good deal of our time waiting. The person who said we do it a third of the time may have been going easy on us. It makes a guy wonder how anything at all gets done around here. But things do get done, people grow old, and time boils on whether you watch it or not.

The next time you're standing at the sink waiting for it to fill while cooking soup mix that you'll have to eat until payday or until a large bag of cash falls out of the sky, don't despair. You're probably just as busy as the next guy.

Cleanliness
vs. Godliness

The idea that cleanliness is next to godliness is a little presumptuous, don't you think? They've been telling us that all our lives, but I'm certain it's just a ploy to get us to pick up after ourselves. Who do they think invented dirt in the first place? How many of God's little critters would you let in on your living room rug?

I realize that hygiene is important to good health, but it's unnatural to be *too* clean. People who primp, pick, buff, and shine are spending way too much time thinking about themselves and their stuff and not enough about other things. The slobs of this world who blunder along whichever way it goes are in the true state of grace. Just compare the houses of the two.

The Cleanly has the kind you look at, the Godly's got the kind you live in. I was at one of those you look at the other day. I didn't have to take off my shoes at the door; I had to leave them at the end of the driveway. The glare in the kitchen was blinding, but I caught enough of a glimpse of the counters to see they were better organized than most surgical facilities. We didn't go in the living room, but my hostess let me stand in the doorway and admire things.

I remember touring the Robert E. Lee mansion as a kid and feeling like this. Little red velvet ropes cross the doorways to the rooms. You can look in, but not touch, and it compels you to speak in reverent tones. So I oohed and aahed reverently as I peered in at the rug and furniture.

The rug looked nice. It was freshly tended with a shag rake, she told me. I can't tell you much about the sofa or chairs. They were covered with that clear plastic sheeting. You know the kind: It has those little nodules on it to make sure nobody sits on it for very long. She had a big white cat on one chair and even it looked groomed, like it had a permanent, or had been dipped in solution to keep its hair from falling out all over the place.

The magazines on the coffee table were laid out in a fan shape next to a cut-glass ashtray. It glimmered with a rainbow warning to anyone who even thought of putting a cigarette near it. I couldn't see much else, as they had the curtains closed. "Fades the rug," she said. "Very nice," I told her, starting to feel like bird crap on an El Dorado.

We had coffee in the dining room. I could see the bottom of my cup clear through the coffee. A close inspection proved there was no little oil slick floating on the surface of the stuff. I was just getting ready to ask my hostess how she accomplished that when the handle of the slippery little teacup dodged from between my fingers. It broke on the iridescent tile, splashing a rather dark stain on her otherwise well-arranged white cat. It screamed into the living room in an impressive holy terror and climbed the curtains in a fabric-shredding frenzy. I never discovered the secret of her coffee, as she was soon showing me to the door and begging me to come again when I couldn't stay so long.

Sulking away like I'd just wet my pants in church, I decided to seek consolation at another friend's house on the way home. Now, this friend's got one of the other kind of houses: the kind you live in. And he's really very good at it. At his place you leave your shoes on to save your socks. "Wanna beer?" he called on my way in. "Sure," I said. "So grab one, and crack one for me too as long as you're up."

Here was a house my hostess would as soon set on fire as walk into, but I was feeling warm and welcome. I shoved some clothes, magazines, and what I think was *his* cat off an old easy chair and propped my feet up on the coffee table. We had a pitching contest with some old pistachio nut shells he had in a bowl. We flung them as close to the ashcan next to the wood stove as we could until they were all gone. He won.

He remained a perfect host by not telling me to keep my hands off things as I rummaged through a pile of old *National Geographics*. And he apologized graciously when I sat back on his sofa and found a handsaw I'd lent him a few months back. We made coffee, good coffee, strong enough that I couldn't see through the jar he offered it in, coffee with that tasty little Colombian grease slick on top. We played a couple of spirited games of living-room broom hockey with a piece of leftover breakfast toast, and I left for home feeling well visited and refreshed.

Yes, this cleanliness and godliness business just doesn't hold any water. I really don't think I'll have to wipe my feet before going through the Pearly Gates, or that Saint Peter will pick lint off my robes as he checks me out against the Big Book. I think instead he'll hand me a bag of pistachio nuts and direct me to a well-worn easy chair. At least I hope so. If I have to sit on plastic seat covers or endure the whine of a celestial Dustbuster, that eternal life they talk about is going to be way too long for me.

Strangers
in My Chairs

Furniture just seems to happen to us. There aren't too
many people who get the opportunity to go out and buy
a houseful of perfectly coordinated furnishings in one
swoop. Royalty with summer homes or rock stars on sab-
batical might enjoy the privilege at one time or another, but
we mere mortals must go about things differently.

Our ideas about furniture, of course, started at home.
For the most part, all the chairs and tables there were too
big for any practical use other than making forts out of on
rainy days. We were all made to sit straight at the table with
our little legs dangling and our chins at plate level. There
wasn't a piece of furniture in my folks' house that endeared
itself to me in any way. Dad's chair was always fought over
among us kids when Dad wasn't in it, but this was due more
to its importance than its comfort. It was like sitting in the
throne while the king was out of the castle.

Those of us who went on to college got little in the
way of furniture education. The standard dorm fare — bunk

bed, desk chair, and lounge seat that sat like a straitjacket —
were enough to quell any notions of posture we might have
brought from home with us. Blaze orange burlap on blond
maple was the general theme, and an apple crate, a couple
of bricks, and a two-by-six were all the personal touches
required to finish off a room. The few stabs we made at
decorating were a festoon of fish netting and an Easy Rider
poster over the bed.

After college came our first real digs, furnished apartments, the term "furnished" being applied loosely. A hide-
a-bed made up of right angles and foam rubber sat beside a
three-legged overstuffed chair that was meant to have four.
Paperback westerns and sociology textbooks made up the
difference. The chairs in these apartments were hideous
misrepresentations of a place to sit. I remember my room-
mates and me complaining for weeks about a foul smell
around one such apartment before one of us discovered the
chair had been on fire. The smoldering mess of stuffing and
lint had spontaneously combusted, no doubt.

Our beds were stained mattresses on bare floors, and
the bricks and boards saved from college rounded out our
suites. Kitchen tables were of the tubular persuasion with
bright red simulated marble tops ringed with cigarette
burns. One advantage to this type of furniture arrangement
was that the place looked little better after we'd clean it up,
so there was no logical reason to even bother.

It seems that only after marriage do people take any
serious notice of furniture. After all, you can't set a shiny
toaster oven, matching cutlery, or a new bedspread on any
old thing. The early years are the hardest because you're
pretty much stuck with what you can afford. This usually
amounts to a coffee table of pressboard and photographic

wood-grain paper. This mode of furnishing is a by-product of the mobile-home industry. If you set a perfectly healthy plant on such a piece it would immediately turn to plastic.

Other appointments to the parlor setting might be two blow-molded end tables and a genuine imitation Old English vinyl recliner. Geologists centuries from now will excavate these artifacts and dub this the Plasticene Era. Some couples never snap out of this mode, and they may be the smart ones. Love comes and love goes, but plastic is forever.

Many among us, if left in one place long enough, will eventually settle on a motif. *Modern* might bring with it deep shags, Laz-E-Boys with fabric on them strikingly similar to that which we left at our dorms, and an airbrushed bullfight hanging on the wall for a touch of class. *Traditional* is the same as Modern, only family portraits are on the wall in place of the bullfight. *Ultramodern* gets us back to metal tubes with a lot of glass and hanging things. Wall decoration might be jagged tin sculptures accented by a stripe running from the front door to the fern.

And still others will swing the opposite way and choose *Antique,* the used look. Acquiring this type of furnishing involves going to a lot of auctions run by people who gave up the carnival circuit to sell furniture. "Dis here buffet was made when King Louie da Fourteen still had all his hair, har har." We proceed to outbid each other for a rickety old dresser with stuck drawers and a blurry mirror.

I have a lot of this Antique stuff in my house, and I like it. Coming home is like going to Grandma's house everyday. A sense of permanence stays in the room with you. I stare at our hutch and wonder sometimes what treasures were stored there by people dead and gone who will never see our treasures so nicely displayed in it. I look at our hodgepodge of aging chairs and think of the strangers who may have taken a load off their feet in them. It's not necessarily beautiful furniture. Some of it is pretty plain. It's just interesting because it has longevity. Built-in memories.

Like a lot of us, I have a favorite chair. It's not very comfortable to sit in, and it's pretty beat-up to boot. It's a teetery old bowback I got some years ago. What's special about it is some carving on the bow. In crude letters gouged out by an unknown forebear reads, "I Love you M.K." I've never stopped wondering about that. Who carved it? Who's M.K.? Did they ever get together? Have children, grandchildren?

When I sit down to breakfast it creaks and croaks its "good morning" to the world. I'm reminded of that simple phrase behind my back and wonder about it all over again.

Now *that's* a piece of furniture.

Symptoms of Fatherhood

I used to swear I'd never be one of those guys who talk about their kids. (Of course, before that I swore I'd never be one of those guys who even *have* kids. So you can see how I am about swearing.) I've found, however, that something happens to a man when his own child is born, something rich and inexplicable and, so the experts tell me, chemical.

There has always been lots of talk about the hormonal imbalances and emotional trauma a mother experiences before and immediately after the birth of a child, but lately attention is turning to the effects of childbirth on the male glandular system. It's really quite astounding once you examine it. For instance, it's been proven that the male brain secretes an enzyme into the optic nerve shortly after the onset of fatherhood that allows a man for the first time in his life to see things in store windows like colored blocks and "Li'l Slugger" baseball jammies. It also enables him to tell a cloth diaper from a dipstick rag and a stuffed teddy from a mounted duck.

Another brain fluid, probably a mild sedative, is let loose in the hearing canal. Upon reaching the inner ear, this solution makes a man's head spin when he receives a smile or coo from his own loin fruit. More important, it also serves as a flap-damper against children screeching in public places or infants whining on airplanes. Sounds that once would make a man's fillings ache or compel him to tear an airline magazine in two now only leave him to stare dumbly at their source with an appreciative smile.

An ambivalent chemical, this same stuff that serves to dampen the sounds of everyone else's children can also actually attune a man's ear to those of his own. His hearing can become so sensitive that he'll bolt upright from a dead sleep should his child so much as gurgle in its crib downstairs through two closed doors.

Another biochemical, probably from a gastric gland, enters into a father's abdominal cavity in the postnatal period. This natural body fluid, technically known as *Papa-Bismol*, is, of course, a stomach relaxer. Foul and foreign substances, such as those to be found in a child's diapers, no longer trigger his gag reflex. It may even allow for closer inspections of them in times of illness or moments of simple paternal curiosity. Other infant malfunctions such as oral ejections (spit-up) or nasal discharges (snot) can be greeted with equal reserve under the influence of Papa-Bismol.

Quite frankly, some effects of childbirth on the male of our species are of totally unknown origin. One of these affects his sense of time and direction. Time appears to move at an accelerated rate as the child matures, and all roads lead home. Neighborhood watering holes lose their appeal, and dads are uncannily on time for supper for the first time in their married careers. It's entirely possible that this disorientation in space and time is responsible for the quirks which appear in a new father's speaking habits.

Normally articulate and well-spoken young men can be found leaning into cradles and bassinets repeating a string of guttural incantations. The ability to interpret language is simultaneously impaired. It's not unusual to have a new father claiming to have heard the word "daddy" from a child who's only utterance to date was that of passing stomach gas.

This stage quickly passes and is replaced by another speech anomaly, the *Couplet Stutter.* This causes the male parent to double words which previously served him well solo. Some examples: "no-no," "yum-yum," "bye-bye." In cases where a word cannot be doubled up and still make sense, the Couplet Stutter gives way to the *Aiee Syndrome.* For instance, the sentence "Junior sees the dog-dog" is meaningless, but "Junior sees the doggie" makes perfect sense to everyone but the kid, who can't understand why Dad has to *Aiee* every noun in the dictionary when he points it out.

These very speech afflictions may be responsible for other, yet-to-be-explained new-father nuances. Men who could not have given a hoot how *Babar Gets to Candyland* in prenatal years can be found engrossed in that particular narrative long after the child has given up for the evening. The story of the Three Little Pigs can lead to mild depression in fathers who don't get a chance to huff and puff the doors down before the kid nods off.

Renewed interest in ogres, trolls, fairies, and pirates generally prefigures the disintegration of formal education.

This just might be what is behind such irrational social behavior as pulling out wallet-sized baby photos in airport lounges or suggesting a petting zoo as an interesting night on the town.

Overall, as you can see from this definitive study, the male is much more likely than previously thought to be adversely affected by biological changes due to childbirth. Of course none of these symptoms of fatherhood has arisen in yours truly, and the only reason I'm aware of them at all is that I'm a voracious reader and get all my information from books.

In fact I'm in the middle of one particularly riveting volume at the moment. It seems there were these three men, and this tub. In an interesting blend of careers there was a butcher, a baker, a . . . hold on a minute. I think I hear something downstairs in the baby's room.

Dadiholics
Anonymous

I lived with the illusion for eighteen months that I could become a parent without getting all "parenty" about it. It's only recently I've been able to admit that I can't. My name is Tom, and I am a Dadiholic. That's right. I've found I can't control my parental behavior, and it's seeping into other areas of my life. I'm starting to get worried. It's not that I feel I've become a danger to myself or society. It's scary, that's all, and I think I might need help. Take the case of the no thankyou's.

Long ago my wife and I decided we would not batter our son with a lot of unqualified noes. There is a stage in children's development (roughly from six months to eighteen years) when it's necessary to discourage them from certain unsavory behavior. In order to soften the blow of this steady barrage of badgering, we chose to add to each "no" a polite "thank you" as a sort of verbal candy coating. We afford this courtesy to almost every other person we refuse, so why not our own child? Now when he pushes peas up his nose, it's "No thankyou." When he gouges out the cat's eyes, "No thankyou." When he melts plastic trucks on the wood stove, "No thankyou." It's easy enough to do and didn't take too long before it became a habit. That's just the problem — habitual use of anything can lead to addiction. Enter woe and despair.

I've found that it's become impossible for me to utter a simple "no" without following it with "thankyou." Whether it's a moon-eyed evangelist peddling salvation at my front door or someone at the bank inquiring if I'm waiting in line, my answer is the same, "No thankyou." So what's the big deal, you're probably asking yourself. What does it matter if I'm a little more polite than I need to be, even if it is a knee-jerk reaction?

I'll tell you why. It's this old truck I drive. It has about ninety degrees of play in the wheel, and though I can keep it between the lines with little effort, it's not always a pretty sight. One of these days a policeman is going to get behind me and feel obliged to investigate. The following scenario is what I live in fear of.

"Pretty fancy driving, mister. Have you been drinking?"

"No thankyou."

"Do you mind stepping out of your vehicle?"

"No thankyou."

"Can you recite the alphabet?"

"Yes please."

"Can you say it backwards?"

"No thankyou."

You can see how I could no-thankyou myself right into a pair of chrome bracelets and an unscheduled tour of the pokey. If I don't somehow regain control, there's no telling what kind of trouble it could lead to.

The other thing I've caught myself doing away from the house is "yaying." Yaying is letting loose with a jubilant "yay" while rapidly clapping your hands together. Common household variety praise, and nothing to be ashamed of. Kids love it and usually follow suit with quick little hands and a grin cute enough to ensure they will live comfortably under your roof for the rest of their lives. The general public, however, does not respond as enthusiastically to a grown man yaying.

I've been having nightmares where I'm sitting in a tavern watching the seventh game of the World Series with a bunch of the boys. "The boys" are all two hundred and fifty pounds without an ounce of fat on them. They enjoy scratching up the beer pitchers with the stubble on their chins and chewing the vinyl cushion from the edge of the bar when the favored team makes an error. In the midst of this I see myself jumping from my stool and involuntarily yaying. I haven't slept a wink in four days, and my night sweats are ruining the bed linen.

I've only decided to go public with this now because I sense there are other dads out there with these same troubles — good fathers, dedicated husbands, and regular guys the world over just coming to grips with their Dadiholism.

I think we should organize meetings. One night a week to get out of the house. We could arm-wrestle or something to break the ice, then get on with the regular business. This might include one member pushing a toy dump truck across the room while the rest of us helped each other resist making motor noises with our lips. Assembly guides to Tinkertoy sets could be ceremoniously burned while we punched shoulders and sang old sailing songs.

Personal fears and experiences, like those I've mentioned above, would be shared with the group. We could exchange phone numbers to be used in time of crisis. If, say, at a hockey game things got out of hand, you could make your way to a pay phone: "Roger, I'm really worried tonight. I've almost yayed three times already, and it's only the first period."

"Calm down, Ralph. Go back in there and throw the ice out of your Coke at somebody, then tear the cup apart with your teeth. You're going to be fine, buddy."

Yes, gentlemen, I think it's time we got together on this thing. Stop suppressing your anxieties and shout it from the roof tops, "I am a Dadiholic." We can help each other. If we don't at least try it, we'll never know, thankyou.

A Housebuilder's Guide to Homemaking

Women have been complaining for years about being strapped with the household chores and the duties of child care with little appreciation, less glamour, and absolutely no pay. But things seem to be turning around a little as more and more men find themselves taking over the responsibilities of the home. I've recently found myself among their number. When my wife returned to work, I abandoned my construction business to tackle a one-year-old, a shopping list, a dirty toilet, and the laundry piling up. I'm not going to bore you with another cute "Mr. Mom" story full of observations that women have been making for thousands of years — namely that raising small children is a complex and moving experience, housework is demanding and endless, and presoaking problem stains really does make the whites whiter and the colors brighter. I'd like to avoid the obvious and talk instead about how I've applied some of my housebuilding experience to homemaking, and how homemaking might benefit my construction career should I ever return to it.

Since I brought up the subject of laundry, let's take a look at a new approach to that nagging nemesis of housewives everywhere: static cling. It's only recently that I've begun to appreciate what a pain in the pants this really is. Socks are welded to sweaters, and nylon turtlenecks spring into little balls as soon as you spread them out on the table to fold. I realize this problem can be neatly skirted with those little blue perfumed foam rubber things you throw in the drier, but that's too easy. My male training and blue-collar experience won't allow me to use those in good conscience.

Instead I've chosen to apply the little bit I've learned about the dynamics of electricity while in the trades. Now, static electricity isn't exactly house current. You can't just unplug it, you have to ground it out. Anyone who's ever touched a water faucet on a dry winter day will understand what I'm talking about. So I thought this grounding principle could be applied to the problem of static cling. I tied one end of a copper ground wire to a rivet on a pair of 501s and the other end to the drier's metal spinner. I started 'er up and in less than a minute found the clothes wound up with that wire tighter than a hay bale. So I tried another method. I removed the wad of supercharged clothing from the drier, put my arms around it, and headed on out to the living room. I shuffled my feet up and down the carpet until I figured the laundry and I had become one unified charge, then I went and touched the door knob. It made a loud snap and stung like crazy, but did absolutely nothing for the laundry. Obviously this couldn't work, and you'd be stupid to try it, but there are other innovative methods I've applied to my housework that do make things easier.

We all know how much time homemakers waste trying to clean house and keep young children out of harm's way at the same time. They rush around from one poison cleaning product to the next, making sure not to leave one out where the kid can get at it. They must use the bowl cleaner, put it away, grab the cleanser, put it away, and on and on until a twenty-minute job takes up to two hours or more. Well, I've found a way around all of this.

I dug out my old tool belt with the leather multi-pouches, hammer loops, and shoulder harness. On my right I have the Comet in one pouch alongside the Drāno, with a scratch pad and a dust cloth where the tape rule used to go. On the other side is the Windex and furniture polish with a squeegie stuck in the hammer loop. That leaves one whole pocket and a few small nail pouches for baby's favorite toys, a change of diapers, some salve, cookies, and a spare bib or two. Now I can clean the whole house, serve my child's every need, and get dinner started without retracing a step. I've already read the paper and clipped half my sale ads before my wife walks through the door. Professional efficiency. That's the way to go.

Then there's one thing I learned around the house that I wish I'd known about out in the field. In construction a guy finds himself coming home with some toxic substance or another spread from his fingertips to his elbows, and nothing short of gasoline will usually take care of it. Now I've found a better way.

I cleaned out the wood stove one day and ended up with hands blacker than Dad's fried eggs. I scrubbed and scraped with every poison I could find, but nothing seemed to cut it. So I went ahead and made dinner anyway. That's how I stumbled onto my discovery. I found that no matter how dirty the hands or how persistent the dirt, making a meat loaf will clean you up slicker than a wet kid. Working the raw meat and soda crackers between the fingers for a couple minutes will erase anything from chimney soot to furniture oil. I tell you, it saved my day, and if you'd ever tasted my meat loaf, you'd admit the added seasoning couldn't hurt anything.

You can see that my transition from housebuilder to homemaker has been fairly painless. I'm the laundry-doin'est, counter-wipin'est, baby-boucin'est little dad you ever laid eyes on. Sure, it's hard work, but it's the challenge I like. Innovation, experimentation, that's the stuff of professionalism, and I have every intention of being the best in my chosen trade.

Now, if I could figure out how a guy can get paid for doing this . . .

Dish
Demeanor

Household controversies range from church of choice to the color of the new family car. But nothing on the long list of excuses for domestic disturbance can produce so much fuss as the proper way to wash a dish. Dish-washing techniques are as many and varied as the floral designs on Melmac plates and are surpassed only by bathroom habits in their inflexibility. You can tell a person by his dish-washing style, but as I say, you can't tell him very much.

Dish washers can be broken into two basic categories. There are *Wash-and-Driers,* who methodically wash a few, dry a few, wash a few, dry a few, put some away, start over, and when they're done, they're done. All the rest are *Wash-and-Drippers.* They wash the whole pile, then stack the dishes precariously in a rubber drainer until the next morning. Wash-and-Driers show a basic insecurity in not being able to leave things go. They're the same folks who can spot a dustball under the sofa from across the room and won't relax until it's swept up. Wash-and-Driers normally work in teams, which can promote marital harmony, but which can also lead to whole new points of contention by allowing two solid opinions near the same small sink. Whereas one partner might want to do the silverware first to get it out of the way, the other will surely prefer to let it soak to make the job a little easier. There is a point of agreement, however, among all dish washers, and it's that everyone hates to do silverware.

Wash-and-Drippers are the free spirits of the kitchen, and can be divided into two subgroups: *right-brained stackers* and *left-brained stackers*. Right-brained stackers will randomly clean cup, plate, or serving spoon without regard to shape or size and creatively teeter them on one another until a dish-sculpture rivaling anything in the modern arts takes form at sinkside. This is all well and good, but it requires a municipal bomb squad to dismantle the stack without breaking anything or waking up the baby. Right-brained stackers of the Wash-and-Dripper persuasion reveal a basic love of expression and are the poets and painters of the twin sink. Picasso was a notorious dish stacker, and his *Crystal Goblet on Salad Tongs in Blue Bowl* stands to this day as the quintessential right-brained dish stack.

Left-brained Wash-and-Drippers would build a good bridge or a level house if given the opportunity. They choose their next dirty dish with care, basing their selections on size, weight, and shape with no regard to order of appearance. Lefties wash cast-iron skillets and large ceramic bowls well ahead of the bone china, so as the stack grows the weight bears on the hardier pieces. No left-brained stacker would ever hang a bowl on a wineglass stem or leave the blades of sharp knives pointing up. They might, however, in their zeal for orderliness, stack dishes so close together that even a day later wet plates can be found tightly layered at the bottom of the drainer. This drives right-brained stackers absolutely bonkers, because being dedicated Wash-and-Drippers, they wouldn't put a towel to a dish at gunpoint.

If an argument isn't had over *how* the dishes are to be washed, one will surely come over *when*. Many married and most all single dish owners are famous procrastinators when it comes to this chore, and some have been known to put it off until there is not an adequate cup or plate left in the house. Once the last empty peanut-butter jar has been drunk from, one of two things takes place. The first is to set aside a rainy weekend to scrape, sort, sanitize, and stack the mountain of tableware. The second and more common practice is to sublet or sell the house.

On the flip side of these casual washers are the folks who virtually clean as they go. We've all been witness to the host who rinses out your coffee cup between servings and has it washed, dried, and hung on a hook before the last swallow reaches your belly. These people, when left to their own devices, would choose to eat their meals over the garbage disposal rather than soil a plate or stain a fork. They scour their sinks with neurotic regularity, and finding a noodle dangling from the bottom of a drain-stopper is likely to send them into convulsions. Invariably alone at the end, most *Clean-as-They-Goers* marry but lose their spouses, sometimes to mental institutions, but mostly to well-adjusted slobs.

I believe my wife was quite fortunate in finding herself a well-adjusted slob the first time around. As we are both of the Wash-and-Dripper right-brained stacker persuasion, we have very few cleanup confrontations. In fact, what we have is a healthy competition. We take turns marveling at the sinkside sculptures each devises with his or her stacking skill. We're a pretty even match on this point, and had assumed this playful rivalry would go on forever. Unfortunately we've run into a problem.

Feeling exceptionally inspired one recent evening, I took it upon myself to use our wedding glasses as the foundation for a dish stack of unprecedented ambition. We had several guests for dinner and managed to use every piece of decent tableware in the house, so I was able to arrange them one on top of the other with a ten-pound iron soup kettle at the summit. It's a marvel of balance and fragility with a certain air of grace juxtaposed by the presence of the soup pot.

Picasso himself might have awarded me a spirited slap in the pants with a damp dish rag at the sight of it. The problem is that we're afraid to touch the thing. Those wineglasses, the very symbol of our unity, are holding up every dish in the kitchen. Neither one of us is willing to risk their demise by dismantling my creation. It's going on a week now, and might go on forever. Who knows how long it'll stay standing, but in the meantime, it gives us something to talk about while we scrape the paper plates.

SMALL
COMFORTS

—— ❖ ——

Small
Comfort

Last year my life found me on some pretty long walks in some pretty big cities, and on most of them I came across street people. I don't mean people who love the street. I mean people who live in the street. Homeless indigents, bums, winos, derelicts. Whatever you want to call them, there they are, crouched in doorways, sprawled on bus benches, and peering from alleyways. I don't get to big cities often, so I don't come across them as much as some do.

Those who meet up with them all the time are better at walking around them than I am. They can pass them up without an ear or eye open. If they feel anything like compassion, they can veil it just enough to appear honestly indifferent. I found that hard to do, but getting caught up in the big-city way of things, I kept practicing. I quit looking over at them and stopped straining to hear their pleas for money above the traffic noise. I quit trying to peer into their beggar cans to see if anybody else had put coins in them. I quit reading their signs asking for jobs, money, food, and help. I started to get pretty good at it.

After a day or two on the streets of Washington, D.C., I could walk dead through DuPont Circle and not trip over my heartstrings if an old man called out for change. I could wave off the aggressive vagrants with one quick backhand motion. I'd look past these people for some far-off sign or building to focus my direction on. By golly, I was getting cosmopolitan and enjoying it. I'd mastered the subway. I'd learned to time my street crossings so as not to appear flustered or hurried. And now I'd gotten rid of any guilt or intimidation I'd ever felt at being a well-dressed white boy in the presence of poverty. What a thrill to stand defiantly on the street surveying my options, just as cool, calm, and numb as a post.

I carried on this way for a while, but then something broke me.

It was getting way past lunch on a free day. My stomach was rumbling, and I was out in search of an interesting place to grab a knockwurst and a beer. I turned a corner and there in a doorway crouched an old man with a block-lettered sign on his chest. It said simply, I'M HUNGRY. I'd seen signs like this before, but this guy *looked* hungry, really hungry, and tired to the bone. With my stomach as empty as his tin can, that simple statement, "I'm hungry," took on new worth.

It struck me as if hearing my little son cry like the weight of all the world was crushing down on his tiny shoulders. I'd drag myself across hot coals to comfort him, and I couldn't pass by this old soul. Two doors down was an Arthur Treacher's Fish and Chips restaurant. "Don't give him money," I thought. "It could get stole from him, or he might just drink it away. Go buy the guy a bag of fish and a cup of coffee. What'll it cost, three bucks?"

I started in the door just as five young businesspeople came out, and I had to stand aside for a moment. That killed it. The self-satisfied expressions on those successful young faces snapped whatever I had going with that old man. As I watched them file past him, preoccupied with their own conversation, I felt the old indifference coming back. I suddenly felt more of their fold than the beggar's, and I moved away from the door.

"Nobody feeds street people," I thought. "What are you doing? Who are you trying to impress?"

As I looked back at the old man, he happened to turn his head and look at me. I was found out. He realized what I was up to. He knew I was wavering and held my gaze. I'd only seen that look in eyes once before. That was in the eyes of a deer I'd dropped but not quite killed while hunting in Southeast Alaska. As I walked up to the dying animal to finish it, there was that same pitiful look of appeal. Every cell in that deer's body hoped beyond hope that I'd change my mind and walk away.

I didn't walk away then, but I did that day in Washington. Walked away clean. I strolled down the street defiant and numb as a post. The only indication of a crack in my composure was the blood in my cheeks and my hands dug deep in my pockets like I'd never pull them out. I could feel that old man's stare burning at the base of my neck, but I wouldn't turn around.

I came back home to Alaska shortly after that day, and I don't see street people anymore. I eat well, all my friends eat well, and I forget about that old guy a lot. Sometimes at night, though, my little son wakes me with cries like the weight of all the world is crushing down on his tiny shoulders. I hold him tight, rock him, and think how I'll never be able to look that old man in the eye again. Not even in my sleep.

Realizing this is no great comfort to anyone.

Gross
Estimates

A mericans have got to be the most anticipated people on earth. Everyplace we look there's the results of this poll or that survey. It's estimated this, predicted that, or early indications of the other thing. It's like having some guy come to dinner and keep telling you, "Now wait, I know what you're going to say," before you open your mouth, or, "I knew you were going to feel that way about it," after you do. And the worst of all is the "See how you are?" when you do something you've always done and he thinks he's clever because he notices it. Nobody can stand these kinds of people in their private lives, and I don't know why we put up with it in public.

Of course, all these polls and surveys are designed to find out which way we're heading so they can ambush us with stupid products we don't need, television minidramas we can't follow, and made-to-order politicians. They start those opinion polls about a year before an election. They ask what qualities you look for in a leader, what issues you would like to see addressed, and how you think the leader should address the issues you would like to see addressed. Come time for the primaries — *whammo!* — there he is, Mr. Right. All bought and paid for.

I suppose there is an estimate somewhere on how many people spend their time estimating people, and my estimate is that we can stand every one of them right on their ear.

The next time a polltaker calls your house, give him the wrong answers. If you want to say Democrat, say Republican. If you mean yes, say no. Don't do this on every single question or we'll get caught up in another prediction. Estimates will show that Americans are becoming wiseguys. Be subtle and we can ring bells in every capital and industry.

When you're at the store, don't pick up the roll of paper towels they tell us has the biggest bounce. None of them bounce. Grab the cheapest roll and go. You're just going to wipe up a mess with it and throw it away, so who cares? And some of these books. You know the ones. They come off the presses with "Number One Best Seller" already stamped on the cover because the publishers are that sure we'll buy them. Let's don't. Who really needs to burn through another international thriller? Innocent man or woman is caught up in something bigger than his or her self. It's up to our hero to (A) win the war, (B) preserve democracy, (C) save the world, or (D) provide titillating sexual fantasy to the masses. Flash scene of Berlin Wall, trench coat, romantic encounter on Lake Geneva, then on to startling conclusion where neo-Nazi conspiracy is exposed through employment of sheer wits, high morals, and the stiletto depicted on the cover dripping blood all over a swastika and a lace brassiere. See, you've heard the story, so skip it next time and buy a psychology textbook or a *House-plants Illustrated* instead. Market analyzers will go nuts trying to figure it out.

You people with the Nielsen rating machines on your televisions should turn them to the public station and leave them there. Watch "Dynasty" and *Blue Thunder* out in the garage on the portable if you have to. It'll only be for a while. It shouldn't take very long. We'll have them pounding their heads on their computer monitors before you can say "trend report."

Just imagine the hundreds of high-level emergency board meetings that will be called to order across the nation. Power brokers, king makers, empire builders, and soda-pop tycoons, every one of them poking at a tender ulcer and asking, "What in the heck are they up to out there?"

We'll never tell. Not until it's over. I want to see Tom Brokaw's face on the evening news as he announces that "The American public is showing a tendency to have no tendencies. Conjecture at eleven."

Once the opinion pollsters and market surveyors have lost their jobs and found honest work counting spawned-out salmon in the Yukon River, we can relax and go back to normal, our point well made.

We'll talk to them in language they understand. Any good businessman will tell you that the advantage lies in being unpredictable. I want those people to look out their upper-story boardroom windows at the milling crowds below, and admit, "Ladies and gentlemen, we have to watch these folks. They're pretty tricky."

Senior Boom

We Baby Boomers were officially spawned during the years 1946 to 1964, and have become, without a doubt, one of the most influential bits of humanity to hit the streets since the Mongol horde swept across Asia. Leaving hula hoops, the Monkees, miniskirts, and underenrolled universities in our wake, we've now progressed to BABY ON BOARD stickers and well-tended stock portfolios. Due to sheer weight of numbers, we get almost everything we want. If we're not sure what we want, there is always some demographic genius out there to show us something we never thought of. If you can figure out a product that the Baby Boomers will buy, you can look forward to early retirement. And that's exactly what the merchants and producers are thinking about, retirement. Our retirement.

You see, it finally dawned on somebody that the boomers ain't babies no more, and are getting less like them every day. Some of us are already in the throes of middle age and nearing the halfway point in our working careers. As we speak, manufacturers of products for the elderly are gearing up for our expected demands when we all decide we're old. Their plans aren't exactly in the public domain yet, but I've managed to find out a few of the things they have in store for us.

I hear that one orthopedic shoe company is planning expansive additions to their facilities, including ten acres of new corrective-sole storage. Some thirty new assembly lines will soon start punching out plain black creepers, and one of the cane conglomerates is stockpiling bamboo walking sticks with little rubber tips. Geritol will soon upgrade its packaging to add a little pizzazz to the experience of being old and worn out. The denture industry is fairly drooling at the prospects of the early twenty-first century. I'd like to suggest they all settle down and think things through for a minute.

The odds of us growing into ordinary old folks are about the same as Jane Fonda running on the Republican ticket with George Bush. I have a feeling we will have about as much use for orthopedic shoes as we did for Lawrence Welk. Baby Boomers as a group have singled themselves out as one of the most self-indulgent generations in history. No new generation likes to do things the way their parents did, but because there are so many of us, we don't do things the way our parents did in the biggest way. Granted there is nothing we can do about getting old, but I have every confidence we are going to do it with our typical flare for contrariness.

For one thing, the health and fitness craze might well assure many of us very long and productive old ages (unless, as I suspect, we find that running aimlessly around in parks during our prime did little but use us up early). We'll see about that, but we're bound to live longer than earlier generations anyway because that's the trend and the medicine men get smarter every day. For this reason there is going to be a whole lot of old boomers around for a long long time. We're going to make an institution out of being over the hill. In just a couple of decades, it's going to be so popular to be an old fart that everybody's going to wanna be one. All I can say is, the marketplace better get ready for us.

Adidas and Reebok better get their heads together on an ankle-support running shoe. Levi's should be planning their shrink-to-fits to shrink a little less as we all fill out. Unpopular sizes like, say, a 42 waist and 28 inseam are going to be pretty hot items before Calvin Klein knows what hit him.

If you own shares in Ex-Lax, you'd be well advised to hang on to them, but only if they do something about the flavors. Something in an Almond Mocha or Swiss Cream would seem appropriate. Same goes for the smell of Vick's, and while we're on the subject, if the medicos don't come up with a cure for rheumatism pretty quick, they're going to have a riot on their hands.

Fashion and entertainment best get ready for a plunge into the past. It's been observed that old people tend toward the styles and sounds of their misspent youth. Grandma loves those old seventy-eights and her print cotton nightgown circa 1910. Muzak had better get those 1,000 Strings renditions of Barry Manilow tunes out of the nursing homes, put some Creedence Clearwater in there, and turn it up. Big-screen TVs around the mineral baths will be seeing a lot of the old Woodstock footage, and *The Big Chill* is destined to replace *Gone With the Wind* as the classic film of choice.

I don't know if getting old necessarily means we'll all turn ornery, but I plan to. I look forward to dusting off some old radical politics and letting my white hair grow over my shoulders just to irritate neo-neo-conservative children who I know won't come to visit. I want to drive too slow in a '68 VW with a rainbow sticker in the window and speakers in the back. I'll wait too long at stoplights and flash menacing gestures at hyperactive upstarts behind me who don't like it. This is going to be great.

Of course I could be wrong about all of this. We may end up just getting old and quiet. We might decide that gin rummy, shuffleboard, and some light gardening are just the thing to fill the golden years with. We could come to think that red jogging shoes look ridiculous on the ends of shaky legs and big, dumb black ones are just the ticket. If we have any hearing left, we might choose not to further threaten it with more loud music. A few thousand strings doink-doinking out a favorite old melody in the background may do just as well. In short, we may all find out by the time we're eighty-five that being sensible is the better way to go. Is that possible? I'm not sure, kids, but I have great faith in us, and I just don't think so.

Mental Safety

C onsumer advocates have for years been trying to protect us from ourselves. They've succeeded in saving us from a myriad of hazardous products from the Pinto to pajamas that burst into flames on contact with a warm thought. It seems that making anything small enough to pass between a baby's lips is now against the law, and everything we buy to eat short of tap water has to be hermetically sealed. My stepladder is burdened with so many instructions and warning labels that I can hardly pack it up the stairs (stairs which must be outfitted with an approved handrail as required by state law).

I'm not complaining about this. Even though a few new rules stretch the limits of reason, I have to admit this is a somewhat safer world than the one I grew up in. We're all going to live longer, and we owe a lot of that to the consumer advocates. If I have a problem with their work, it's that they are not addressing all there is at fault with manufactured products. Safety is a biggie, for sure — nobody wants to spend his hard-earned dollars on a death wish. Value is also a grand consideration — it's getting harder and harder to spot a rip-off in an economy that can't even decide what a dollar's worth. But there's a whole lot more to a good buy than a safe product for a fair price. There is a mental health quotient also at stake here.

Psychiatrists have recently coined a new term, *Agent Blue*. It refers to whatever it is behind the drastic increase in depression, violence, and suicide in our society. Now, I'm not at all sure, but I think I have an idea of what a great big part of this Agent Blue is, and it's something our consumer raiders should investigate. I'm talking about bad ideas embedded in good products. There's a lot of stuff in this world that we all long for, require, and use that has a certain amount of misery built into it.

Take, for example, the tags in some clothing. I have a pair of long johns I paid close to twenty bucks for. They are of some state-of-the-art fabric that is warm, durable, and so comfortable I feel like I'm climbing into bed every time I put them on. But there was this tag in the back. It was made out of something just short of stainless steel and gave me the sensation of having a piece of shattered flowerpot down my britches. I tore it out after the first wear.

That opened up a whole new bag of worms. The tag had been sewn on with about two thousand stitches per inch, and although the tag was gone, the stitching remained. It provided all the comfort of a serrated knife sawing away at my fourth lumbar. No amount of chewing and slashing would get rid of the stuff. So I have to wear my new long johns inside out.

Now why would a company produce a garment of such obvious merit, then booby-trap it with a thing like that? It's either a KGB conspiracy or there's a very bitter person at the helm of some sewing machine. Whichever it is, it's irritating, and should be looked into.

While on the subject of garments, there's another little mystery that for years has contributed nothing to my peace of mind, namely the tendency of the pant legs on Levi's to migrate. After several washings, the side seams are screwed around so far it looks like your legs are welded on crooked. If you haven't noticed, they're not giving Levi's away these days, and we're paying substantial amounts of dough to look like genetic misfits. It's a little thing to be sure, but it might be just these little things behind our deteriorating mental condition.

Luckily we live in a potentially just world, and there are compromises to be made that could relieve some of the tension.

For years I've been looking for a glue that might actually work. We've had super glues, crazy glues, wonder glues, mighty glues, and easy glues, but precious few glues that stick. I recently bought a new soup pot, and it came, of course, with a label stuck to it. This label refuses to go away. I've scrubbed it, boiled it, scraped it, applied every toxic chemical known to a kitchen to it, and it endures. More than a few times over the last two weeks I've wiped my brow and exclaimed, "What kind of glue did they use on this thing?"

Now, here's my compromise. If the gluemakers would sell us whatever it is keeping that label on my soup pot, and if the pot manufacturer would in turn use any other trade glue on its labels, we would live in a near-perfect world. The things I glued together would stay stuck, and the labels on cookware would gracefully fall off before I got them home from the store.

What's *your* gripe? Potato-chip bags that blow out at the bottom while you're trying to open the top? Impenetrable peanut packages on airlines? Could we cut down on airborne violence if we didn't have to carry knives to get at the snack? Why do you have to pull the engine of some Italian cars to change their spark plugs? For that matter, why are Fiats listed on the Foreign Trade Exchange under "Durable Goods"? These questions need to be answered.

Write your congressman. Call Nader. Boycott. Do whatever it takes. Just don't sit around thinking because a baby can't choke on it, or you can't fall off of it, that it's okay. A baby couldn't choke on an Edsel, and you couldn't fall off a pair of 501s and get hurt very bad. But I hope you see the hidden danger here.

Look every potential purchase over carefully. Read the side of the box. If it appears to contain even a little Agent Blue, remember: it's a bargain at no price, and unsafe at any speed.

I Aim
to Please

It's pretty obvious that Americans can't find enough things to spend their money on. Pet rocks, fifty-dollar rag dolls, Dodge trucks — the list goes on and on. People will pay for darn near anything if it's sold properly. The problem is just thinking up stuff to sell. Every time I hear of some brilliant new con, I kick myself for not thinking of it first. I've always fancied myself a bit of a businessman, and it irks me to see somebody else beat me to the punch.

When I was out East, someone showed me a tin can which the label claimed was full of "Fresh Maine Air." What a great scam. I've seen the cans of what they try to sell to tourists around here as "Gold Pan Material" — it's actually dirt and gravel, but it is canned *something*. In Maine some freethinking entrepreneur has found a way to sell *empty* cans to people. Why didn't I think of that?

We've got pretty nice air around here too, and canning lines that sit idle most of the year. "Fresh Alaska Air" would drive Maine air right off the market. I'd go through with it, but I hate to steal ideas, and the high overhead of Alaska canning operations would make it cost-prohibitive. I thought about having the cans made in Thailand at lower prices, but feared the class action suit that would surely come if someone were to discover that what was billed as a whiff of pure arctic air turned out to be a snootfull of downtown Bangkok. I put the whole business aside and was scheming some more when I heard someone had aced me again.

"Adopt-a-Ghost" it's called. Kind of a cross between a Cabbage Patch Doll and absolutely nothing. Your ghost comes with a name and brief character description so you know how to act around it. I don't know if it comes in a can too, but that seems like a pretty handy way to package a spook. Casper in a can. Americans *love* things in cans. They might offer three convenient sizes, one to suit every household's ectoplasmic needs. It's a tremendous idea that's humbling by its sheer genius.

I was desperate to get with the program and think up something to sell America when it came to me in the middle of a beer commercial: we love to be flattered. That's how they sell us all that junk — they make us feel good about ourselves for buying it.

So what I've decided to do is bypass the products altogether and sell pure sweet flattery. Everybody wants some recognition. You too, right?

How about for twenty bucks I name my dog after you for a day? Wouldn't it be swell to know I'd spend a whole day calling for Chuck, Kirby, or Bob? Bend down to scratch his ears and say, "Good dog, Bill." Put out the food bowl with a "Here ya go, Stephanie." (Women's names are okay because he's been neutered and doesn't care about that too much.) You'll also receive a Polaroid snapshot of me and the dog with your name written on it someplace, and the satisfaction of knowing that for a full twenty-four hours you've had a namesake.

There's no end to this business. Send me ten dollars and I'll start nice rumors about you. For five bucks I'll ask you where you bought your hat, or who cuts your hair. And for a dollar — that's right, one dollar — I'll put your name on my "Good Guys" list and leave it on the coffee table to browse through at my leisure.

So get on the stick and buy yourself some strokes. I think you folks are the cat's meow. (That one was on the house.)

Miss America

I watched the Miss America contest this year. I don't remember when I last saw one, but nothing much has
changed. There was the same middle-aged emcee doting on
the hopefuls, the current Miss America bubbling over last
year's magic moment, and of course the final ten contestants
in attack formation smiling their best Ultra-Brite smiles. I
read somewhere that they put Vaseline on their teeth so
they don't dry out and get their lips stuck to them. Good
idea. It wouldn't look good to give a teary-eyed promise to
spend the rest of your life benefiting needy families in Ap-
palachia by singing operettas in a bathing suit if your lips
were stuck in some idiotic grin. They've thought of
everything.

It appeared as though they'd all had their vertebrae sur-
gically fused so that the only moving parts were legs that
propelled them along at an ideal linear speed, like a fleet of
golf carts. Their heads turned smartly from side to side, and
their hands rose up to wave in that mechanical back-and-

forth motion as if working some huge control knob. In a sense, I guess, that's what they were doing.

Young women all over the country were looking up to this group for inspiration. Out of these ten would come one Miss America, the quintessential young single American female. College-educated, career-oriented, fashion-conscious, and built like a five-hundred-dollar privy.

Each gave us her little biography and ambitions. "I'm a senior at Backwater U. majoring in Communication. I hope one day to head up public relations for large charity organizations that help *all* the people of the world. Until then, please take note of my lovely breasts and mole-free shoulder blades. Thank you."

As the house applause faded to a styling mousse commercial, I couldn't help but wonder if anybody was buying all this. I pictured an Adrienne in Des Moines. She's not painting her nails, she's biting them wondering if she's going to make the rent this month. She works part time at the phone company and takes night classes in computer science. Someday she's going to make enough money to get out of this town and take a job on the West Coast. Get away from all her bozo boyfriends and get a new car. Then she might do something different with her hair and look into world hunger. For now, she can't afford to do either. In fact, she couldn't afford to do much of anything this Saturday night but watch this stupid pageant on TV and chain-smoke cigarettes to stay on her diet.

And there were our ten beauties lined up and waiting for the judges' decision. Hundred-dollar hairdos enshrined in lacquer. Makeup from petroleum by-products to take the edge off the bright stage lights. Skillfully applied lip gloss outlining skillfully applied smiles. There were enough complex carbon molecules wafting off the group that Adrienne couldn't safely light a cigarette within a hundred yards of there.

All these thoughts entered my mind as I waited for the grand finale, that moment when Adrienne and I and the rest of the country would be given our next Miss America. The artificial smiles would give way to the weeping passion of victory or the scowl of defeat.

Then the most amazing thing happened, or failed to happen, I should say. It made me wonder what I've missed since I saw my last beauty contest. Miss America didn't cry. She accepted her crown and marched down the runway dry-eyed and confident. None of the cute pouts I've come to expect. No trembling lips choking back tears of amazement at becoming everything she'd ever wanted to be. I felt cheated of the pleasure of seeing that overwhelming flush people get when they've won true fame and fortune. It wasn't "Little ol' me?"; it was "You bet it's me." A true child of the eighties firmly grabbing another rung on a well-designed career ladder.

Watching her make her way down the runway held all the emotional appeal of seeing a new car roll off the assembly line. Adrienne walks around it, looking it over. She opens the glove box and looks at the manufacturer's sticker. MADE IN AMERICA. Ain't she a beauty?

Lost Mail

Acts of God occur everywhere, but nowhere with as much frequency as on the high seas. One of His more recent performances was to bounce around a container barge on thirty-foot seas in the Gulf of Alaska. That made for a lot of water in all the wrong places, and, sure enough, some cargo got lost in it.

No big deal, really; it happens all the time. But there was something about this cargo that caught my interest. It seems that a whole container of U.S. mail went overboard and, presumably, sank. That hardly sounds earth-shaking either, but what got me going was the Postal Service announcement acknowledging that 20,680 pounds of mail was lost. It seemed like such a strange way to put it. Before then, I'd never really thought of mail by the pound. I'd get a little mail, or a lot of mail. Sometimes I'd get a stack of it, or, after returning from a long trip, a pile would be waiting for me. But I've yet to ask my wife if we got any mail and hear her say, "Oh, only about eight ounces." Of course that's all changed now.

Since this came up I've been guessing the weight of my mail. You'd be surprised how light it is. Even counting magazines and free samples, I figure I average about four pounds a week. That's when it hit me what a catastrophe losing this container of mail really was. Twenty thousand, six hundred and eighty pounds of mail is a lot of mail. Based on four pounds a week, that's ninety-nine years' worth. How'd you like not to get your mail for a whole century? Another way of looking at it would be to assume we each get about four pounds a week. That container represented a week of mail to over five thousand people. Now, that's a tragedy.

Just think of it. All those little "I love you, Grandma" refrigerator drawings lost to the briny deep. Picture a "Dear Oliver, if you don't answer me this time I'll know we're finally through" returning to pulp on the ocean floor. Imagine "I know it's stupid to send cash, Phil, but I didn't have time to get a money order" being sucked in and spit out by an irritated halibut. Sentiments lost, relationships ruined, and friendships strained. And that's not even counting the merchandise.

Alaskans live by mail-order catalogues. Somewhere in the Japanese Current we now have little schools of L. L. Bean sweaters, Sears bed linen, Eddie Bauer boot liners, and personalized note pads by Spencer Gifts all headed with the salmon fry for the high seas. What's the Soviet trawler captain going to think when his crew shows him the "Rambo Commie Basher" doll they dredged up that morning? It could touch off a serious international incident.

Just as I was really starting to slip into a dither over this whole mess, I took another long, hard look at my last four pounds of mail. It consisted of a women's underwear catalogue, a catalogue of gifts for gifted children, three magazine renewal notices, a sweepstakes, two political action committee newsletters (one left, one right), and a life insurance offer from J. C. Penney.

There was nothing there. Except for the underwear catalogue, there wasn't a keeper in the bunch, and the only reason any of it made it to my desk was so I could figure out how much it weighed. Judging from the amount of real mail I get as opposed to the other kind, I figure I get about a pound of the good stuff for every ton of the other kind. Using this formula, there were probably only ten or eleven letters on that barge. That really helped me to put this thing in perspective and cope with this tragedy on the high seas.

Twenty thousand, six hundred and eighty pounds of U.S. mail lost forever. Big deal.

Chain
Reactions

I got a strange letter in the mail today. It's one of those Xeroxed chain letters, and I have no idea who sent it to me. The purpose of this letter is not to make money or collect recipes; it's to spread good luck. I'm supposed to make twenty copies of the thing and send them out within four days. It says to send them to friends and associates I think might need good luck. Like I don't think everybody could use a little.

The letter starts out: "Kiss someone you love and make magic" — as opposed to kissing someone else and making time, I guess. It goes on to detail the success stories of a few of its previous recipients. A guy in the air force received seventy grand for cooperating, and another guy named Joe got forty grand but lost it when he broke the chain. Gene Welch lost his dog, tragically, after receiving the letter and failing to pass it on, but here's the good news, he got seven thousand some-odd dollars before its death. Good for you, Gene.

It tells about a guy who received the letter in 1953 and won a two-million-dollar lottery. Another guy got the letter but mislaid it. He lost his job, then found the letter, mailed his twenty copies, and was given a better job. Right, we get the picture.

The whole thing seemed pretty harmless and just a little silly until I got to the last line: "Dalan Fairchild received the letter and, not believing, threw it away. Nine days later he died."

Oh, now, this is just great. A letter that started out inviting me to kiss someone and make magic is now threatening to kill me if I don't play along. To get rid of this curse, I gotta go pay twenty cents a copy at a Xerox machine, buy four and a half bucks' worth of stamps, and pass the curse on to twenty of my friends. I don't know who sent this letter to me, but I think a little more of my friends than to lay a deal like this on them, even if I am superstitious. It seems like they get enough guilt, fear, and anxiety from their regular suppliers without me sending along unsolicited free samples.

I picture some poor twisted soul sweating in a walk-up apartment in L.A. He's close to tears and has just about had it with everything and everybody. As he polishes his rifle and contemplates the unspeakable, the postman pushes an envelope through the slot in his door. "Kiss somebody and make magic. . . ." By the time he gets to the end of the letter all remaining strands of sanity are severed and we get a big headline in the morning paper. Like I say, people don't need this kind of anxiety floating around loose.

Besides, this whole thing doesn't make mathematical sense. If somebody did get this letter in 1953 like they say, then it's been around for a while. Assume for a minute that everyone in the pyramid did what they were supposed to and sent along twenty copies within four days. It would take only a little over a month before the number of letters in circulation exceeded the number of people that exist by some five times over.

So who gets all the leftover good luck? Could this be a scam after all? Maybe it's some international conspiracy of casino owners trying to water down all the good luck in the world until none of us has any worth mentioning.

The letter tells us that some missionary in South America named Saul Anthony DeCroff originated this scheme. He may have worked out the math on this thing too. You can bet that with twenty-five billion letters in circulation, sooner or later somebody's bound to either win a car or drop dead within four days of getting one. That makes good ol' Saul DeCroff look pretty clever. But to what end? I don't know what church he's working for down there, but they better call him back to headquarters. The good reverend's been in the jungle too long.

I'm assuming that you've received this letter too. If I got one, then everybody did. If that's so, then listen up here. Don't rush off to Kopy Kwik. Don't give in to fear. I have a better idea.

Instead of spending what would amount to around eight bucks on Xerox machines and postage to perpetuate this hogwash, keep four bucks for yourself, buy something for your sweetheart, and send the other four bucks to me. If there's as many of you out there as I think there are, we will become one of the largest financial concerns in the world overnight. Trust me, I worked it out on my calculator.

Since I do have a calculator, I'm probably the best one

to manage our corporate holdings. I'll only withdraw enough to cover my basic administrative costs and what I'll need to keep up the limos and Lear jets. You'll get a nice letter every quarter, or as soon as I get to it, letting you know how things are going and asking if there's anything in particular you'd like me to buy, like Yellowstone Park, or Vermont. As a stockholder, you'll get into these places free of charge.

Your dedicated chief executive will keep it a personal organization. I'll send you pictures of my kid as he grows up and maybe a nice card around the holidays.

This sounds like just another scheme, I know, but I'll bet you twenty postage stamps it's more than you're going to get out of that chain letter.

Burger
Blues

This is an embarrassing thing to admit, but the first place I ever ate at in Alaska was a McDonald's restaurant. That was in Fairbanks eleven years ago. I found it hysterical that I could get to faraway Fairbanks and find a Big Mac dispensary at my service. I ate there just to say I did and took note of the sign on the door claiming it was only the second McDonald's in the whole state.

I'm reminded of this lately by the construction of our very own McBurger stand right here at the end of the road. Whatever I found so amusing about that second-only Alaska McDonald's escapes me now. People here take the appearance of this and other fast-food joints very personally. An invasion of their privacy.

McDonald's has come to represent everything bad that is happening to Alaska. It's all blamed on the newcomers from everyplace else. The golden arches are an easy symbol for "Everyplace Else." That's where all the surly cowboys with crude oil under their fingernails come from. That's where carpetbagger developers come from. For God's sake, that's where *tourists* come from.

It's also the place where I and a whole scad of other born-again Alaskans come from. "Outside," we call it, and there's hardly one of us didn't try to pull the door shut behind him on the way in. It's pretty typical, really. For being the most adaptable critters in all God's creation, we sure do kick and scream when somebody tries to change things.

We've all got our little ideas about what Alaska is and should be, and we want it kept just that way. I had an old-timer tell me once that Alaska is being able to piss off your own front porch, and if it ever got to the point where, by God, he couldn't, then he would pack it in. I suppose he's still around. You can still pee off your front porch here if you're so inclined and your house points the right way. But there are other things not so easy anymore. Longevity bonuses and local hire laws are going the way of home marijuana crops. Alaskans are having a heck of a time accepting that the U.S. Constitution applies to them too.

Anchorage has some of the worst air pollution in the nation and cradles our very own TV preachers and homeless indigents. Rising high above it all are the golden arches, twin monuments to banality. "Over Fifty Billion Served," it says. My God, that's more than the pipeline serves and it's all in burgers.

It seemed like such an impossible number that I had to figure out how big it really was. I did some arithmetic, counted up all the zeros, and found that fifty billion hamburgers would cover one square mile twenty-three feet deep. That's not taking into account the ones on the bottom being all squashed together. The thought of it disgusted me.

I looked over our beautiful Kachemak Bay landscape and imagined this blight of ground meat and food additives sitting on it. Then it struck me. You wouldn't even have to see it. There's about forty crevasses I can count from here that would hide that pile of burgers.

So what's the big deal? We could take everything that outfit ever made right down to the last McNugget and hide it where nobody could find it. I wouldn't want to be the one to do the job, but just the thought of it calmed me down. It's a testimony to the size and ruggedness of our state that such an awesome entity as the world's largest fast-food empire could be digested by it whole, leaving not so much as a bad smell behind.

Alaska's people could take a lesson from her land. If a few hamburger stands are all it takes to break the spirit of Alaska, then we must have had a pretty precarious hold on it in the first place.

A Year of
Peace

During the Christmas season there was a banner along-side the road I drive home, bidding PEACE ON EARTH. I liked that. It was your typical holiday fare, but so much better than a mere "Merry Christmas" or "Noel" (I still can't figure out what that means).

Peace on Earth — as opposed to peace on the Moon or Pluto, I suppose — is a nice sentiment. I was a little disappointed when I noticed today the banner is gone, packed away in a garage or basement for safekeeping until the spirit of the season once again moves the owners to unfurl it. It's a shame there has to be a season for that sort of wish. I'd have thought none the less of them if they'd left it up.

Now that 1986 is history for everyone except tax accountants, I wonder if many of us remember much about it. All the "Year in Review" folderol in the media lately has done its best to remind us time and again of the *Challenger* disaster, upheaval in the Philippines, unrest in Central

America, and scandal in the White House. Natural disasters, technical failures, graft, disinformation, and weaponry seemed to dominate the headlines as they have every year in recent memory.

War toy sales reached historic highs in 1986. Not only at Toys-R-Us, but also in Congress, and in more than one unlikely country overseas. A strange statistic to emerge out of a year that was proclaimed the International Year of Peace by the United Nations. Maybe you didn't know it was. I don't think it made the "Best of '86" shows. Too many good train wrecks and too much bang-bang footage from Nicaragua to squeeze in a mention of something as uninteresting as peace, I suppose.

Of course not everyone neglected our token year of pacification. Several hundred individuals took it upon themselves to walk across the continent in the March for Peace. They arrived in Washington, D.C., eight and a half months later, triumphant, exuberant, exhausted, and ignored. Maybe you heard about this march. It made the news a few times. Like when it went bankrupt and the marchers had their porta-potties repossessed. Nice little humorous tidbit to round off the half hour before we went to sports and weather.

I recently read an account of this expedition, and the participants said they were mostly well received on their travels. They allowed as how the small-town folk of America would come out to greet them, wave, and cheer them on. Whether or not this was due to some philosophical alignment remains a mystery, but having lived all my life in small towns, I can testify that a herd of cattle going down Main Street would have elicited about the same response. It was the marchers' accounts of the negative reactions that really got to me. They made mention of the "one-finger peace sign" and the oft-repeated slogan "Peace Sucks."

Now, everything is a matter of taste, but of all the personally undesirable futures that might possibly lie before us, one of peace is certainly not among them. Even the last great man of war, General Douglas MacArthur, wrote in his memoirs that "no one prays for peace with as much earnest as does the soldier."

How anybody could have a problem with the idea of a peaceful world escapes me, but it might have something to do with conditioning. We've been trying to kill each other ever since we learned how to throw rocks. You don't get rid of that sort of behavior overnight. Rocks, having progressed to guided missiles, stealth bombers, and orbiting lasers, have rooted themselves firmly in our economy. War is everybody's bread and butter, and, by golly, don't you be messin' with my supper. I can't imagine why we came to be this way, and I'll be the first to admit it will take more than four hundred people on a walking tour of the country to undo it. As luck would have it, they were not the only ones with peace on their minds last year.

On a more local level, the Alaska Performing Artists for Peace cooked up a little cultural exchange with the Soviet Union. A very plausible idea, you must admit. If any Americans could find a common denominator with the Russians, it's us. We both live in really weird places. We share a hemisphere, a climate, a border, a native culture, and more than a couple of fish. If Alaskans can't get along with the Soviets, nobody can, and these folks went about trying to do just that.

Although most of the trip was funded out of their own pockets, one of our Homer participants told me a chilling tale of his efforts to raise local funding for the exchange. It seems that more than one fine and benevolent organization declined to donate because they thought the word "peace" in their title was "too political."

Gag me with a claymore, folks. The term "political" means to me that there are some opposing parties to a given idea. Communism is political. Capitalism is political. Who's gonna take out the garbage is political. But peace? C'mon. Is there a person on the face of this earth that hasn't stood up at one time or another and yelled, "Holy mackerel, what's a body gotta do to get some peace around here?"

What we gotta do is not easy to say, but until we figure it out, our desires might be best summed up by the words of one Yupik Eskimo. While on this Alaskan tour of the Soviet Union, the man had occasion to present a fur parka to a representative of Chairman Gorbachev's wife. His presentation speech went something like this:

"We of this small known segment of the universe deserve the very best, and the very best that we can give each other is peace."

I don't know how much this Yupik knows of politics, or if he even cares, but I trust Mrs. Gorbachev enjoyed her gift. God and bureaucracies willing, we'll have a few Russians over here next year bearing similar gifts. It might not do any good, but it sure as hell can't hurt anything.

"Peace on Earth." Wouldn't that be something to write home about? Maybe I'll go ask those folks with the roadside banner if I can put it back up for a while. I know I don't speak for everybody, but I hadn't grown tired of seeing it just yet.

Hard
Comparisons

I've never found it a healthy practice to compare myself to other people. It only leads to either smug satisfaction or abject self-pity, neither of which becomes me. I sometimes feel that other people are my competition — whether it be for money, smarts, popularity, or spiritual awareness — and even though it does no good, I continue to wage silent battle with my fellow travelers. I'd be a lot better off figuring out what makes me happy, and doing what I can to stay that way.

Of course this is easier said than done, and no matter how noble my intentions, I continue to hold myself up against other people whether I want to or not.

There are two times I've done this that stick out in my mind more than others. These two in particular stay with me because I won the contest I should have lost and lost the one that never should have been a challenge.

The contest I won took place in a swank hotel bar in Boston a year ago. I was on my maiden publicity tour, and the publisher of the book was treating me pretty good. There were a couple presidential visits commemorated in brass by the front door of this joint, and limos and Rolls-Royces were parked four deep on the street. I felt entirely out of my element, but decided to wallow in the good life just in case it never came around again.

While I was sitting in the bar one evening silently enjoying the fruits (or at least the hops) of success, a very drunk man broke me from my thoughts. I guessed him to be in his late thirties, and you didn't have to know a lot about clothes to see that his evening attire probably cost more than my truck did.

He was alone and trying to spark some conversation around the bar by talking too loud to nobody in particular. He claimed to be the heir to a huge corporate fortune and to own a controlling interest in a worldwide cosmetics company. He bragged that he inherited his pile at the tender age of eighteen, and moaned that everyone's been trying to take it from him ever since. He was closing up his Boston town house and building a "little ten-room" up at Kennebunkport, Maine, "to get away from it all." He wondered if you could get decent servants up in that wilderness.

The word "servants" raised my hackles, and I started to listen more closely. He hated his cars. His Rolls was always in the shop waiting for parts from "those damn Brits." He'd blown three transmissions in his Porsche in less than a year. The Mercedes "rode like a tank, and what's the use of driving one anyway now that all the pimps have them?"

He had to fly the SST to London in the morning and complained all the way out the door on unsteady legs how his "brains go right through the back of his head" when he rides that thing with a hangover.

I sat in my off-the-rack clothes nursing my cheap domestic beer and gloated. Even though my entire net worth wouldn't rotate the tires on his fleet of cars, I was the more fortunate man. He'd found more to complain about in a ten-minute tirade than I could come up with in a month.

I spent my last night in the good life with a different view of it. The next day I would fly coach back to Alaska, where I would be reunited with family, dear friends, and contentment, to name just three of the things that have obviously eluded that miserable soul at the bar. He had everything I should have envied, but all he got from me was pity. I won.

I would lose everything I won a year later in Seattle. Just a few weeks ago while on a similar tour, I had occasion to look out the window of another swank hotel. They were still treating me good, but I was getting a little tired of it. I had a cold and I missed my family. While pining away waiting for room service to bring me my version of a cold remedy, I spotted a man down on the street.

He was pushing a grocery cart of garbage bags full of God only knows what. He couldn't have been that old, but he carried himself like a *very* old man. It was obvious that everything he owned was in the cart. He had on three or four beat-up coats to ward off the Seattle rains, and my heart went out to him. But just as I was about to slip into pity he did the most incredible thing.

He pulled a rag out of his coat pocket and began polishing the public drinking fountain on the corner. "Some kind of nut," I thought. Then he pushed on and started cleaning up a parking meter. A few feet more and he was on a newspaper box. Every few wipes he would refold the rag to present a clean face and diligently go about his chore.

A store owner came out and started talking to him. I thought he was chasing him off, but it was soon apparent they were friends. The store owner gave him something. A few pedestrians walked by and greeted him as he went at his task. I was fascinated.

Here was a man who had lost everything, or maybe never had it. He had every reason to lie under a trestle somewhere and drink bad wine until it all went away, but he didn't. He worked his way up the street making friends and doing some small thing for the privilege of being there.

I was beaten hands down. There I sat in a room that cost more money than he'll see in a year, and I was depressed. Had he ventured a look into my window, he'd have seen a long face in a fancy chair. He might have felt sorry for me. Sorry that I was alone in a strange city without the benefit of all the good people he knew. He won.

I guess you could call this contest even, but I'm not so sure. All the standard lessons are there. Every luxury in the world can't buy happiness, and all the hard times won't necessarily break it. There's no good reason to be intimidated by anyone as we go through these little comparisons with each other. You win some, you lose some. It's best not to play the game at all. Especially in this little world we live in, a world in which anything can happen. Like these two guys of mine could turn out to be one and the same person.

Now, *that* would be intimidating.

PART
·3·

NOT
LETTING GO

———— ❖ ————

Eulogy for
an Ancient Eskimo

O ne of the deepest fears we all share is that of dying alone and without recognition. Not recognition in the sense of a *New York Times* obituary or a national monument, but just a simple acknowledgment that we've passed. Something in the deepest part of our being requires that our life mean something to others. For our death to go unnoticed and unrecorded would be virtually to deny that we were ever here at all.

We humans have always had our share of problems, but by far the biggest one is our tendency to wear out, drop dead, and rot away without a trace. Since we've yet to figure out how to keep from dropping dead, we've devoted a lot of time over the centuries to figuring out better ways to leave traces of ourselves.

Scientists are still poking around the pyramids in Egypt trying to decipher all that's there. Probably the fanciest tombstones ever built, these crypts of kings are the prime example of our desire to be remembered. From records of their daily lives to the treasures they decided to take along with them to the afterlife, these things served to defy the pharaoh's own mortality and say to future generations, "See how I was."

Our culture is lucky this way. We know a lot about how we used to be because of our determination to be remembered. Down through the millennia, men and women great and small have chronicled their deeds for us to study. Three thousand years after his passing, the Boy King Tut lives in the books of schoolchildren and historians. Simple fishermen from biblical times have their names repeated from pulpits and pews, classrooms and kitchens the world over. We have our Michelangelos and Martin Luthers, our painters and popes, saints and scientists, every one of them destined to live on in the minds of their descendants for as long as their descendants have minds.

Somewhere about the time one of these lucky ducks, Galileo, was dropping things off a tippy tower in Pisa trying to get a handle on gravity, a lesser-known man was trying to get a handle on the weather in another part of the world — Utqiagvik, "Place Where We Hunt Snowy Owls." It would one day be known as Barrow, Alaska, "Place Where a Pizza Costs Close to Fifty Bucks," but that wouldn't be for another four hundred years or so.

In the meantime there were more important things for this guy to worry about. There was one helluva storm brewing out over the Arctic Ocean, and he didn't like the looks of it. He'd heard the elders' stories of the dreaded *ivu*, winds that would send the loose pack ice bulldozing onto land at blinding speeds. His house was dug into the frost perilously close to the beach. He paced the bluff listening to his mukluks scuff the fall tundra and worried. Should he head inland until this all blew over? No, he needed to stay here for the seal hunting when the sea finally froze.

He looked forward to the winter, to being tucked away safely in his house of driftwood and sod. The dim glow of the burning seal oil would light the faces of his visitors, fellow hunters with their tales of bravado. Recounting the bounty of the whale harvest. Sharing their strategies for tracking the caribou. Speaking quietly of ancient times and strange things. The *ivu*.

No, he would stay. He returned to his house, out of the wind, and lay on his bed of baleen. Watching the shadows of the seal oil lamp play on the walls, he daydreamed to get his mind off the sound of the pack ice scraping and cracking outside. He recalled the hunt that landed the bowhead whale whose parts he now rested on. He fingered the bags of food tied to his waist and his fine shirt. He was a lucky man. He drifted off to dream of his father, and *his* father. He slept and dreamed of children, and their children, and theirs. How they would know of him and what a fine and fortunate man he was.

A terrible noise rose out of the sea and woke him. He grabbed at the shaft of his harpoon in reflex, but there was no enemy to fight, only tons of ice crashing down through his house and onto him. It was over. Death had come.

Our fortunate Eskimo had just joined the ranks of the Boy King and Julius Caesar, with one exception: he left no mark. The ocean's gravel covered him, and it's possible not a soul who knew him ever learned what became of the man. Nothing of him remained for the children to know, or theirs to teach. He realized the deepest fear of all mankind, to die alone and unknown.

Some four hundred years would pass. The "Place Where We Hunt Snowy Owls" became the place where white men hunted lots of whales. They brought with them their ways, their religion, and their names. Utqiagvik is now a city of 3,000 Americans and the descendants of our lost Eskimo are driving cars made in Detroit. They live in modern homes with sheetrock walls and pay a lot for a pizza.

He might have liked pizza, most people do, but that's not important. What's important is what he *did* like, what he didn't like, and just exactly what he was. It's important to his heirs, who live their lives precariously on the edge of America and the twentieth century, who cling desperately to the heritage that produced them.

The need to know is powerful. The need to be known is at least as great. The two together can do incredible things.

Just such a thing happened not too long ago in Barrow. A powerful fall storm, much like the one that killed this man, washed huge chunks of earth into the sea. A modern Eskimo village was being threatened. A modern Eskimo paced the bluffs listening to his mukluks scuff the fall tundra. He worried and watched, and while he was watching he spotted something.

A single frozen mukluk-clad leg was sticking out from a gravel bank. An ancient Eskimo, harpoon at his side and bags of food tied to his waist, lay on a bed of baleen. As the storm raged on, specialists were called in. Archaeologists, reporters, photographers. Work began to protect this incredible find. There would be no way to study it now until spring. Money would be needed. Heavy equipment.

Modern shelter. Barricades the best minds of our day could muster would be erected.

But there are many powers in this world greater than the wants of men. The storm wound up to a force that hadn't been seen in years. Although the *ivu* never came, there was enough damage done without it. When things settled down, the current residents of Utqiagvik tallied their losses.

Apartment buildings and houses teetered on the ocean's edge. Roads were washed away, the waterfront a shambles. Disaster aid from a governmental system inconceivable to the mind of our good man poured in to repair the damage. But there was a loss that will never be recovered. Our man was gone. Washed clean of this earth, and despite the greatest efforts of men, passed on to the ages.

Scientists would mourn him for the information lost about an era of great mystery. His descendants would mourn the opportunity to learn of themselves and honor him with burial in a faith they now hold dear. A writer who knows little of science or Eskimos would see a picture of his leg on the back page of a newspaper. It would cause him to wonder about such things as death, posterity, and the lives of ordinary men and women.

There the man lay in black and white. Arrows on the page pointed out his "toe" and "heel." The toe was pointed down. The caption made note of the baleen bed, harpoon, and food bags. The writer's imagination got the better of him, and he befriended this old Eskimo with a foot in two centuries. The writer consoled himself as he thought many times, "Rest easy, old friend. Your passing has not gone without notice."

Ohlsen Mountain

It was about a year ago that workers removed the dish antenna from the Ohlsen Mountain radar site. The Ohlsen Mountain facility was part of the old Defense Early Warning System which the military set up to watch for incoming ballistic missiles. The whole system was made obsolete and abandoned years ago, but the antenna and some old buildings still stand atop the naturally flat-topped mountain.

Our front window looks out on Ohlsen Mountain. It's a few miles away, and not the most arresting feature in our view, but it's right smack dab in the middle of it all the same. I didn't think that antenna bothered me, and never realized it did until they took it down. It was only today I gave it any real thought at all.

When we look out our windows, we see some pretty well-put-together hills. Right below us sits an old red barn with a metal roof and fading paint. If I knew it only from a photograph, I'd have placed it in the New England countryside. Over and beyond the green hills, including Ohlsen Mountain, stand the white granite peaks and glaciers of the Kenai Mountain Range. There are better views of the world to be had, but probably not much better.

During our long summer evenings, it's nice to sit in the window and admire the landscape. As the sun sets behind us, the shadow of twilight makes its way up the green hills until just the very tops are all that's left of the day.

That's when that antenna would really come into focus. Because it was made out of metal, the sun would spotlight it. Being the tallest point of land in our vicinity, it was always the last thing to go dark. Long after the red barn was buried in shadow and the spruce groves and alder patches were lost to the dusk, there'd be this lone radar dish, gleaming in self-importance. It was the last thing I saw before I looked away and went to bed. It pointed straight up in the sky but wasn't aimed at anything anymore, having been relieved of duty by better watchdogs in outer space or someplace. Still, it was an effective reminder of the dangerous world we live in, like a nervous gunfighter watching his back in a crowded room.

It couldn't have done anything to stop a missile, but it could see one coming. Give maybe twenty minutes' notice to Omaha or Dubuque. Time enough for prayers and curses. Time enough for our guys to shoot back. These were the kinds of thoughts I used to take to bed with me.

I guess it was only last night I realized I was sitting in the window longer than I used to. I noticed that the white peaks across the bay are now the last things to go dark. They turn a pale rose color, and sometimes, if the angle of the sun is just right, some of the glaciers take on a power of their own, as if the ice itself were on fire. Sort of poetic, but not being a poet, I'm not sure what to do with the experience. It's fine with me just to sit and admire it.

They say that body of land over there hails from South America, that it drifted up here millions of years ago and married itself to the North Pacific plate. The collision pushed those mountains up in the air where it's cold enough to hold glaciers that reflect bright light into the window where I sit. These are the kind of thoughts I take to bed with me these days, big thoughts spanning millions of years of history and holding out the implied promise of a million more to come.

Seems like I'm sleeping better this summer, but I might be imagining it. I can't say if the last thing a person sees before he hits the hay has anything to do with the way he sleeps; all I can say is I'm glad they finally took the antenna off the top of Ohlsen Mountain.

State of Spring

Springtime in Alaska is more a state of mind than it is a state of affairs. The days do get longer, but only so we can watch it snow all the way into evening. There are no sure signs that summer's on the way.

Spring is supposed to be a period of grace, a sort of mental pause in which to gather our wits about us after a long, hard winter. Alaskans are robbed of that. By the time it feels like spring it's already summer, and time to go out and be somebody again. It's like being sent off to work without our morning coffee. There are no spring songbirds out my bedroom window bidding me to come alive. Just the sounds of a neighbor rocking his car out of a frost boil.

Real hints of spring are hard to come by. The only signs I've seen for sure are the ones the highway department put up to tell us our studded tires are now illegal. I love those signs. When studs are outlawed, only outlaws have studs, and I like the image. I pull on the ol' Levi's jacket, snap my chewing gum, and speed down the dry pavement savoring the criminal whine of metal on asphalt. It ain't exactly the Sundance Kid, but not bad for a married guy.

Other spring indicators try to get my attention, like the genetic curse that triggers me to clean things. Once our yard glacier recedes, I while away the hours picking things out of the mud. I sort it into two piles: my stuff and somebody else's stuff.

I don't know how or why junk migrates in the winter, but it does. Exotic garbage turns up in my yard. Campaign posters, yogurt cups, and chrome parts of unfamiliar cars sneak onto my domain under the cover of snow, while some of my own stuff defects.

A fairly new double-bit ax left out in a December snowstorm has mysteriously slipped away. I suspect it eloped with the cap to my propane tank, or the extension cord I used for the Christmas lights. I wish them nothing but the best. I pile the muddy things I recognize as mine next to the garage, to be ignored at a later date. Other junk is heaped in the back of the truck, and when it's full I lose interest in cleaning anything.

The truck sits in the pool of pudding my wife and I use as a driveway. I suppose that's another sign of spring I've failed to mention. Our perennial bog returns, a boot-sucking mass of sinister mud that presently has my truck in its slimy grip. What's the use of tidying up? It's like washing windows while the living room rug is on fire. Nothing is going to look good with that going on, so I quit and sulk for a while.

It just isn't fair. Other places get springs full of cherry blossoms and tulips. The air turns sweet, and people turn frisky. All we ever get is a mess to clean up.

I remember the springs of my youth, when I had no trouble getting into the swing of the season. My adolescent sap rose to fever levels. The school year tapered down to a matter of weeks when misdirected energies could be applied to any number of ill-conceived notions. A whole new summer lay ahead to be spent a year older than the one before. Added privileges, maybe even a job. God help me, maybe even a *car.* It was too much to handle. I'd sit in algebra class staring past the green maples into a new era. Teachers tried in vain to hold my attention while my knees bounced and my feet worked the pedals of an imaginary GTO. I was immune to their efforts. They had no idea they were competing with destiny.

Some destiny this turned out to be, slogging around in an unkempt yard, kicking absently at the frozen earth and cussing a truck that couldn't hold a candle to my dream wheels of yesteryear. It's filthy and stuck and full of vile things that have to be taken to the dump, and I can't stand the sight of it. It makes me tired and I go sit down behind the garage.

There is this one spot on the south side of the garage that's always warm. The sandy ground is bare and dry, and the cool breeze doesn't find its way back there. It's a good place to sit. That's where the dog is, and dogs always know the best places to lie around.

It gets kind of hot when the sun comes out and feels good to open the coat and pull a few buttons. Sun on bare skin, not too bad. If I close my eyes I can be almost anywhere at any time, even on my folks' back stoop with the smell of freshly turned earth from gardens and farms on the wind. Not bad at all.

You know, with a couple more days of this, the sun might dry that muck right up. As soon as the frost is out of the ground, a guy will be able to dig in it. Maybe I'll put in that barbecue pit we've talked about every year. Have some friends out for steaks and volleyball, or just sit around and smack gnats. We could have a real nice place here if we fixed the yard up a little. I should put that fence up, too. Wouldn't that set the place off?

I start working an imaginary post-hole digger with one foot, while counting off how many posts it will take with the other. I could haul some slab wood from the mill for the rails. Probably get all of it in one load as soon as I get that junk out of the truck. Good a day as any for a drive if I can get it free of the mud.

Put on the ol' Levi's jacket and take the dog for a ride. Go to the dump. Check out the mill. By God, I think I'll even run that old truck through the car wash while I'm in town. What the heck. It's spring.

Back to School

He couldn't have weighed much more than his new raincoat. It was so new, in fact, that it wouldn't let his arms hang the way they should. They stuck out from his sides at an odd angle, and he could no more scratch his nose than he could turn his head strapped into the hood. He stood stiffly beside the road and watched me coming from a long way. As I passed him he looked at me with his lip curled under his front teeth in fear.

When I found him again in my rear-view mirror, I saw it wasn't me he'd been looking at at all, but the big yellow school bus behind me. "Oh, that's right," I thought. "First day of school." I wanted to turn around and go comfort him, but was called off by something remembered in his expression. Yes, the kid was scared, but his eyes were fixed on the bus with such defiance that I knew he didn't need any counsel. He was going through with it. Brave as any soldier, he was going to get on that bus for the very first time. I drove on while a similar bus in a similar rain charged out of my memory in fourth gear.

I hadn't been to kindergarten. That's what had me worried. I knew my colors and I could count past a hundred, but I couldn't spell at all. My mother assured me I didn't need to spell to go to first grade. That's what they wanted to teach me. But I wasn't so sure. My older brother was way up in the third grade, and he could spell like crazy. He had me convinced I was a mental defective and the nuns at our small parochial school would serve me for hot lunch the first day if I didn't get my act together.

Determined to measure up, I asked my brother what it took to spell. "Lots of paper and some pencils," he said. The pencils were covered. I'd already sharpened the life out of all three fat number ones in my Roy Rogers pencil box, and their big pink erasers were good and broken in. It was the paper that had me worried. Mom had told me the school would give me what I needed, but I couldn't trust her. She wasn't going to school, and my brother, who was, had explicitly mentioned paper. So I stole the whole stack of typing paper from the kitchen drawer and slipped it under my brand-new yellow raincoat.

Standing by the mailboxes with my brother, I was probably as scared as I ever have been since. Six years old and functionally illiterate. Buckled into an impossible raincoat I wasn't sure I could find my way out of without maternal assistance. The only thing I had going for me was a Roy Rogers pencil box, a Davy Crockett lunch pail, and over four hundred sheets of stolen typing paper. The hardest thing I ever did in my life was step onto that bus.

I'd like to be able to say that all my worrying was for naught, but it wasn't. Actually, as I reached this mythical place called Saint Sebastian's Elementary, my worst fears were realized.

Upon approaching the first-grade classroom I was greeted by Sister Antonio. I'd never been so close to a nun before and wasn't sure just how to act. When she smiled and said, "Good morning," it was as if a burning bush had spoken. Until that moment I had never heard a nun speak. My only experience of them had been watching them in church in their mysterious black-and-white robes. I had some twisted notion that they were all related to Saint Peter — a good friend of Jesus' — and none of these people were to be taken lightly. I nearly swallowed my tongue as I stumbled past her into the room. That's where the real trouble started.

All the desks were in neat rows, and each one had a little folded card on top. "Find the desk with your name on it and take your seat, Tommy," I heard her say from the door. Other kids I'd never seen before were gracefully finding their places and admiring their name cards. I didn't even know what my name looked like. I stalled around the aisles until there were only two empty seats. Taking my best shot, I marched up, plopped down my Davy Crockett lunch pail, and collapsed with relief into Tammy Beech's chair.

The details are fuzzy from there, but I think I was found out during roll call. I vaguely remember Sister Antonio looming over my desk and saying something like, "You don't even know your own name?" This was the last thing I needed pointed out in the presence of my very first peer group. Still in my raincoat, I clumsily got out of my chair and dislodged the four hundred–odd sheets of paper that were precariously stashed underneath. They cascaded across the floor in an impressive display and proceeded to soak up the mud and water left by thirty first-graders. First-graders being how they are about wiping their feet, it's a good thing I brought as much paper as I did.

To say I could've died would be an understatement. I blushed so hard my ears rang. The thing I remember most about picking up that paper was the presence of the burning bush right behind me in eternal silence, the cruel giggles of my classmates, and the pounding of my broken little heart.

Of course, I lived through all this and went on to finish my first year of school. I got used to Sister Antonio and, believe it or not, she even taught me how to spell. I was never served up for hot lunch, and I played Joseph in the Christmas play.

All these memories came back to me when I passed that little guy on the road. All the fear and uncertainty that come with a strange new land. All the pain and humiliation that go with screwing it up. And everything we learn in the process. It never stops, and it never seems to get any easier.

I must say, though, how encouraged I was by that small face along the road. Biting his lip in terror, but with pure resolve in his eye, he reminded me all over again of the best lesson I ever learned. If you want to go somewhere, you gotta get on the bus.

Last Dollar

I've been at different stages of being broke all my life. My last dollar has slipped through my fingers more times than I care to remember.

The first last dollar I ever spent was earned on a paper route. Every morning I would diligently teeter out of the driveway on a wreck of a bicycle and deliver the morning news. It was a dismal occupation even on its best days, but it provided me with the first real money I ever had. What a heavenly feeling to march into the bank and open a savings account with a whole five dollars. Five turned to ten and ten to twenty, until pretty soon I felt the riches of the world lay at my feet. My parents advised me that what money I made was mine to do with as I pleased.

It didn't take me too long to fix on something I wanted. As bicycles were a big part of my life at the time, a replacement for my wreck was the obvious choice. I recruited new subscribers on my route to spur things along, and as the route got bigger, the size of the bike I needed increased in direct proportion. About the time my route grew to such a size that nothing short of Mom and the family station wagon could get me through it before school, I reached the magic number.

Taking my entire wad into Three Rivers Schwinn, I walked the familiar path to that big black beauty in the window. Mustering all the self-importance that ninety-five self-made dollars could confer on a ten-year-old boy, I told the manager my intentions. I had him fit it up front with a two-bushel basket. I commissioned him to install a generator light, handlebar hooks, and side carriers, and even got a rear-view mirror with the change. I walked out of that store the best-outfitted paper carrier in three states.

I had everything I wanted in the world. For a time things went along smoothly. Then one dim morning, while I was loading papers onto my customized truck of a bicycle, it dawned on me. I *did* have everything I wanted in this world. Suddenly, and without provocation, I lost my will to work. Why go on aimlessly earning when I sat astride all the happiness money could buy? My paper route became the first victim of a character flaw that would mold my life for many years to come. It didn't take long for my last dollar to go, but I still had my bike, and life was good.

They say all things must pass, and this one certainly did. As childhood made its wary way into adolescence, my interests grew beyond black bicycles with half-ton payloads. Certain members of the opposite sex began attracting my attention. Although I wasn't exactly sure what it was, I was certain everything I wanted in life somehow involved them. Of course the operating costs of pursuing this enigma soon found me flipping hamburgers for ninety cents an hour. I spent my last dollar every Saturday night during this period, but life was good again and getting more promising by the day.

A hot grill soon gave way to a dime-store stockroom when I decided that true inner peace could only be reached with a new stereo. Not long after my last dime-store dollar was handed over to the Sony Corporation, the frustration of being a biped in a four-wheeled society snatched happiness from my grasp once again.

After a long, hot summer in a furnace factory, I found myself content behind the wheel of a '55 Pontiac Star Chief that smelled of chickens, and on my way to college. The last dollar from a night job as a janitor went toward a fine new guitar, and life became good once again. What with poverty being somewhat of a badge of honor on college campuses, it remained good for a very long time.

I don't know exactly when it happened, but sometime after entering the real work force I stopped earning for contentment and just started earning. Money no longer represented particular fancies. It became a necessity. Last dollars turned into a serious and dangerous thing.

There was no paying for the groceries and rent and taking the rest of the year off. Vehicles broke down at the worst possible times and had to be replaced with less than the stuff of dreams. New furniture, real estate, and tropical vacations were sometimes realized, but more often foiled by every conceivable expense between income tax and illness.

After marrying each other, my wife and I discovered the principle of buy now, pay later. We sold our souls to a thirty-year mortgage and a succession of car payments with matching insurance policies. All our disposable income is calculated a year in advance and spent the year before. Our last dollar shows itself every thirty days and will continue to appear on schedule for as far ahead as we can see.

Sometimes I wonder what we're really working for, and I sit in the living room to brood. There must be some comfort in this.

The wood in the stove shifts and I'm grateful for the heat. The phone rings bringing news from family and I'm glad we can accept the charges. My wife pulls into the driveway in a car that's at least half ours, carrying groceries that are all ours. A ten-dollar refund came from Sears so she bought a bottle of wine. Sitting upstairs, we watch the moon rise over the mountains and talk about our day. Amusing stories replace problems, and we decide we love our jobs. The wine makes us sleepy, and while leaning against a not-so-fancy couch there isn't much left to say.

Not much, that is, but what I've always said: life is good to me. Like it always has been. Every last dollar of it.

Pretty As
a Picture

've been told that I take lousy pictures. It's not that my
shots aren't technically okay, it's just that my pictures
seem to bring out the worst in people. I hope that's not a
sign of something. If looking through another person's eyes
would be a good way of finding out how he sees the world,
you'd think that looking through his camera would be the
next best thing. Well, I think very highly of people; in fact,
some of my best friends are people. So why are all the pictures I have of my friends ugly?

Other people's pictures have folks in them with a lot of
white teeth. They're looking right at you with big smiles
and flattering character lines etched across their faces. Maybe they're smelling a fresh flower with eyes half closed in
thoughtful appreciation, or toasting you with a drink at a
long-gone celebration of some momentous sort or another.

My pictures will capture people in conversation, which
is a big mistake. You can video-tape a conversation, but you
can't take a snapshot of it. People's mouths make really fun-

ny shapes when they're talking, and if you shoot a person saying even a good word like "wonderful," you'll freeze their lips in some oddball position like a monkey's. I'm famous for doing that, and people who know me don't like me hanging around with a camera.

I take a lot of candid pictures at parties and picnics. Those can really get you into trouble at a slide show. I always manage to capture some poor guy glancing at the rear end of the wrong woman. Of course almost every man does this at one time or another, but even an innocent look, when caught on film, can become eternal lechery. I usually end up throwing away half the pictures I take. It's not that they're deceiving. They're just too honest.

It's true what they say about a camera never lying, but you certainly can lie to a camera. We do it all the time. At least we exaggerate things a little. The first thing you'll hear when you point a lens at someone is, "Wait, I'm not ready." So you wait while your subject brushes the crumbs off his chin, puts out a cigarette, or throws an arm around the person next to him like they've been standing that way all day. You get your picture, but it's blown all out of proportion. Everybody's having a little more fun than they really were, and liking each other more than they actually do.

We've all been guilty of putting on a show for the camera at one time or another. You're with your sweetheart traveling somewhere. You've been walking and complaining about the price of the room, the blister on your heel, and the rude waitress at the café. Then you stop somebody on the street, hand them your Kodak, and put on your very best "having a wonderful time" smile. Ten years later you'll look at that picture in a scrapbook and remember what a great trip it was, whether it was or not. It's a worthy thing to do, plant these little seeds of contentment in our lives should we someday doubt we ever had any.

It's good practice to take these opportunities to mug up to a camera. There never seems to be one around for the real special times. That make-up embrace after a long and dangerous discussion. The look on your face as you hold the phone and hear that you got the job. The quiet ride home from the hospital after learning that suspicious lump was benign, only something to watch but not to worry about. Those are the moments that should be preserved, to be remembered and relied upon when harder times take hold. Those times when a photographer like me will catch you at a party with a loneliness on your face that you didn't think would show. Or bitterness tugging at your lips during a conversation you didn't intend to be overheard.

We all slip up like this sometimes, and sooner or later we get caught with our guard down. I think that's why I end up with pictures like I do. I like it when people leave their guard down. We all know our best side, and it's nice to keep that faced forward whenever we can. But I don't mind having pictures of the other sides. My collection of faces may not be as attractive as other photographers' albums, but they're my friends, and they all look just like people to me.

Working
Slobs

Not everybody can put his finger on the single dumbest thing he ever did, but I can. I barely got away with my life. I was twenty-one, and I'd just been hired on by a cannery to help build a new four-story steel building. It was winter, all the iron was covered with snow and ice, and the foreman needed another squirrely little guy to work the high beams and bolt the roof members together.

"You afraid of heights?" was all the foreman wanted to know. "No," was all I had to answer. Needless to say that was not entirely true, but at the moment I was more scared of not getting the job than I was of high places. He strapped a leather tool bag to me that held about ten pounds of wrenches and another ten pounds of nuts and bolts. "Have at it," he said, and pointed to an overextended aluminum ladder that reached almost to the top of the framework. The fact that it only *almost* reached the top is significant because that's what prompted me to attempt a stunt that I've yet to match in the way of bonehead maneuvers.

When I climbed to the end of this ladder — a broken-down old thing that would have made any OSHA inspector gag on his citation book — I realized I couldn't reach the top of the beam I was supposed to go to work on. Fully stretched out on the last rung, I was still a good six inches short of my objective and, undoubtedly, my job. So, wielding all the common sense a young man in dire need of work could muster, I jumped.

Like I say, I got away with it. My mittened hands made the edge of the iron to the first knuckle and I was able to monkey my way onto it. It was a lucky break. If the fall hadn't killed me, a rusty re-bar sticking up out of the snow on a twelve-inch center would have. What people throughout history have laid on the line for God and country, I'd risked for six-fifty an hour.

I can never recall that incident without a wave of anxiety overtaking me. I see my own young face frozen in astonishment. A broken body impaled on nine dollars' worth of steel reinforcement. Four dollars' worth of nuts and bolts and a few worn wrenches scattered around me. We've all done things in our life we'd handle differently if given another chance, and this might be one of mine.

If I was on that same ladder today I wouldn't jump. I'd climb down and tell the foreman he needed a longer ladder. Or more likely, I'd complain about the safety of the whole operation and demand a job on the ground. That would be the smart thing to do, but sometimes there are greater rewards than being just another smart guy. Like hugging a piece of frosted steel with your eyes closed until your heart calms down enough to sit up. Like having the veteran iron-worker on the next beam shake his head with an admiring grin and say, "So they sent a wildman to help me, eh?" Being invited into the old-timers' circle on the first day of the job and listening to your veteran partner recount your deed to an appreciative coffee shack audience. Overhearing your foreman explaining to the contractor that the new guy is shaping up fine. "He's a good worker": the highest honor that can be bestowed on a working slob. Yeah, I wouldn't have the guts to try it again, but I think I'd want to.

I'm not sure why all of this has come to mind just now. Maybe it's because I'm not working this year. Oh, I'm working, I guess, if you can call poking at letters on a plastic keyboard "work." I'm not convinced that it is yet. After spending all of my adult life trying to be a "good worker," I feel like I'm sloughing off.

All my friends are workers. They come by the house sometimes with concrete on their pants and Band-Aids on their fingers. I offer them beers, and their first three gulps are big and thirsty. I don't get very thirsty anymore, and my hands are healed and pink. For the first time in ten years the cuticles have actually attached themselves to my finger-nails. I can't remember them ever being that way, and they look strange. I can open my hands up all the way and it doesn't hurt. You wouldn't think a person could miss a thing like pain, but I remember that ache with some fond-ness. That feeling when you lie down in bed after eight hours of finishing concrete. Your knees untie themselves and your shoulders melt into the pillow. I miss the morning shower bringing to life the cuts and scratches from the day before. I don't know, I guess it was such a *worthy* feeling.

And I miss the company. I work alone now, and the few people I need to talk to for my writing are smart, careful people. They think about what they're saying and try not to offend. They are not the kind of people who would lunge for slippery beams from an overextended ladder, or appreciate anyone else who pulls stunts like that. I don't talk about that stuff much anymore, but I think about it.

I think about it when I pass a construction site. I hear the *patunk-patunk* of an air nailer and remember what it was like when a good crew got on a head of steam to finish a job. Skilled people plying their trade, taking a chance, making a buck. The crude jokes as thick and annoying as the rattle of the air compressor. Leaning on pickup trucks at the end of the day with a few atta-boys. Maybe piling into a tavern for a quick and spirited beer that would shame anything Miller ever put in a TV commercial.

And I think about it when I hear about a guy blown away when the steel beam he was guiding touched a high power line. Or a friend who stepped into the blind spot of a dump truck and got his legs broken. I remember how dangerous it is and what working people put up with to make a living. Mostly I remember the pride that came with being that way.

It might all be looking better to me in hindsight, or these pretty pink hands of mine could finally be getting on my nerves. Whatever it is, I feel this ache sometimes. It's not the ache that comes of hard work, though. I think it's the ache to work hard again.

Orphans

I am constantly amazed at the way things happen. Unexplainable coincidences occur that add an air of mystery to an otherwise predictable world. The very best of these leave positive evidence of a supreme and playful Being. I've always denied being superstitious, but these occasions of the uncanny make me want to reconsider. I look at them as omens, and like as not, I live my life by them.

There was a time a dozen years ago when I sat in a dorm room at a Michigan college and felt the flatlands of the Midwest closing around my neck. I had to get out of there. The drudgery of school was driving me nuts, and I was tired of leading a life that could be summed up in twenty-five words or less. I needed to *do* something.

I had a good friend I hadn't seen in a couple of years. His family had moved to another state, and he too was pursuing an uneventful student career. In high school we had dreamed together of thumbing rides into the sunset —

Colorado, California, the Great Northwest, and on our best days, Alaska, the spiritual mecca of all would-be adventurers.

I went to the phone to call him. I wanted to talk him into bagging college and heading out on a lark with me. When I picked up the receiver there was no dial tone. I rattled the button and finally heard a "Hello?" It was my friend. He'd called me for the first time in six months while I was about to call him for the first time in a year. What was on his mind made it even sweeter. He was ready to go, and did I want to come along?

Needless to say, I never looked back. Any doubts I might have had about sacrificing my education, disappointing my parents, or ruining my life dissolved with that one divine coincidence.

It turned out to be a good trip. Many omens and adventures later find me living in my mecca and pursuing the career I was training for at college in the first place. So nothing was sacrificed after all. My friend and I separated early in the journey, but he ended up here too. He lives in Healy and does surveying for the coal company, also his field of study in that other life.

This is just one example of some of the markers I've used to map the path I walk on. You can see how, after a few of these timely twists of fate, I might come to rely on them. They tend to hold things together for me. Sort of a reassurance that I am indeed still on the trail. Each is a blaze on a random trunk in a forest full of trees.

The reason I'm bringing all this up is that I've just wandered across another one of these blazes. Today I received a postcard from a well-known artist in Seward. She just wanted to drop me a line to compliment me on something she'd read. Flattered, I returned the favor with a bit of raving on a painting I'd seen of hers.

It was of the Jesse Lee Hayes Home in Seward, an old orphanage. It was abandoned, I believe after the '64 quake, and duly gutted sometime later. It stands now as a haunting memorial to displaced and lonely children, many of them innocent victims of a rapidly evolving frontier. In the painting she had depicted the spirits of these children boiling from the empty entrance of the orphanage and sweeping into the sky. I'm not a great connoisseur of art, and I don't know if it's even one of her better works, but it left a big impression on me.

You see, I used to live there. It was the first place I ever called home here in Alaska. A bunch of us were working at the cannery in Seward, and the old orphanage was our unofficial bunkhouse that summer. There were maybe ten of us there at any one time. All just a couple years out of the house, we took to calling ourselves "the orphans." We were young men with no discernible futures or aspirations, and we'd sit around candles late at night singing songs and talking fish. It was a wonderful summer.

I never knew what happened to all the other orphans. Some returned to schools, I suppose. Others headed off to see more distant lands. One, I understand, is a writer in New Hampshire, and another is still with the canneries, now in Southeast Alaska. The rest I know nothing about other than first names.

I haven't dwelled on it a lot over the years, but as wonderful summers are apt to do, that season in Seward comes to mind from time to time. That's when I'll think of all the orphans and what's become of us.

I went through this when I first saw the painting, and again today as I wrote to the artist about it. It struck me as I redescribed her work to her how much like her spirit children we more fortunate orphans were. All young and without real direction, we burst from our summer friendships with the same energy and reckless abandon.

That's more poetic than I like to be, but there's a purpose to all this. While I lingered once again around that wonderful summer, the phone rang. It was another of those incredible coincidences. On the line was Paul, one of my orphans. He was in the area and just had a thought to get ahold of me after ten years for old times' sake. Call me a liar if you want, but I have witnesses.

He came by the house, we had a beer, talked some fish, exchanged addresses, and that's about the size of it. Paul was retiring his commercial fishing career and heading to California to pursue something less risky, but nothing in particular. We marveled a little at where we'd each ended up, and promised to stay in touch. Maybe we will. You know how those things go. Somebody moves and forgets to tell you. More important people and things get in the way, and pretty soon you become a misfiled card in an old friend's Rolodex. It's nothing personal. Nobody can ever guess what the future might bring.

I gave up guessing a long time ago. I don't mind not knowing where I'm headed. As long as these little blazes keep reassuring me that I'm still on the trail.

Nice to see you, Paul.

WOW

Among the thousand and one truisms that were hurled at us as expectant parents was one I especially wanted to believe: "You are going to learn the most important things from your children." It sounded so promising, and when accompanied by a smug veteran-parent grin, it appeared to hold water.

I looked forward to learning about these "most important things," but soon after our boy arrived I decided it was all a lot of tripe. If the most important things are pricing Pampers, holding tempers, and coming up with six-hundred variations on the word "no," then I figured people's ideas of "important" are purely subjective.

My partner in crime and I have spent the last twenty months with our child teaching him everything from rolling over to the dynamics of liquids in cups not carefully handled. All the while I held on to the hope that one day the teaching would leave off and the learning begin. Apparently it was just a matter of time, and the time, at last, has arrived.

We recently had occasion, as a family, to spend the night at the house of some friends in town. They have an extra room down in the basement, and we were set up with the bed and crib in the same room. No big deal. The kids went to sleep early, we had wonderful late-night conversation, and retired to our accommodations. I slept well but woke up too early, realized I was in a strange place, and couldn't go back to sleep.

In our natural habitat my wife and I don't share a room with the baby. We normally first come to know he's awake by a series of screams from downstairs that would put any self-respecting banshee to shame. But lying there wide awake in an unfamiliar house offered me the opportunity to hear my child wake up for the first time. This is where the learning came in.

Let me establish here that there are only a few words in our boy's vocabulary. "More" is the one we hear most often and can refer to anything from fun to food. "No" comes in a close second as he repeats it just about as often as he hears it. "Hello," "Bye-bye," "Momma," and "Daddy" make up the rest of his standard casual conversation, and that's all the words he's got. All, that is, but one.

By far his most distinguished and seldom-used expression is the word "wow." He only says "wow" when something really impresses him. If Dad lets a frying pan catch on fire and juggles it out the front door into the snow, it's "wow." If we turn around backwards on the way to town and hit the ditch at thirty, it's "wow." If the house were to burn down around him with the Messiah whispering reassurances into his ear the whole time, I'm confident he would sum it all up with "wow."

My reason for going into all this is, like I said, I had

occasion to hear him come to life one recent morning. I'd been awake for over an hour, but nobody else was up. I lay there silently straining to hear any encouraging sign that there might be people and coffee about. I thought about my day, a Sunday, and took inventory of the chores at hand. We would have to get organized and make the drive home. Once there I'd have wood to put up, a door to fix, a few letters to write, and some bills to pay. My wife would clean the house, as she does every Sunday. The boy would refuse to take a nap, as *he* does every Sunday. Luck willing, we would have a little time to spend together before Monday once again descended on our lives. All this was less than the stuff of dreams.

As I was lying there brooding, I heard my child stir. He rolled over — I assume he opened his eyes — and said "wow." Suddenly, I felt like a heel.

With all my training to "think good thoughts," "look on the bright side," and "take it a day at a time," I woke up to a near-miserable world. This little boy who knows nothing of optimism woke up, saw he had a new day, and gave it his grandest praise. I learned something.

It dawned on me that this innocent little child was at the place I wanted to be. To wake up in the morning, take a look at the world, and say "wow" is probably about as close to contentment as a person can ever hope to get.

Contentment is a rare commodity. The more we learn about this world, the more anxious we get. There is trouble afoot. There are heartbreaks, failures, tragedies, and an endless list of selfish desires that are never realized. Sooner or later we come to resent our own existence. I'm sure our innocent child will eventually eat this forbidden apple and wake up, as most of us do, to say only "ugh."

I wish I knew what I could do to never let this happen. I wish he could teach me the way he sees things now so that I could help him hold on to it — and so I could remember how it's done. That truly would be a "most important thing" — if this tiniest of guides can show me from his crib how to open my eyes in the morning, see that I am alive in Paradise, and say "wow."

Father's Day

This Father's Day business is kind of new to me. I've only recently become a father, so I'm not sure what to expect, but I like the idea of it. It's sort of like inheriting another birthday at midlife. We become the centers of attention and objects of affection for a whole sweet Sunday. And we get presents. I guess that's what interests me.

It doesn't interest me in a selfish way, really. I'm just curious what type of present a dad like me would get. I don't feel I cut quite the figure of a father that, say, my dad did when I lived in his house. He was big, wore suits, and smelled of cologne and shaving cream. We could get him ties or Old Spice and end up being pretty good kids for the effort.

You couldn't get me a tie. I already have one, and it's in the back of the closet with the knot still in it. I couldn't keep a straight face if you got me Old Spice or a soap-on-a-rope. My dad might have laughed at soap-on-a-rope too, but he would have hung it on the showerhead all the same.

I got him a rock one year with a magazine picture pasted to it. I made it myself. It was meant to be a paperweight, but he could have used it for a doorstop, too. Actually, he could have derailed a train with it. The magazine picture was pretty good-sized, and I had to use a big rock to fit it all on. I think the only reason he kept it around was there was no place he could throw it away.

My son isn't old enough yet to design me paperweights, so he and his mother will probably go for something a little more conventional. But just what is a conventional Father's Day gift these days?

Judging by the sale ads in the newspaper, it seems that everything in a hardware store is a "Great Gift Idea for Dad." I thought that kind of thinking went out of style with soap-on-a-rope. It would be like putting floor mops on sale for Mother's Day. To assume that all the family men in America share a common desire for a set of matching screwdrivers is to be more than a little presumptuous.

Fathers are changing. I think that's why I feel a little funny about all this. Gone are the days when you could stand the old man next to a new barbecue on Father's Day, slap a beer in one hand, a spatula in the other, and tie an I'M THE BOSS apron across his pot gut. A lot of dads would rather have a Cuisinart. I know I would.

It's a risky business for a man to buy a woman a kitchen appliance these days. He's likely to be accused of "forcing roles" or what-not upon her. But give a guy a blender, and stand back. He'll wear the blades off of the thing playing with it. Want shakes? Got shakes. Pâté? Try this liver. He'll have it mastered in no time then sit back grinning like a fool, not realizing he's just done what everybody's been trying to get him to do for twenty years.

It's becoming common knowledge that most of today's fathers do more than spit good and go to work. They are, often as not, up all night with the sick kid, rolling Pampers down the grocery aisles, and maybe a little late for work right alongside the working mothers.

So how about something for the working father? Like a men's diaper bag. I'm not exactly sure what a men's diaper bag would look like, but it would make a nice gift. If it was anything like a game pouch or a saddlebag, I'm sure it would do. There's something about a quilted blue bag lined with a floral print that fails to define a guy's masculinity. You can tell me it's all in my head, but it's not. It's hanging on my shoulder. If one more bonehead tells me he "likes my purse," I'm either going to break somebody's nose or break down and cry. It's hard to decide which with an accessory like that at my side.

So you can see that the realm of great gift ideas for Dad has grown a little beyond the tool and fishing tackle departments. That's not to say those aren't great gifts too, but don't let anybody fool you into thinking that we're not hanging out in kitchens and sizing up car seats with the best of them.

Who knows what sort of Father's Day gifts I'll accumulate over the years. As my son grows up and gets to know me, I'm sure he'll pick out just the right thing. I might not be as easy as Old Spice and a necktie, but I'm pretty easy, and just about anything else would do fine.

I just hope that somewhere among those future Father's Day gifts, whether I get my diaper bag and Cuisinart or not, there's something along the lines of a large rock with a picture pasted to it. There isn't a dad in the world that couldn't use one of those.

Not
Letting Go

M y mom just sent me a box full of stuff she cleaned out of the attic. Everything's in it from my high school diploma to my infant feeding schedule. It's a pretty important little bit of history that couldn't mean much to anybody but me and my folks.

The first thing out of the box was a print of Mom and Dad's wedding picture. They had six of them made, one for each of the six kids they knew they were going to have. Mom looks like a young Rita Hayworth in a bridal gown. Dad strikes quite a figure himself with a full head of hair and a naval uniform. He is tall and trim with medals on his chest. They look good together. Like they know what they're doing.

There's a small spiral notebook in the box, a record of the first six months of my life written in my mother's young hand. It's sort of humbling to review. I tasted my first cereal thirty-two years ago this coming May 9. I cut my first tooth the following June 3, a tooth that probably earned me a nickel under my pillow a few years later. I got my first hair-cut on Tuesday, July 26, and the record leaves off a few days later. On the last page I weigh eighteen pounds, three ounces.

None of us really remembers being a baby, and it's sort of nice to see this evidence that I once was. Under the note-book I found a packet of cards. They're congratulation cards that friends and relatives sent my folks when I was born. None of them mention me by name, so I must not have had one yet. One of them is a florist's card from Peter and Billy. Peter was my father's name before it was Dad. Billy was my older brother, who's now a mechanical engineer in Phila-delphia named Bill. One card starts, "Welcome, little dar-ling." It's from a grandmother who died sixteen years ago.

Am I boring you with all this? Probably. Who knows why people save these sorts of things. For just this reason, I suppose. To be able one day to send it off to a grown child and say, "Once you were ours." We forget that, I think. After all, we spend most of our young lives denying it. Something inside tells us to fight our parents every inch of the way until we leave home or get thrown out.

I see it already in our own young son. The rebellious acts of treason. Cries of defiance from a screwed-up little face. Always testing, always stretching the bonds to the breaking point, then returning. No parents can watch their children finding their legs under them without a little sad-ness. As we nervously monitor their awkward progress step by ill-placed step, we know that one day we'll have to watch grown legs carry them out of our lives.

A contemporary version of the box my mom just sent me is beginning to take shape in our bedroom closet. I nev-er really knew what we were going to do with all that junk until now. Silly records and sentiments that couldn't mean much to much of anybody. They won't amount to a lot compared to the disagreements we're bound to have over the next twenty or thirty years. We'll give them little thought as we suffer through the pratfalls of his becoming a man.

God willing, he will become one. I hope a happy one with a good mind, a safe home, and a family of his own. I hope he's vital, and strong-willed. I hope he's good at what he does, and does good with it. Mostly I hope he'll be able to look one day into a box full of yellowed notebooks and curling photographs and ponder for a minute the fact he once was ours. Then I hope when he's a father he starts putting together a box of his own. There are certain silly things in this world that shouldn't be let go of.

About
the Author

Tom Bodett was born in 1955 and grew up in Sturgis, Michigan. He has been a cannery worker, a logger, an independent building contractor, and a commentator on National Public Radio's "All Things Considered." He is the author of a previous collection, *As Far As You Can Go Without a Passport,* and is currently the national radio spokesman for Motel 6. He lives with his wife and son in Homer, Alaska.